Practice and Learn

WORKBOOK

Get Ready, Get Set, Learn!

Grade 1

10 9 8 7 6 5 3 2 1

Practice and Learn

WORKBOOK

Get Ready, Get Set, Learn!

Grade 1

Practice and Learn

WORKBOOK

This book belongs to

____

Get Ready to Learn!

Get ready, get set, and go! Boost your child's learning with this exciting, colorful book. Designed to help children practice and master many needed skills, the **Practice and Learn Workbook** is bursting with 368 pages of learning fun! Use this book for . . .

- enrichment
- skills reinforcement
- extra practice

All your child needs to get started are pencils, crayons, colored pencils, markers, and a little encouragement from you!

You'll also find a sheet of more than 500 colorful stickers. Use these stickers for . . .

- decorating pages
- rewarding outstanding effort
- keeping track of completed pages

Celebrate your child's progress by using these stickers on the reward chart located on the inside cover. The blue-ribbon sticker fits perfectly on the certificate on page 368.

Now let's get ready to practice and learn!

Table of Contents

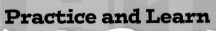

Practice and Learn WORKBOOK

First Grade Fun

Picture Shapes

Directions: Find the triangles and circles in the picture. Color the picture.

Color Bears

Directions: Color the bears.

blue

green

red

yellow

black

white

purple

brown

pink

What Do You Hear?

Directions: Say the name of the picture. Listen for the beginning sound. Write the letter.

____ ountain

____ enguin

____ emonade

____ ey

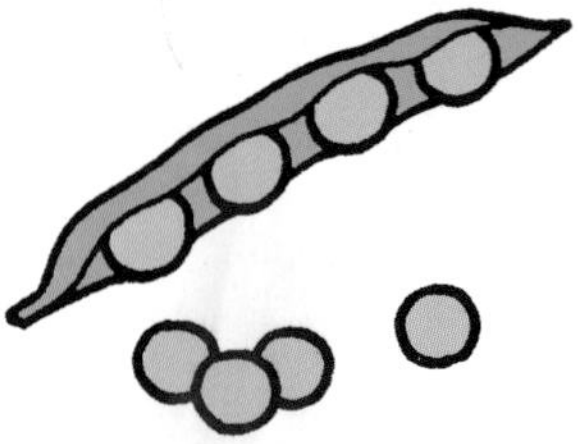

____ eas

____ ine

____ eopard

____ oon

____ ainbow

Ice-Cream Treats

Directions: Find the answers. Color the pictures.

0 = yellow	1 = pink	2 = brown	3 = green	4 = white

Jets

Directions: Circle the pair of rhyming words on each jet. Color the pictures.

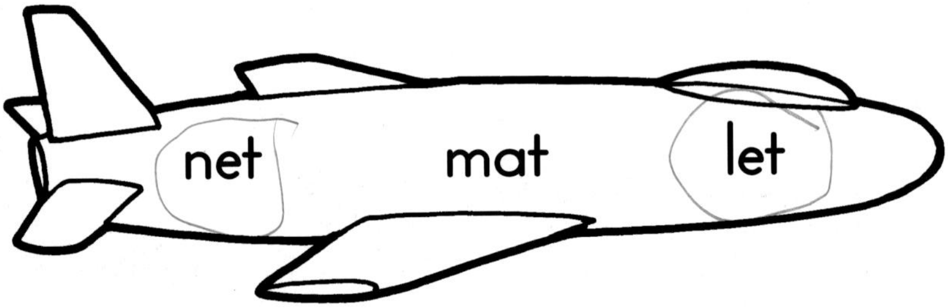

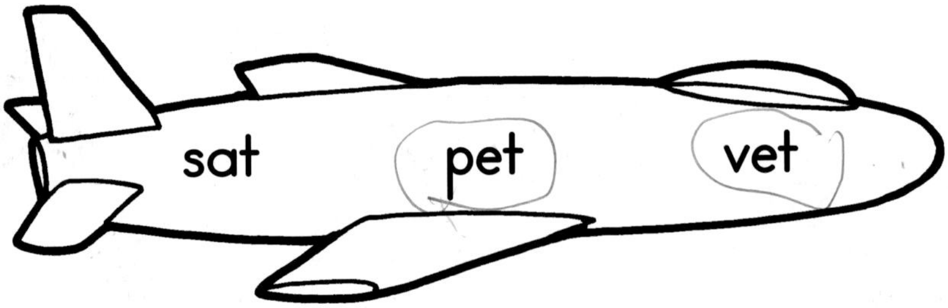

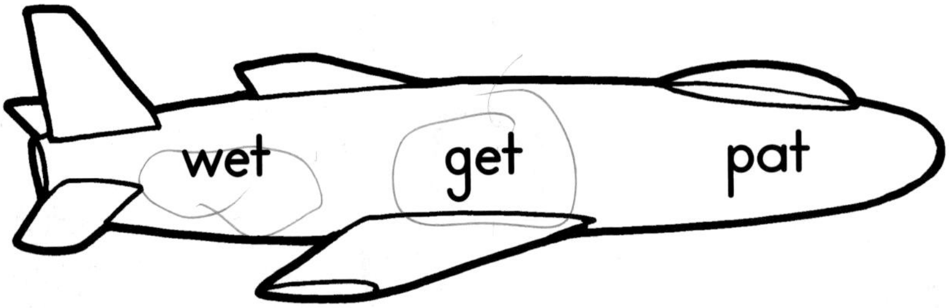

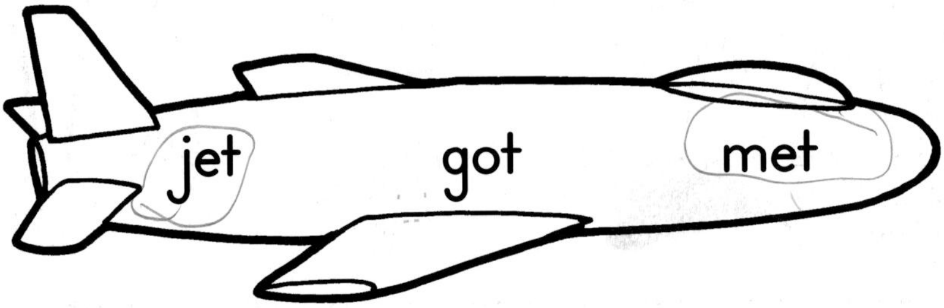

Out in Space

Directions: Color 2 planets. Color 3 space ships.
Color 4 stars.

Things That Are Purple

Directions: Color the things that can be purple.

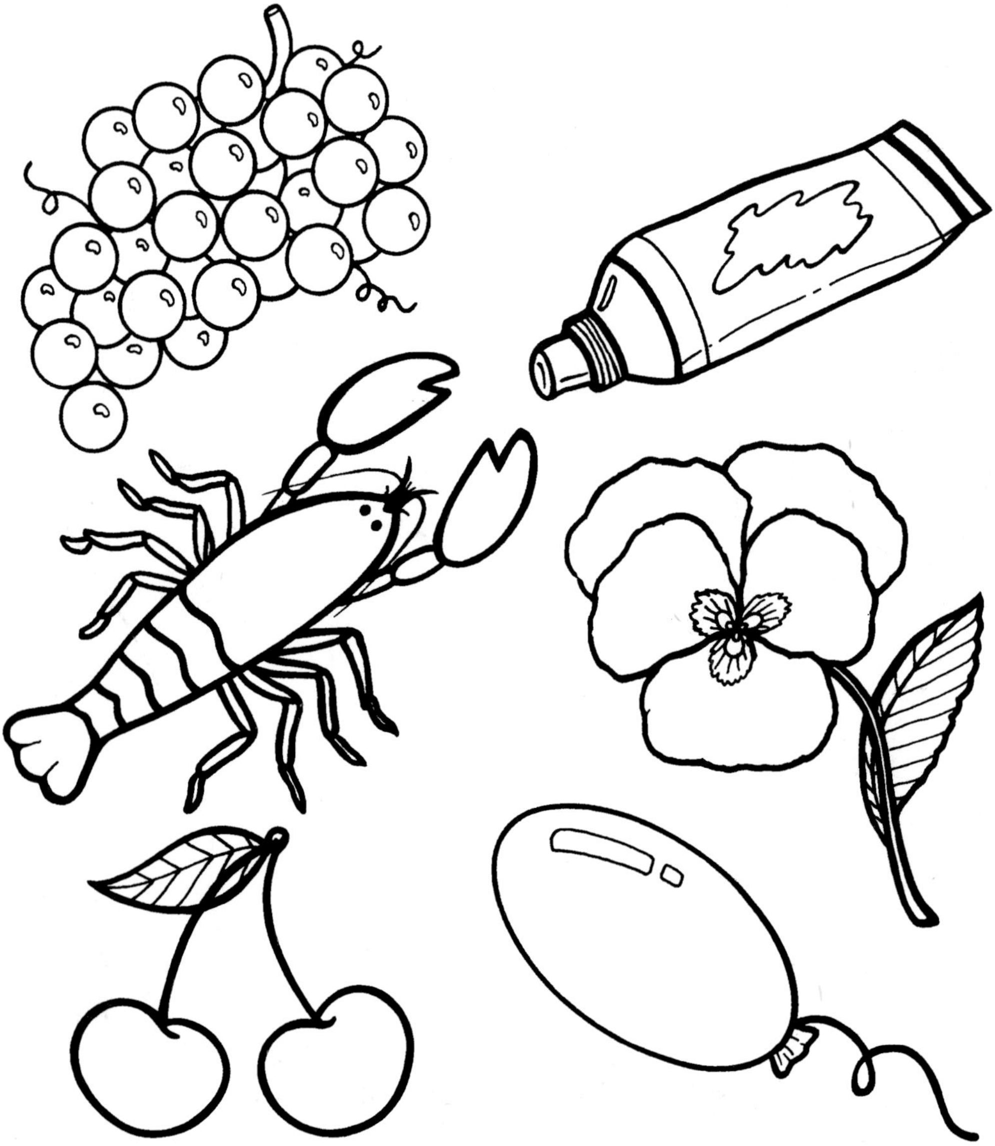

An Apple a Day

Directions: Who is saying hello to you from this delicious apple? Follow the dots to find out. Then color the picture.

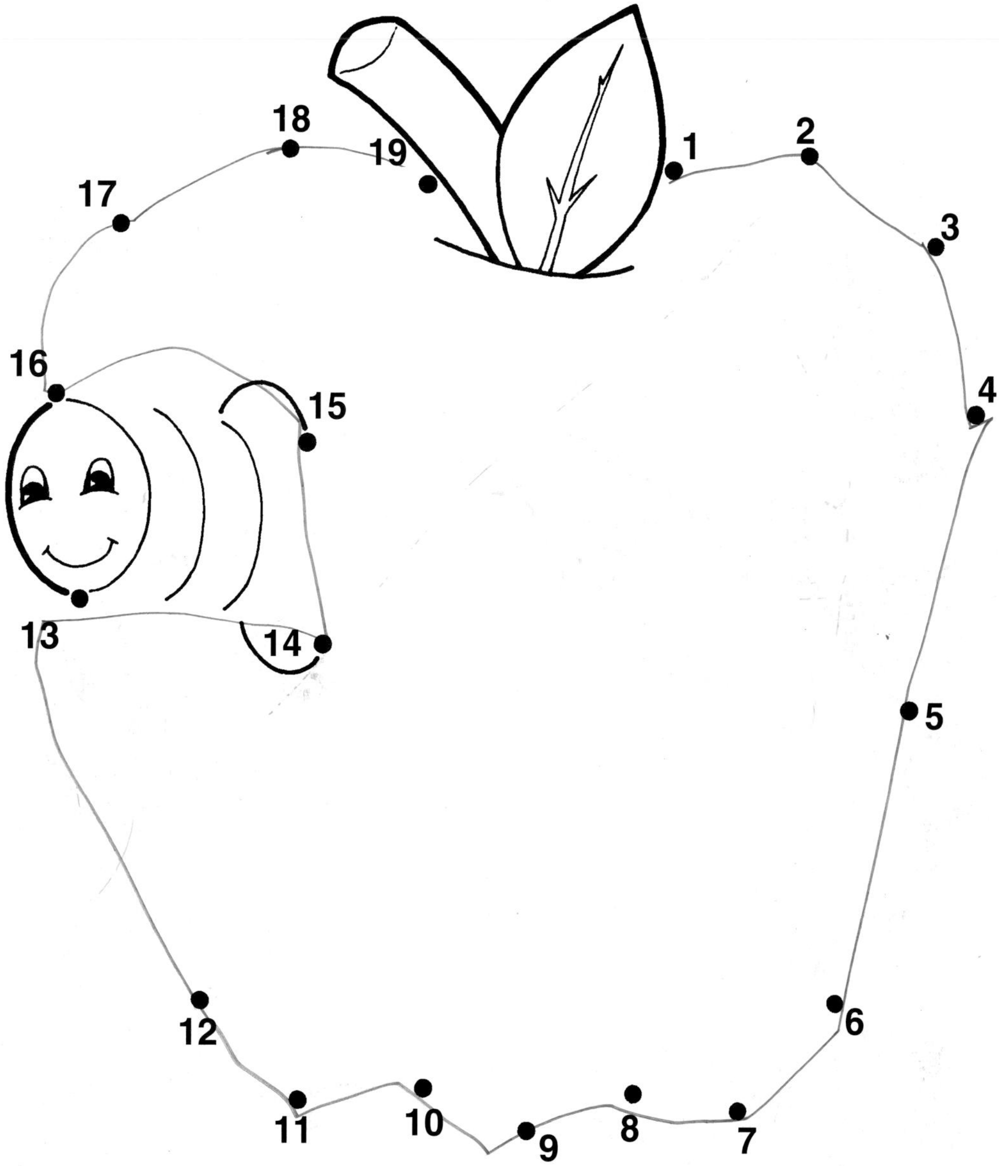

Same Sounds

Directions: Draw a line between the pictures with the same beginning sound.

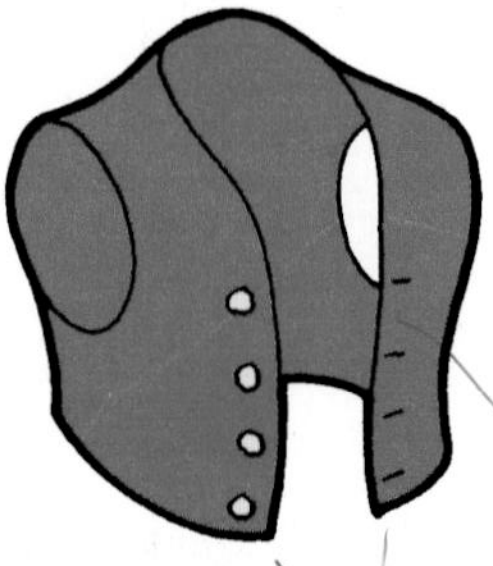

A Basket of Flowers

Directions: Deliver the basket of flowers to the house by following the maze.

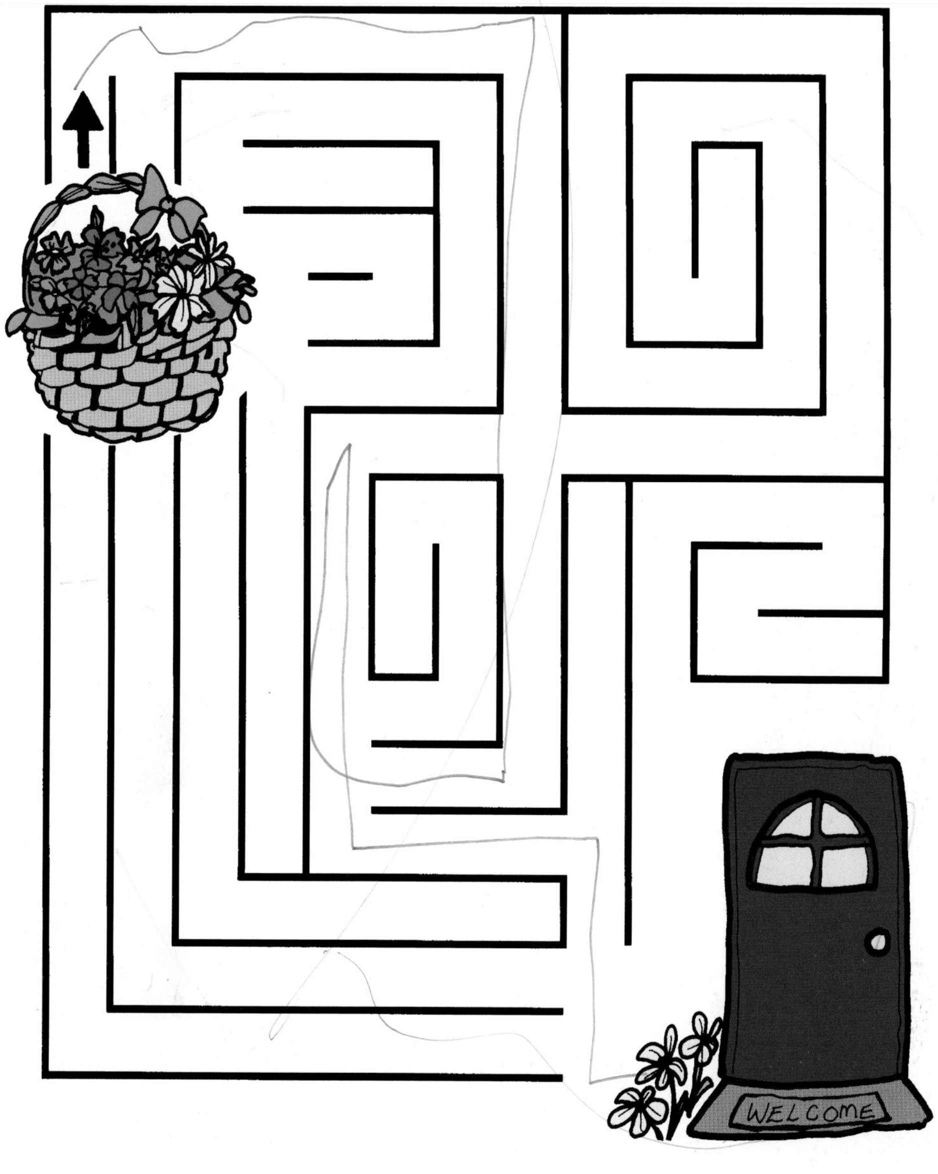

Flying Kites

Directions: Help the girl find her kite. Solve the problems. Draw a line from the girl to the kite with an answer of 12.

They Rhyme!

Directions: Say the picture names. Draw lines to match the rhyming words.

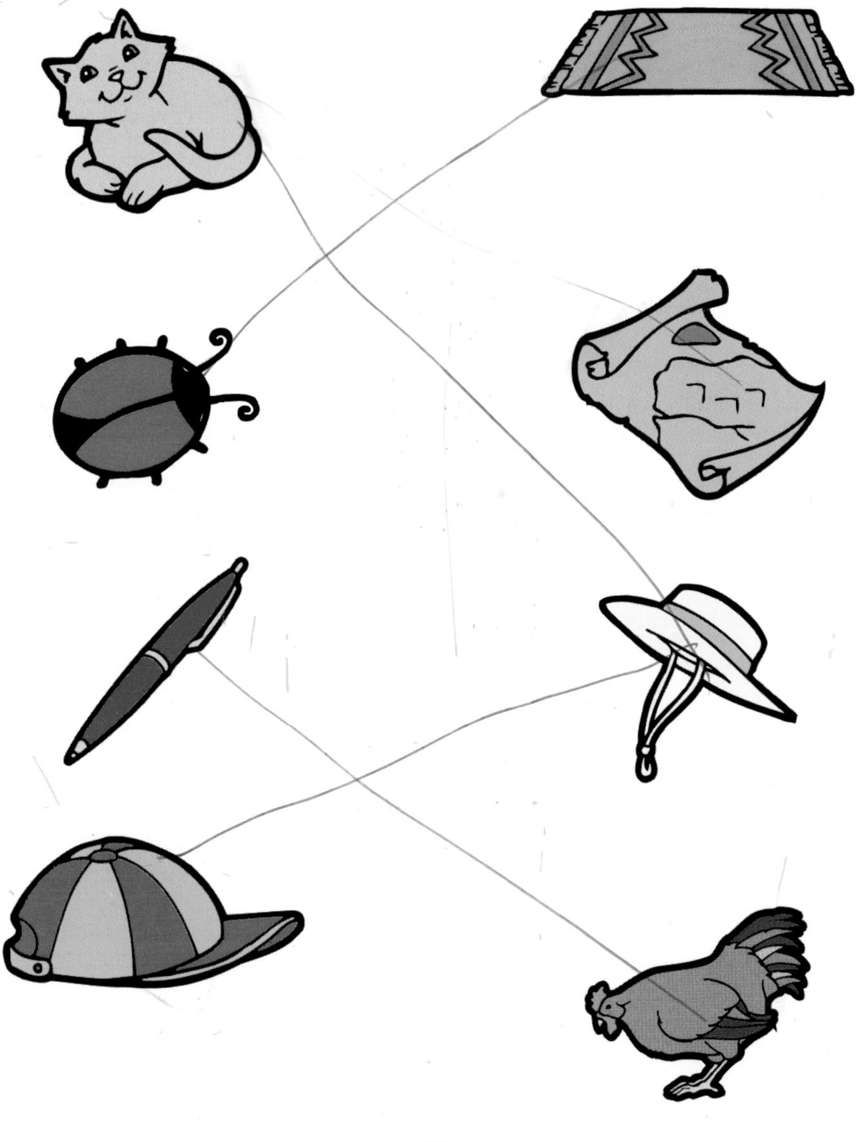

Missing Parts

Directions: Draw in the missing part of each picture.

clock

cat

rabbit

car

A Bee in a Tree

Directions: Look at the picture. Read the story.

A bee flew by my tree. The bee did not see me. I am glad! That bee would take my honey if he saw me in the tree.

Directions: Read the questions. Circle the correct pictures.

1. Who flew by?

2. What is being eaten?

3. Where is the person sitting?

ABC Order

Directions: Write the words in ABC order. Color the picture.

well	bed	pet	hen

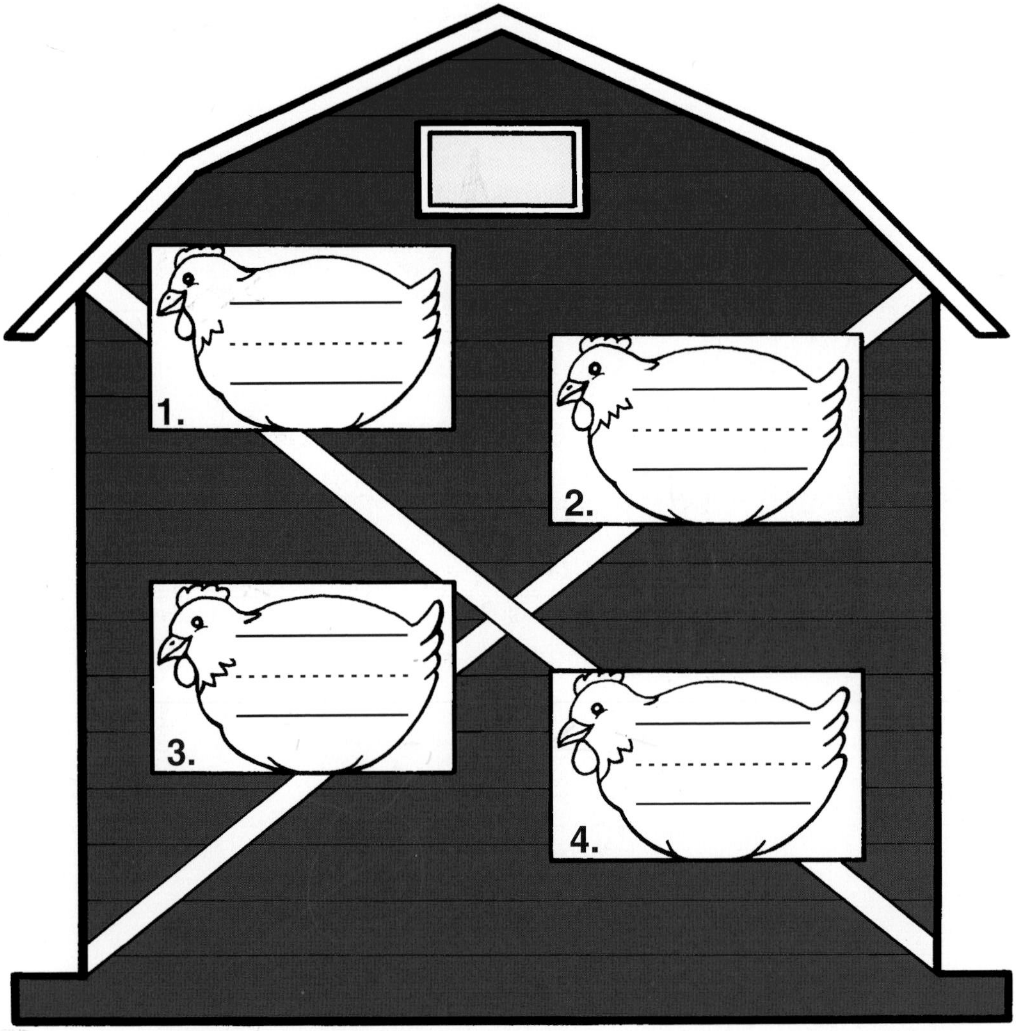

What Is On the Tree?

Directions: Color everything you might find on a tree.

Flowers

Directions: Color the tulips with **long *u*** words red. Color the other tulips yellow.

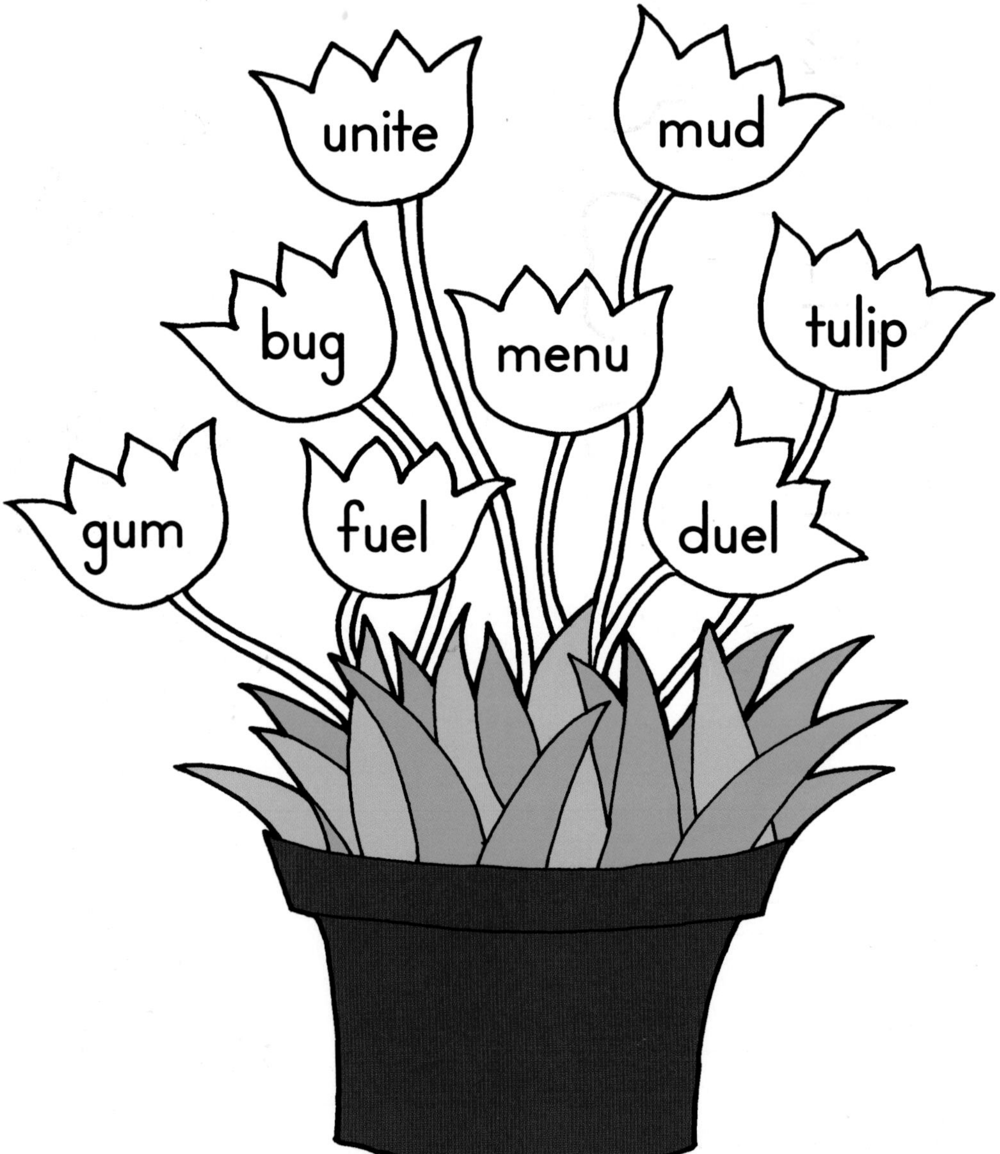

Doggie Bones

Directions: Draw a line to match each equation to its answer.

9 – 2 = ____

7 – 4 = ____

10 – 9 = ____

6 – 6 = ____

3 – 1 = ____

8 – 4 = ____

Match Them Up

Directions: Draw lines matching the pictures to their words.

fork

fox

lamp

nest

web

worm

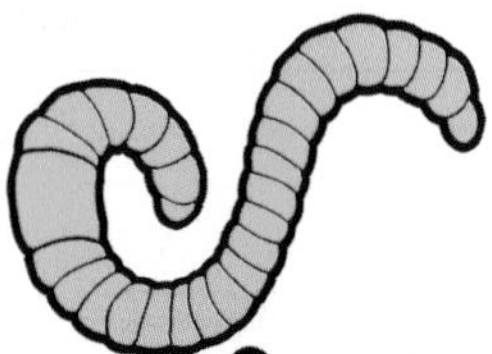

A Picnic

Directions: Color 10 hot dogs. Color 11 apples. Color 12 ants.

Put Them in Order

Directions: Number the pictures in order. The first one has been done for you. Color the pictures.

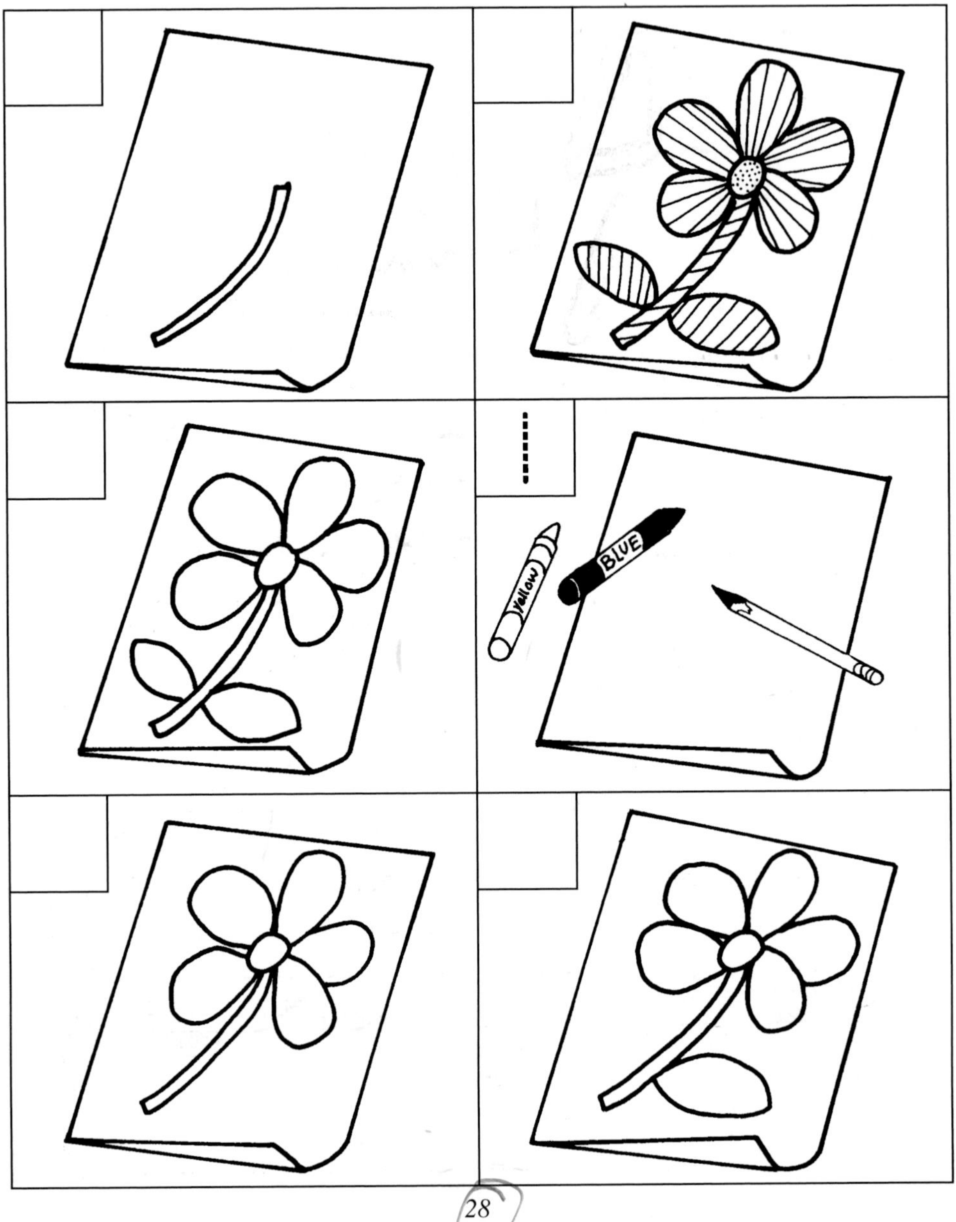

Tool Box

Directions: Cross out each answer in the tool box as you solve the problems.

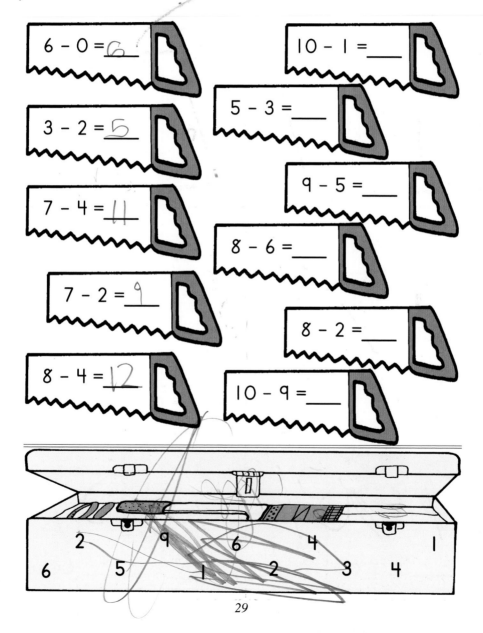

6 - 0 = 6

3 - 2 = 5

7 - 4 = 11

7 - 2 = 9

8 - 4 = 12

10 - 1 = ___

5 - 3 = ___

9 - 5 = ___

8 - 6 = ___

8 - 2 = ___

10 - 9 = ___

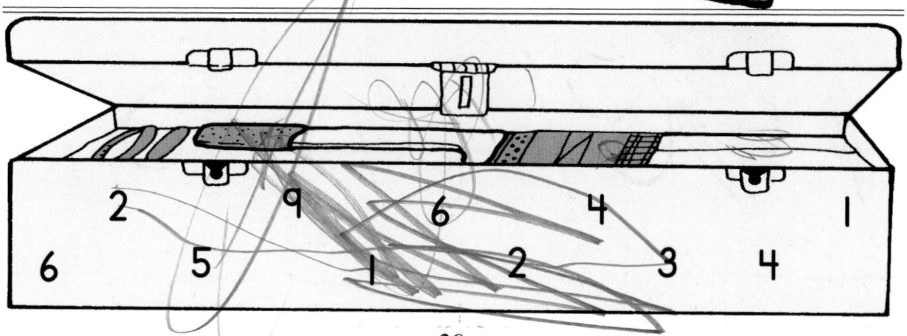

Beginning Sounds

Directions: Say the name of the picture. Listen for the beginning sound. Write the letter.

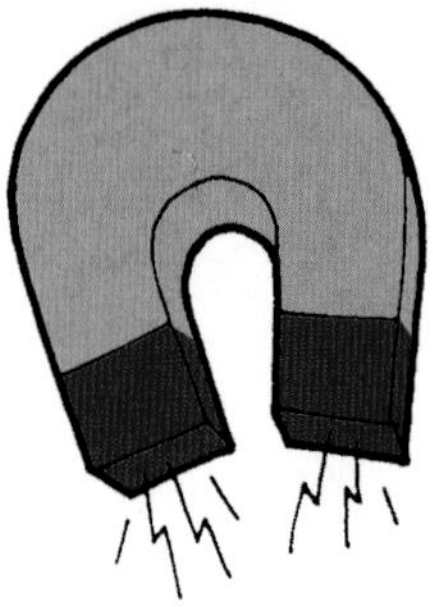 _____ agnet	 _____ izza	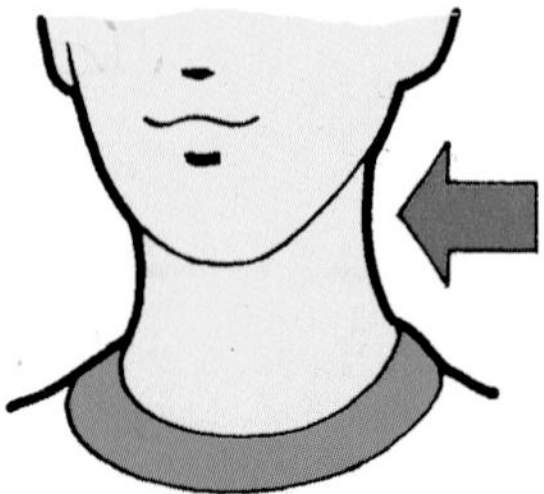 ch_____ eck
 _____ uilt	 _____ ite	 r_____ uler
 _____ izard	 c_____ ing	 _____ ocket

Octopus Bath

Directions: Write a story using the beginning below.

One day I came home from school and found an octopus in my bathtub.

What's the Order?

Directions: Write the words in ABC order.

a b c d e f g h i j k l m n o p q r s t u v w x y z

van	can	fan
pan	man	tan
~~and~~	ran	

Got Rhymes?

Directions: Color the spaces with the rhyming *ot* words green. Color the other spaces yellow. What do you see?

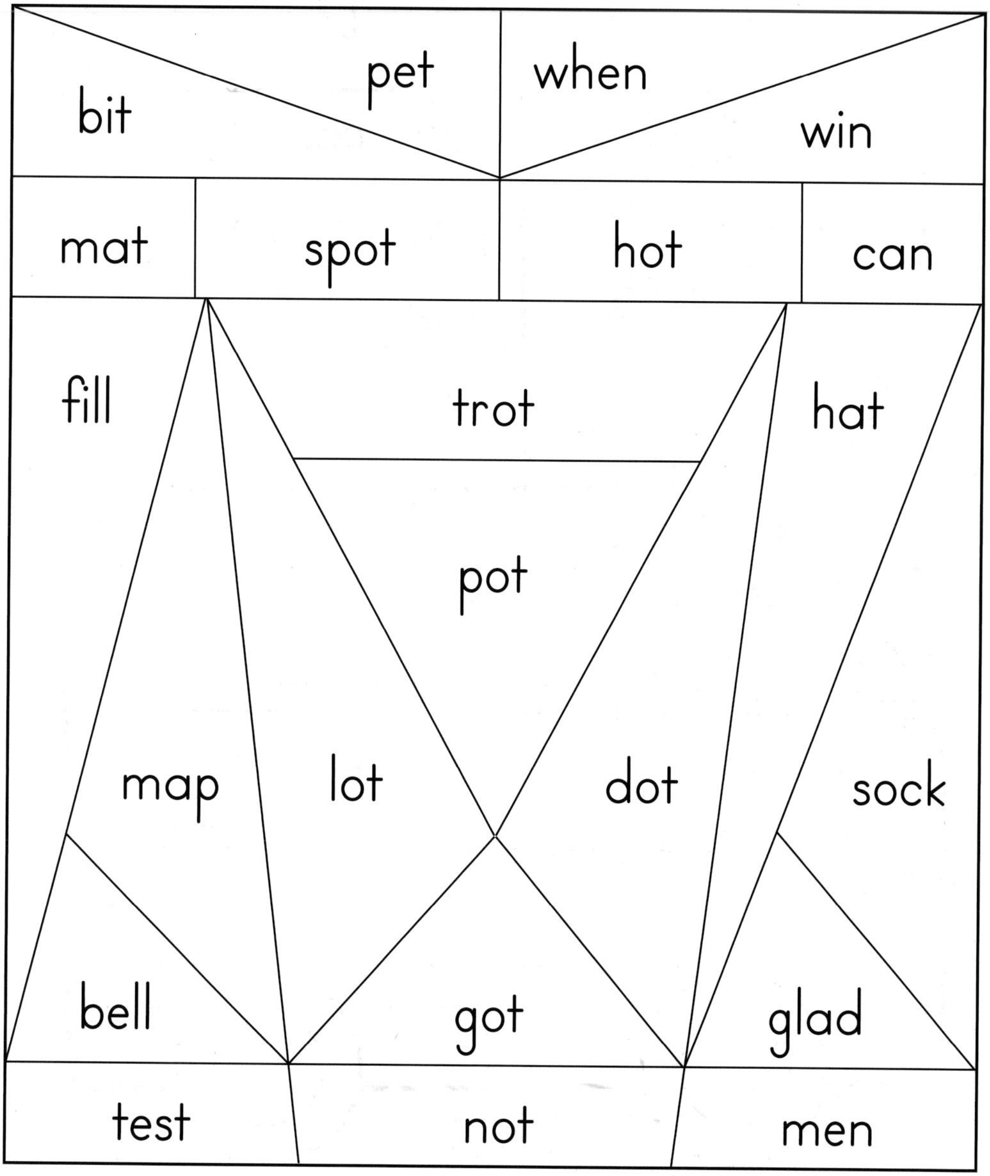

Red Hearts

Directions: Color the hearts red.

Our Feathered Friends

Directions: Connect the dots to find the picture. Color the picture.

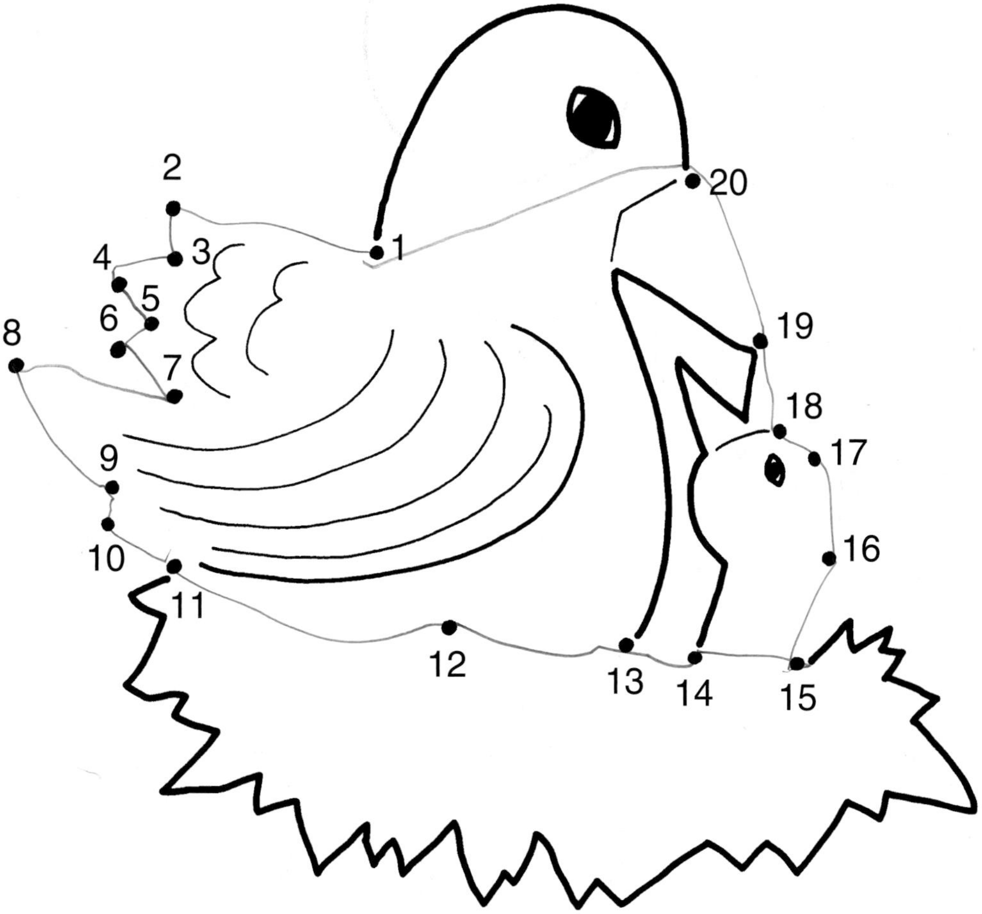

Making Sentences

Directions: Put these words in order to make sentences.

1. I cherries. the ate 

2. swim pond. the in Fish 

3. ride I my can bike. 

4. net. strong This a is 

Fast Food Math

Directions: Cross out each answer in the hamburger as you solve the problems.

5 - 0 = 5

7 - 1 = 8

4 - 2 = 6

8 - 3 = 11

4 - 1 = 5

10 - 5 = 15

7 - 6 = 14

7 - 3 = 10

8 - 8 = 16

9 - 6 = ______

Number Clues

Directions: Read the clues to find the mystery numbers.

1. I am thinking of a number.
It is greater than 21.
It is less than 23.
What is the number? ____

2. I am thinking of a number.
It is less than 40.
It is greater than 30.
You say it when you count by 5s.
What is the number? ____

3. I am thinking of a number.
It has a 2 in the ones place.
It has a 7 in the tens place.
What is the number? ____

4. I am thinking of a number.
It is less than 20.
It has a 0 in the ones place.
What is the number? ____

5. I am thinking of a number.
It is less than 10.
It is odd.
It is greater than 7.
What is the number? ____

6. I am thinking of a number.
It is greater than 50.
It is less than 60.
It has a 3 in the ones place.
What is the number? ____

Fishing for Numbers

Directions: Add the numbers. Color the picture.

9 = orange	10 = brown	11 = blue	12 = yellow

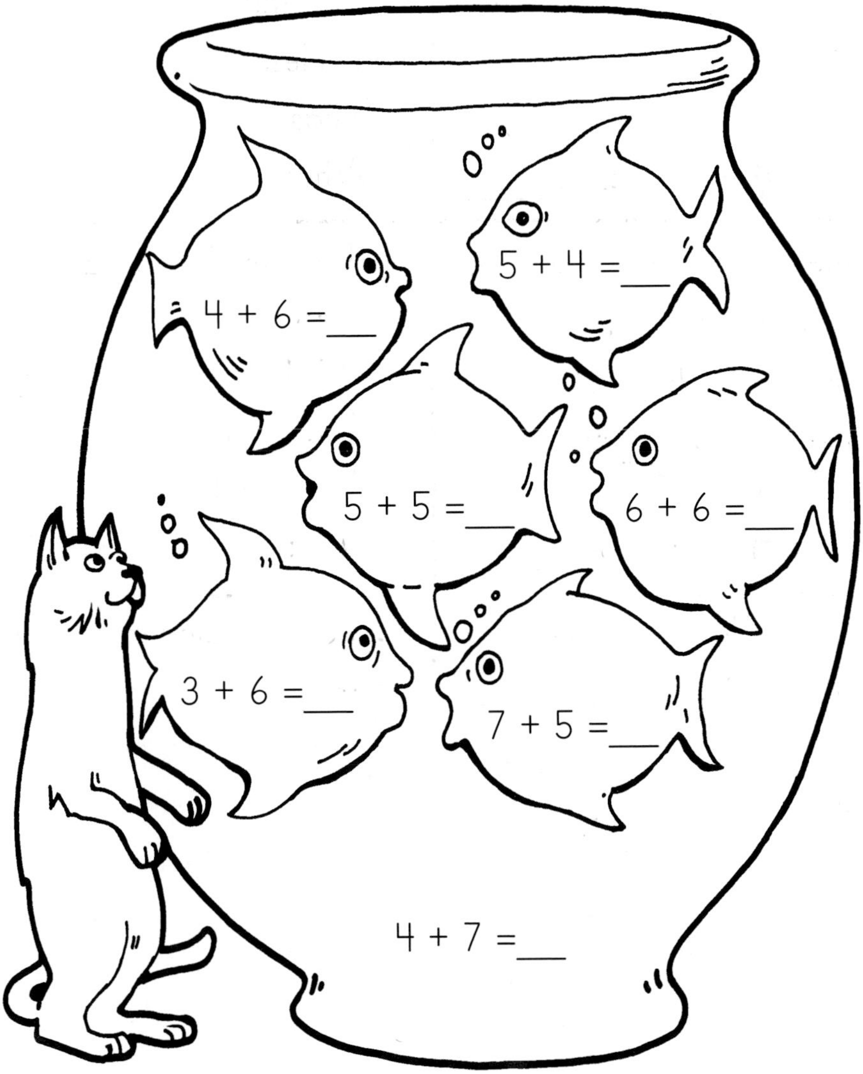

Fan Fun

Directions: Find and circle the *an* family words.

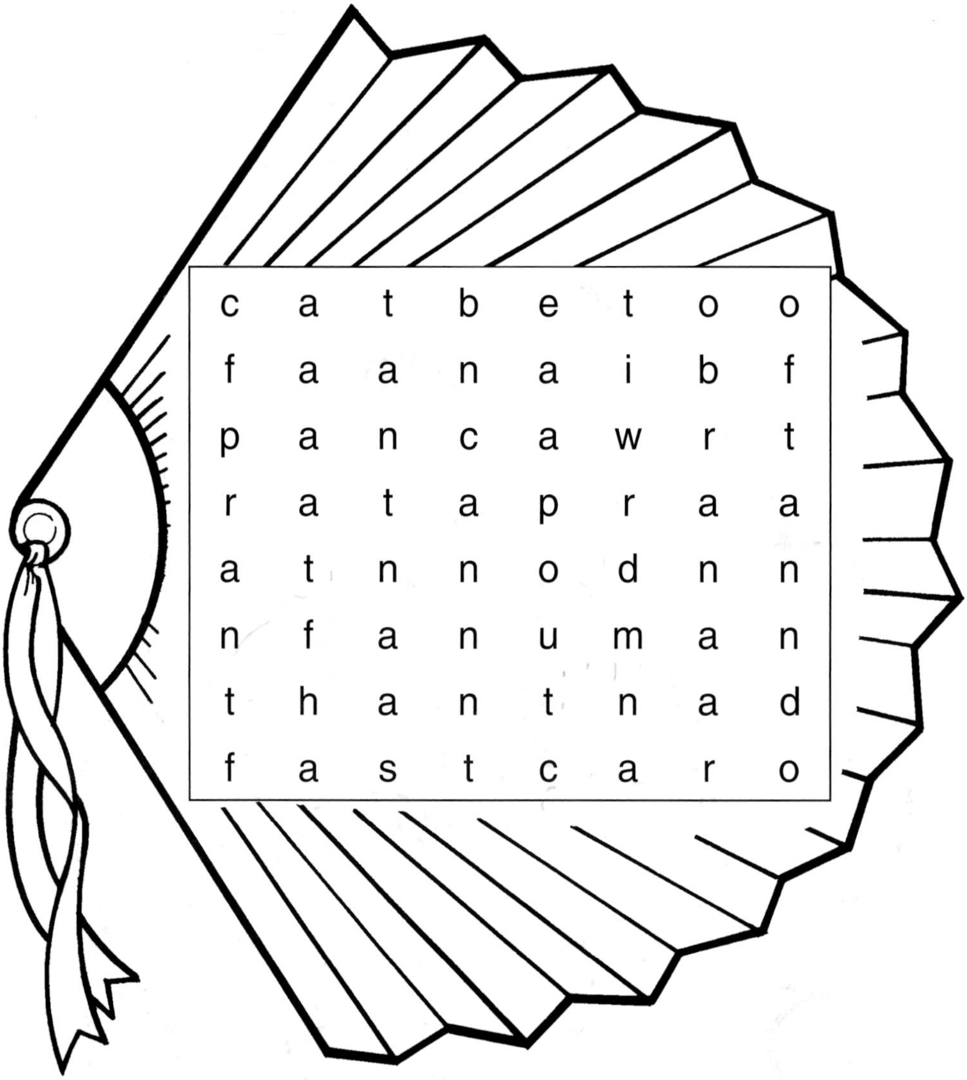

c	a	t	b	e	t	o	o
f	a	a	n	a	i	b	f
p	a	n	c	a	w	r	t
r	a	t	a	p	r	a	a
a	t	n	n	o	d	n	n
n	f	a	n	u	m	a	n
t	h	a	n	t	n	a	d
f	a	s	t	c	a	r	o

tan	**pan**	**man**	**ran**
can	**bran**	**fan**	**than**

Colorful Clown

Directions: Color the clown.

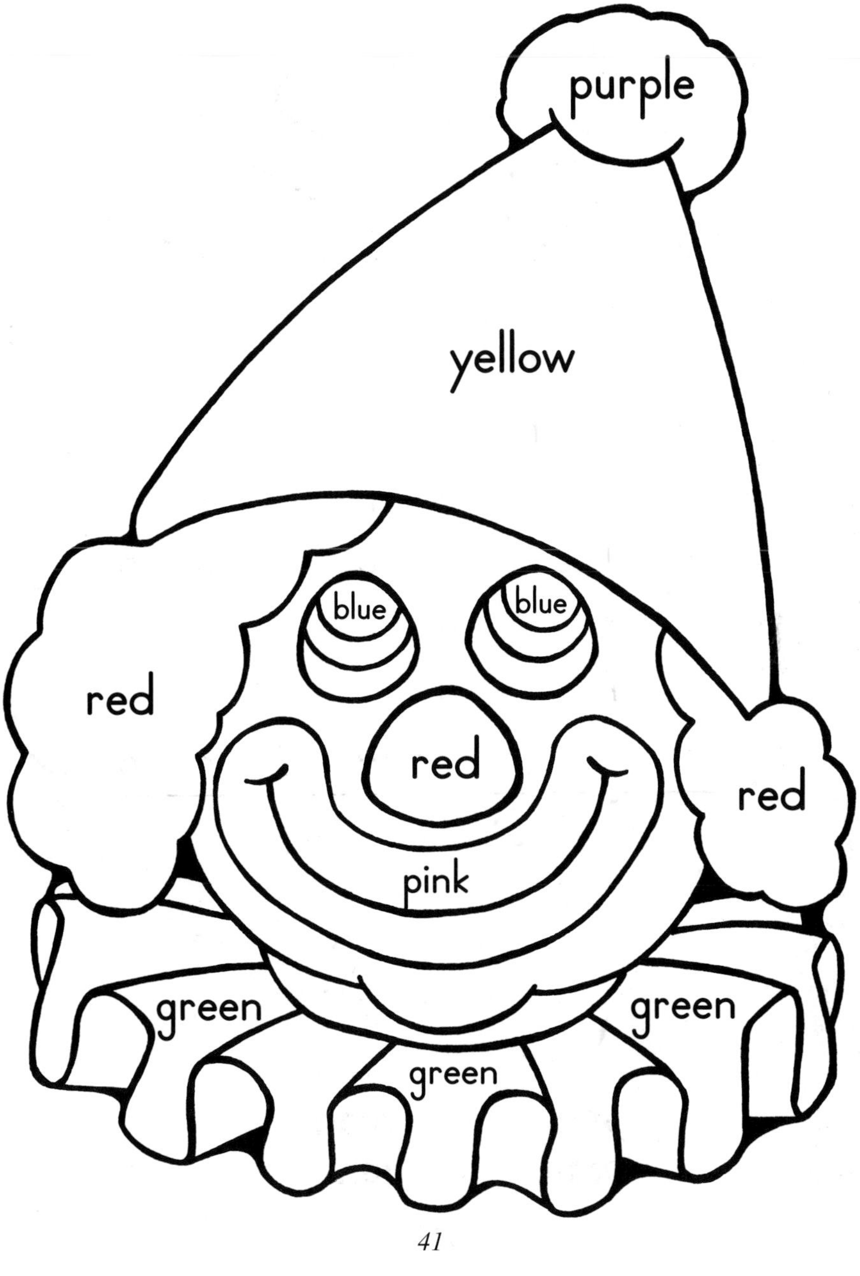

Crossword Blocks

Directions: Fill in the crossword blocks with the correct words.

broke joke poke smoke spoke woke

1.

4.

2.

5.

3.

6.

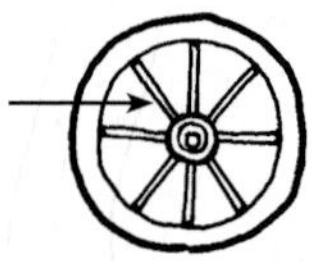

Rhyming Coats

Directions: Color the rhyming coats red. Color the other coats brown.

Things That Are Brown

Directions: Color the things that can be brown.

Which Flower?

Directions: Help the bee find the right flower. Solve the problems. Draw a line from the bee to the flower with the sum of 14. Color the picture.

What Goes Together?

Directions: Draw lines to connect each set of two things that go together. The first one is done for you.

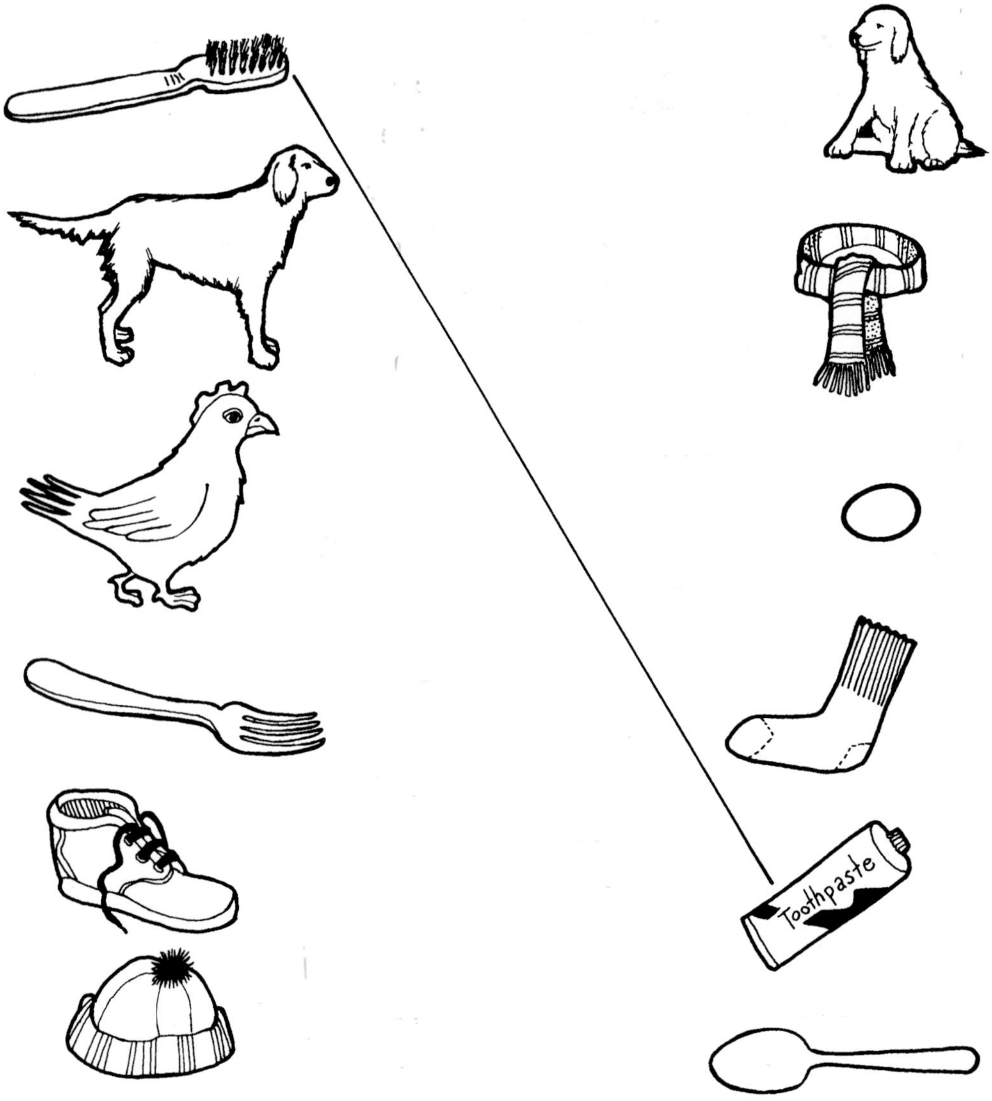

Baa, Baa, Black Sheep

Directions: Look at the picture. Read the poem.

Baa, baa, black sheep,
Have you any wool?
Yes, sir, yes, sir,
Three bags full;
One for the master,
One for the dame,
And one for the little boy
Who lives down the lane.

1. How many bags of wool are there?

2. Who has the wool?

3. Where does the little boy live?

Cute Rhymes

Directions: Circle each word in the puzzle. Color the picture.

s	d	s	u	i	t	k	s	i	r	f	w
s	m	d	e	r	b	f	t	i	o	r	f
m	z	x	n	b	x	l	s	l	d	u	u
k	u	n	w	e	o	u	h	f	e	i	n
c	u	t	e	l	a	t	e	m	h	t	e
n	w	a	e	j	w	e	x	r	g	n	d
q	k	d	j	v	f	g	o	m	u	t	e

School Days

Directions: Add the numbers. Color the picture.

7 = yellow	8 = red	9 = brown
10 = yellow		11 = green

Ending Sounds

Directions: Look at the pictures. Say each word. Write the ending letter on the line to complete the words.

1.  do___

2.  tu___

3.  cu___

4.  pi___

5.  ha___

6.  ca___

7.  su___

8.  su___

More Beginning Sounds

Directions: Say the name of the picture. Circle the beginning sound.

1.  k l	2. 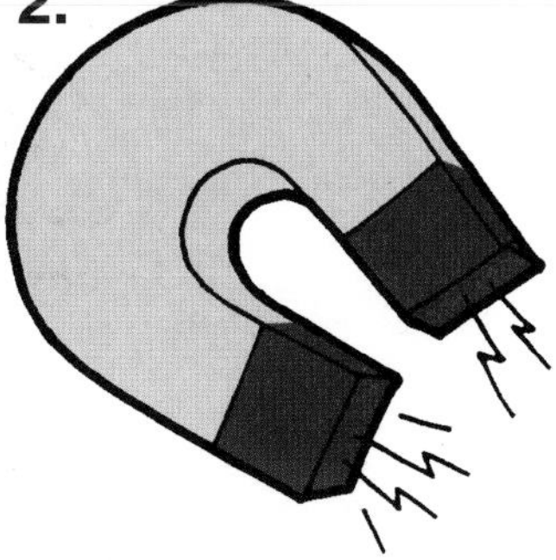 l m	3.  k m
4.  p q	5.  k q	6.  r v

The Chicken and the Egg

Directions: Help the chicken find her egg. Solve the problems. Draw a line from the chicken to the egg with the sum of 9. Color the picture.

Rainy-Day Colors

Directions: Use this key to color the coat.

5 = yellow	4 = blue	3 = green

Crack the Code

Directions: Look at the code. Write the letter in the blank above each number. Write the word on the line.

a	b	c	d	e	f	g	h	i	j	k	l	m
1	2	3	4	5	6	7	8	9	10	11	12	13
n	o	p	q	r	s	t	u	v	w	x	y	z
14	15	16	17	18	19	20	21	22	23	24	25	26

___ ___ ___
8 5 14

___ ___ ___
20 5 14

___ ___ ___
4 5 14

___ ___ ___
13 5 14

___ ___ ___ ___
20 8 5 14

Light Bulbs

Directions: Unscramble the words. Write them correctly on the lines.

1. hligt
2. rhtgi
3. thifg
4. ihtng
5. itgsh
6. tgrhib

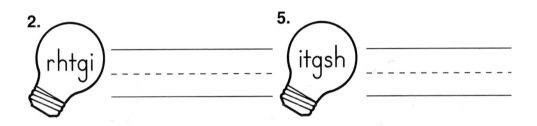

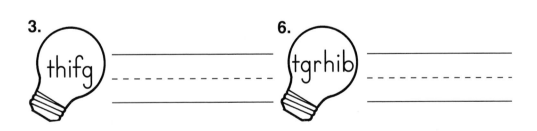

bright	fight	light	night	sight	right

Growing Crops

Directions: Color 6 tomatoes. Color 7 pumpkins. Color 8 ears of corn.

Addition

Directions: Count the things in each box. Add the numbers.

1. 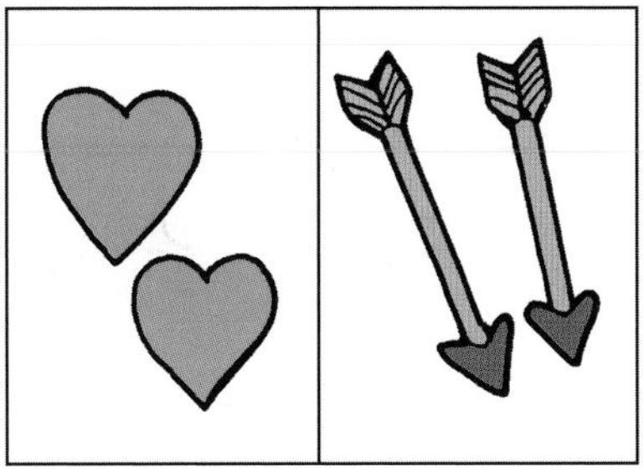

2 + 2 = ____

2. 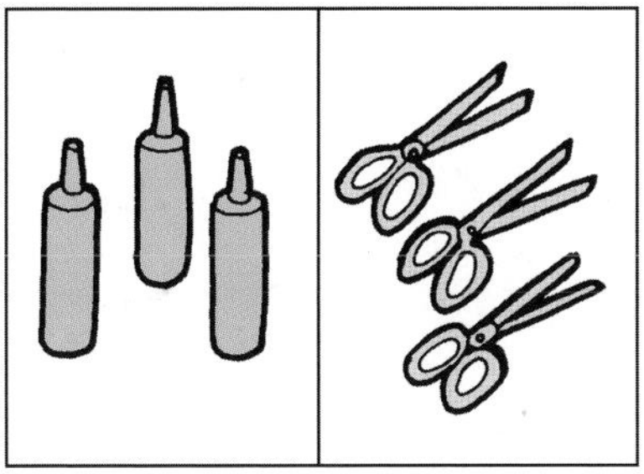

____ + ____ = ____

3. 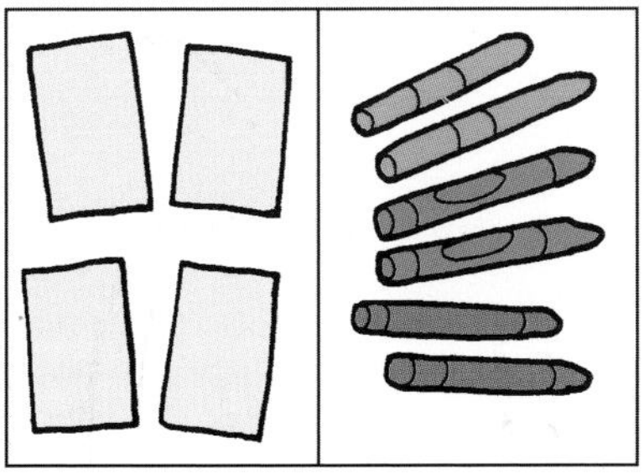

____ + ____ = ____

4. 

____ + ____ = ____

5. 

____ + ____ = ____

6. 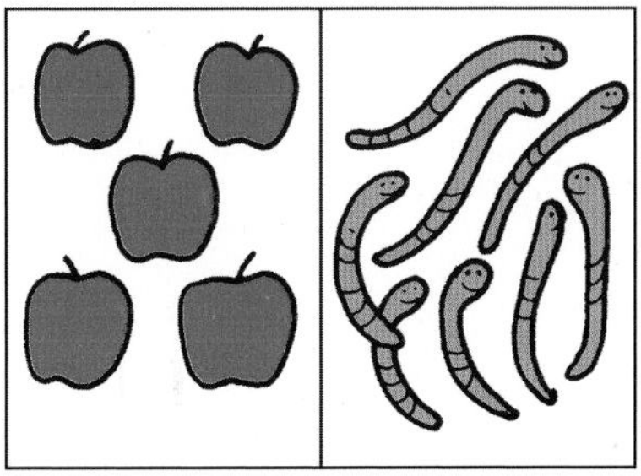

____ + ____ = ____

A Peanut Story

Directions: Read the story. Answer the questions below.

A peanut sat upon the track.
Its heart was all a-flutter.
Along came engine number nine —
Toot! toot! — peanut butter.

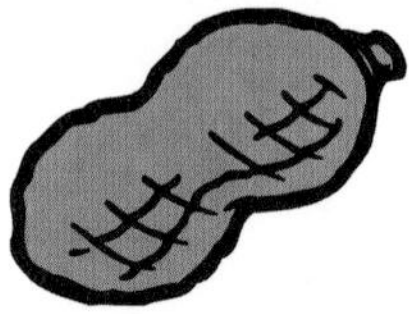

1. Where was the peanut?

2. What came down the tracks?

3. What happened to the peanut?

Balloons

Directions: Cross out each answer in the balloon as you solve the problems.

0 + 6 =

1 + 10 =

2 + 3 =

3 + 5 =

4 + 7 =

5 + 9 =

6 + 8 =

2 + 9 =

8 + 2 =

9 + 5 =

10 + 9 =

Making Contractions

Directions: Read the two words on the leaves of each flower. Write a contraction in the center of the flower using the two words from the leaves. The first one has been done for you.

1.

2.

3.

4.

5.

6.

7.

8.

9.

Under the Sea

Directions: Color 8 starfish. Color 9 fish. Color 10 seashells.

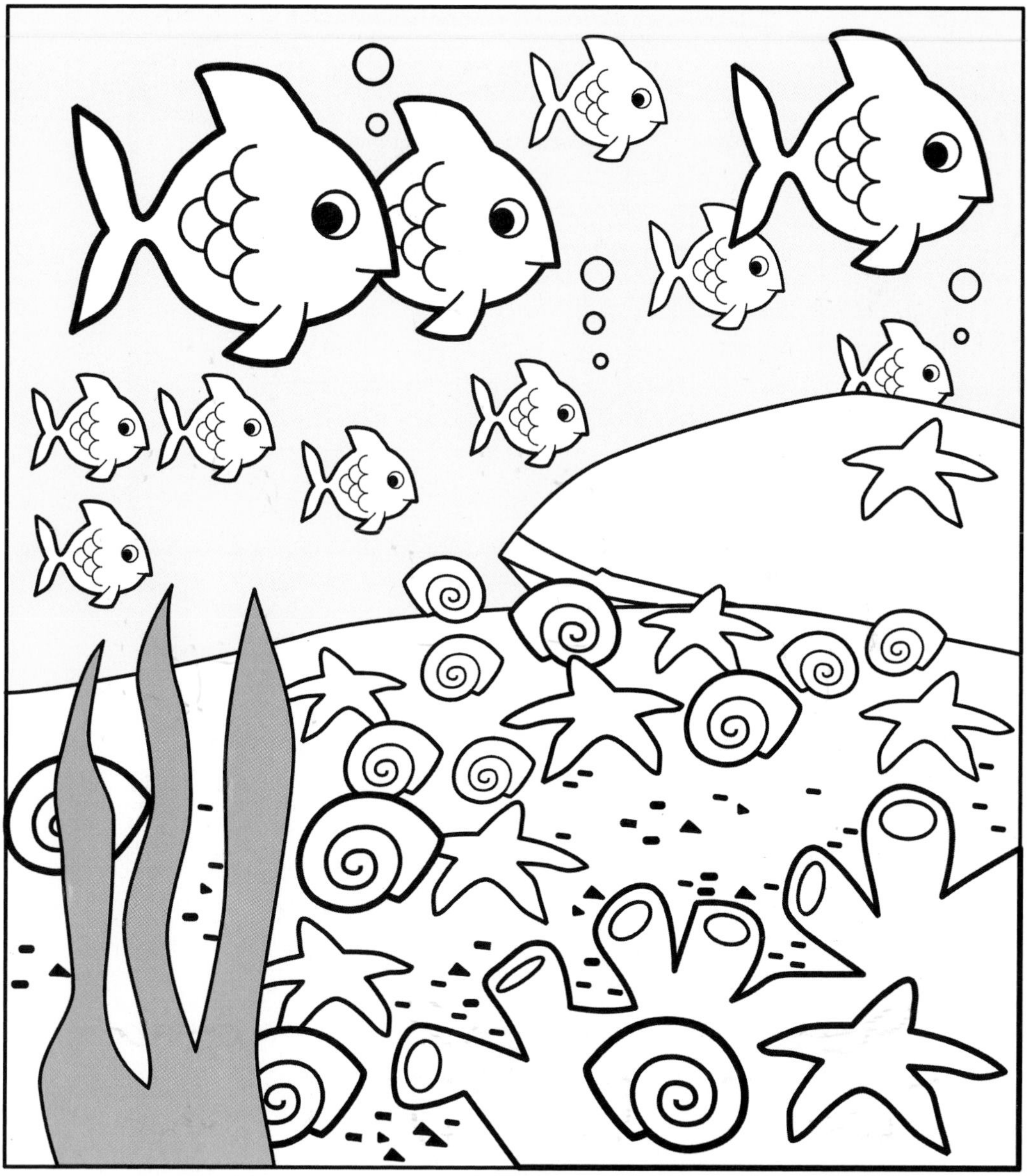

Happy Birthday!

Directions: Fill in the puzzle. Use the clues at the bottom of the page to help you.

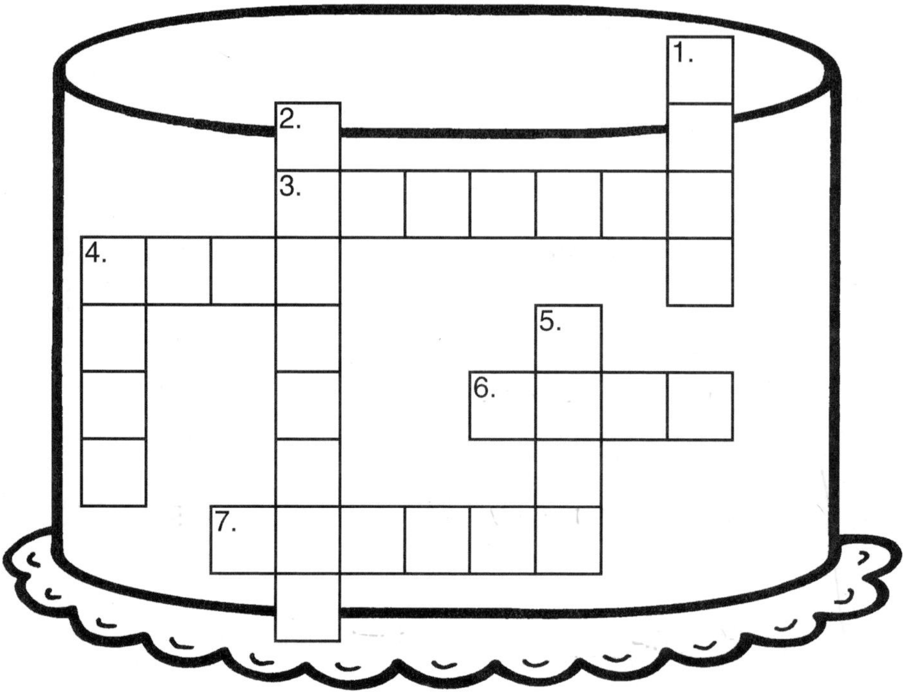

Across

3. 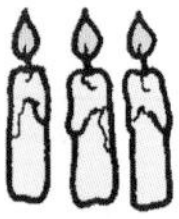

4. 

6. 

7. 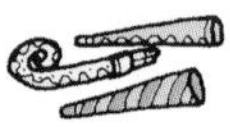

card
cake
hats
wish
ice cream
favors
game
candles

Down

1. 

2. 

4. 

5. 

How Many?

Directions: Fill in the number that completes the title of the rhyme or fairy tale. The first one has been done for you.

1. Snow White and the __7__ Dwarfs

2. __1__, __2__, Buckle My Shoe

3. Goldilocks and the __3__ Bears

4. The __9__ Little Kittens

5. The __3__ Little Pigs

6. __10__ Dalmatians

7. __9__ Blind Mice

Sheep on the Farm

Directions: Circle the words in the puzzle.

b	e	e	p	r	b	f	d	w	i	s	d
m	s	m	n	b	x	n	e	l	d	w	u
k	h	k	e	e	p	f	e	f	e	e	p
a	e	l	a	e	a	w	p	m	h	e	e
n	e	a	n	j	e	e	p	r	g	p	e
q	p	k	j	v	f	g	o	w	e	e	p

beep	jeep	peep	sweep
deep	keep	sheep	weep

Sweet Dreams

Directions: Read the story. Answer the questions below.

At bedtime, my father reads a story to me and tucks me in my covers. Then we tell each other about our days. He says that he is proud of me. I always have sweet dreams!

1. What is the first thing the father does?

2. What does the child tell the father?

3. How does the child sleep?

Rhyming Flutes

Directions: Color the flutes that rhyme yellow. Color the flutes that do not rhyme green.

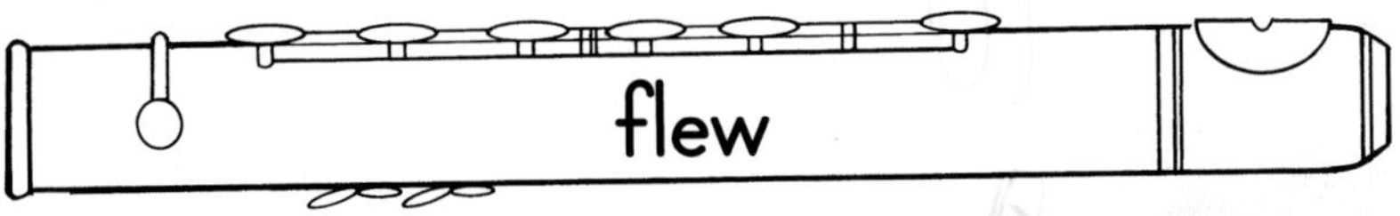

Practice and Learn

WORKBOOK

First Grade Activities

Uppercase Letters

Directions: Copy each uppercase letter.

A B C D

E F G H

I J K L

M N O P

Q R S T

U V W X

Y Z

Lowercase Letters

Directions: Copy each lowercase letter.

a b c d

e f g h

i j k l

m n o p

q r s t

u v w x

y z

Short "Aa" Words

Directions: Blend the letter sounds together as you say each word. Then circle the picture it names.

p → an

r → am

c → at

t → ag

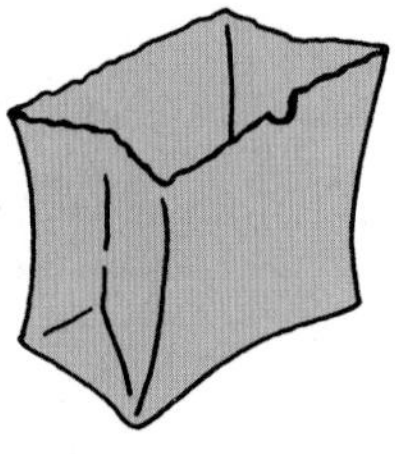

Short "Ee" Words

Directions: Finish each word with "et" or "en." Color the pictures.

j

p

h

t

Directions: Finish each word with "est" or "ell." Color the pictures.

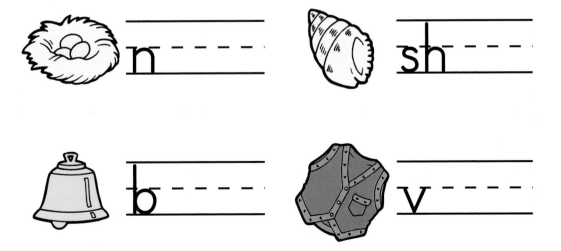

n

sh

b

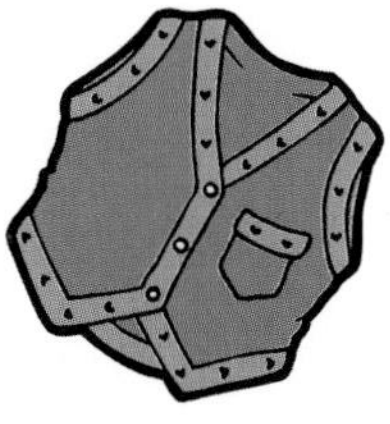
v

Short "Ii" Words

Directions: Unscramble the words. Write them on the lines.

lip	**mill**	**sit**
hit	**grin**	**pill**

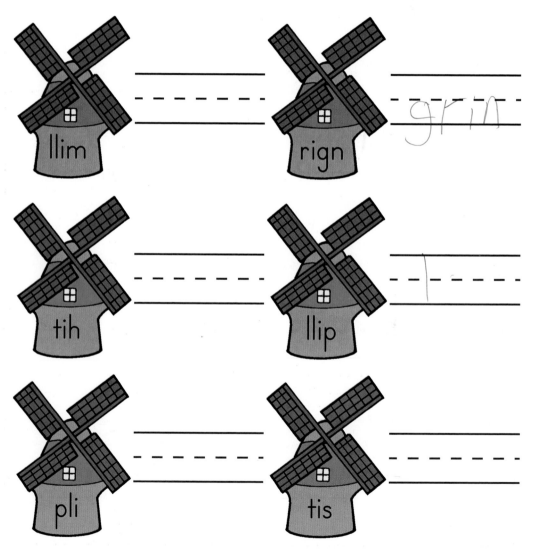

grin

Short "Oo" Words

Directions: Write the name of each picture below. Then, circle the letter that represents the short *o* sound.

1.
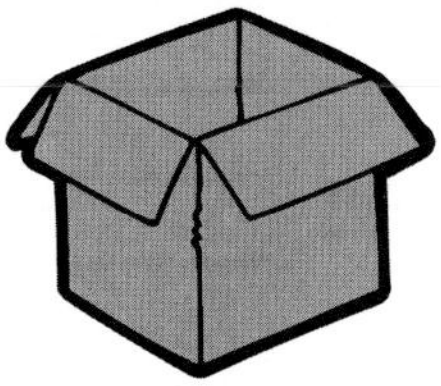

2.

3.

4.
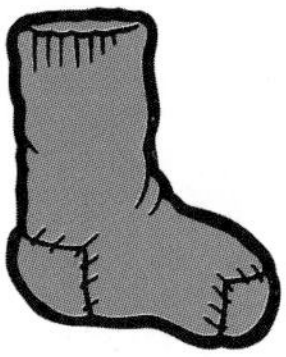

5.

6.

7.

8.

Short "Uu" Words

Directions: Unscramble the short "u" words. Write them on the lines.

ppu ____________ uppm ____________

umpj ____________ pu ____________

pcu ____________ mupl ____________

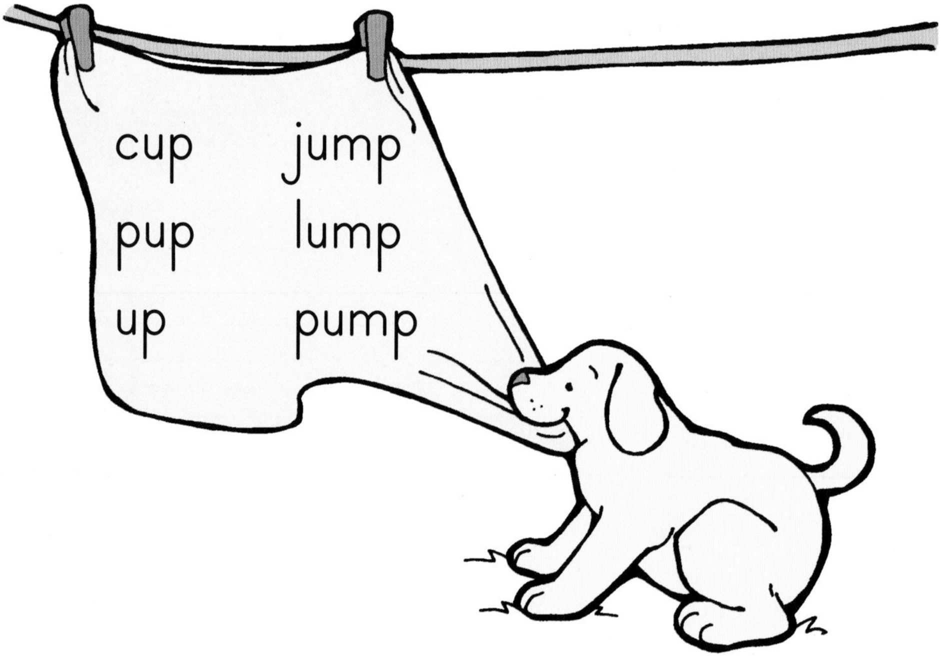

Long "Aa" Words

Directions: Fill in missing letters under the pictures. Then write the words in the correct word family below each picture.

day	date	hay
make	bake	lake
say	gate	late

_____ay

_____ake

_____ate

Long "Ee" Words

Directions: Finish each word with "ee" or "ea."

w ____ d

f ____ t

h ____ t

k ____ p

n ____ d

wh ____ t

sh ____ p

m ____ t

n ____ t

f ____ d

bl ____ d

sp ____ d

Long "Ii" Words

Directions: Look at the pictures. Use the words in the box below to name the objects.

1.

2.

3.

4.

5.

6.

dice	ice	pine
night	mice	vine

Long "Oo" Words

Directions: Finish each word with "old" or "oat."

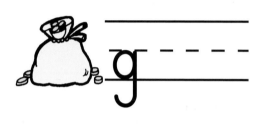

g

b

g

c

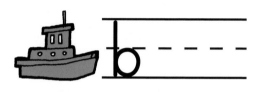

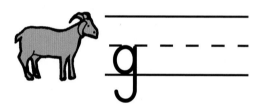

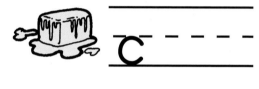

Directions: Finish each word with "oke" or "ow."

r

arr

b

br

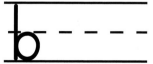

Long "Uu" Words

Directions: Unscramble the words. Write the long "u" words on the lines.

cube	huge	tube
dune	mule	tune

Missing Vowels

Directions: Say the picture names. Write the missing vowels.

1.

b ___ t

4.

r ___ ck

2.

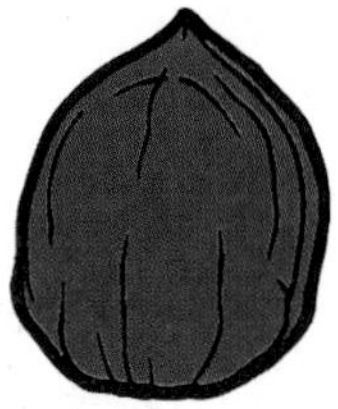

n ___ t

5.

b ___ x

3.

m ___ c ___

6.

t r ___ ___ n

"Bl" and "Br" Blends

Directions: Circle the pictures that begin either with the "bl" or "br" sound.

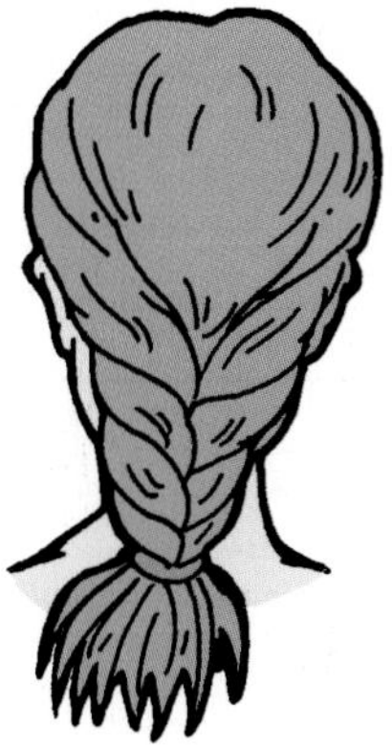

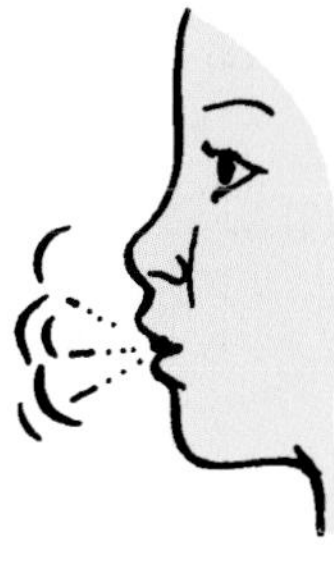

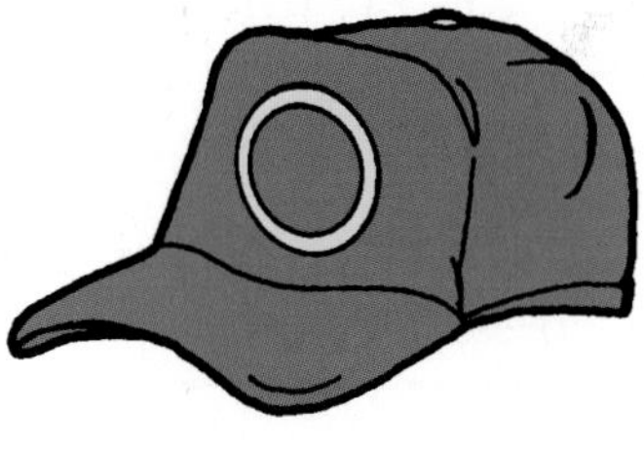

Many Blends

Directions: Say the name for each picture. On the line, write the blend you hear at the beginning of the word.

Listen for the **r** blends as in **trap** and **grass.**

1. 	**2.** 	**3.** 

Listen for the **l** blends as in **flag** and **slide.**

4. 	**5.** 	**6.** 

Listen for the **s** blends as in **smile** and **swim.**

7. 	**8.** 	**9.** 

Ending Blends

Directions: Say the name for each picture. Find the word that names the picture. Write it beside the picture. Underline the ending blend.

skunk **~~desk~~** **ring** **plant** **jump**

1. 
desk

2. 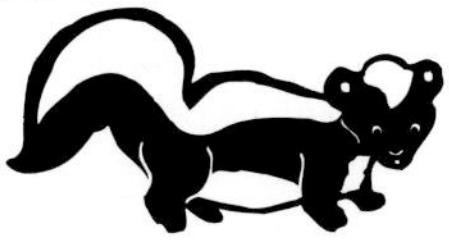

3. 

4. 

5. 

Words in a Family

Directions: Say the name for each picture. Write the beginning sound. Then, read all the words in each word family out loud.

1. an	 f an	 c an	 v an
2. et	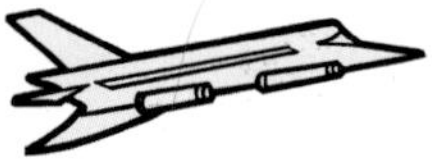 j et	 n et	 p et
3. and	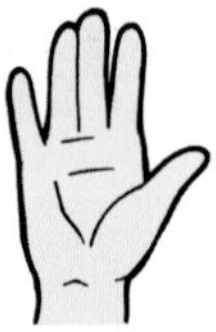 h and	 S and	 b and
4. op	 m op	 p op	 h op

Short or Long?

Directions: Say the name for each picture. On the line, print the vowel sound that you hear. If the vowel is **short**, fill in the bubble labeled **short**. If the vowel is **long**, fill in the bubble labeled **long**.

1.

○ short
○ long

2.

○ short
○ long

3.

○ short
○ long

4.

○ short
○ long

5.

○ short
○ long

6.

○ short
○ long

7.

○ short
○ long

8.

○ short
○ long

9.

○ short
○ long

Which Short Vowel?

Directions: Read each sentence. Circle the word that best completes the sentence and write it on the line.

	**1.** The dog sat in the ________________ .	set sun sick
	**2.** The pig is on the ________________ .	mop map mat
	**3.** The bug is in the ________________ .	top net nest
	**4.** I put him in the ________________ .	tub tan top
	**5.** He can ________________ .	dig den dot
	**6.** A fish has a ________________ .	fat fin fell

Two Meanings

Directions: Look at each pair of pictures. Write a word that names both pictures. Use the words from the Word Bank to help you.

1.  ____________ 

2.  ____________ 

3.  ____________ 

4.  ____________ 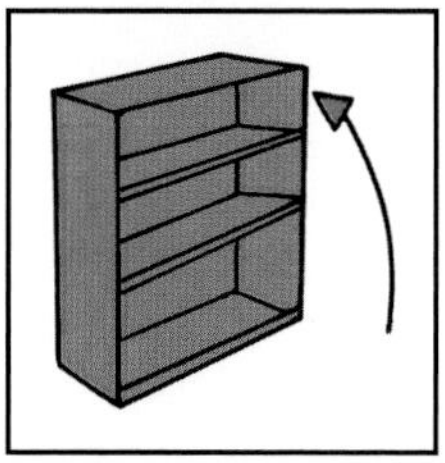

5. 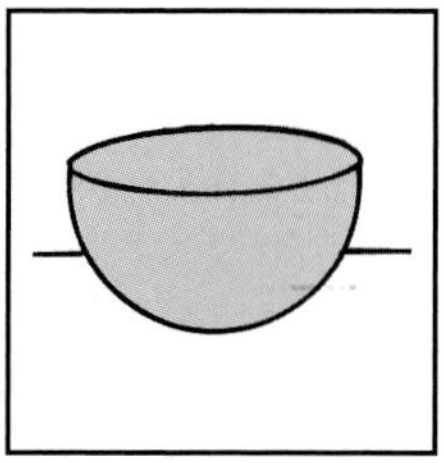 ____________ 

Word Bank

pot
bat
top
saw
bowl

Rhyming Sentences

Directions: Complete the blank in each sentence with a word that rhymes with the underlined word. Use the words from the Rhyming Word Bank to help you.

Rhyming Word Bank		
truck	hat	fish
box	book	frog

1.  Look at the ________________.

2.  The fox is in a ________________.

3.  On the log sits a ________________.

4.  The cat wears a ________________.

5.  There is a duck in my ____________.

6.  I wish I had a ________________.

Myrtle Turtle's Sight Words

Directions: Myrtle is a sight word turtle. She had to hide in her shell in a hurry. She scrambled her sight words. What a mess! Write the sight words correctly on her shell.

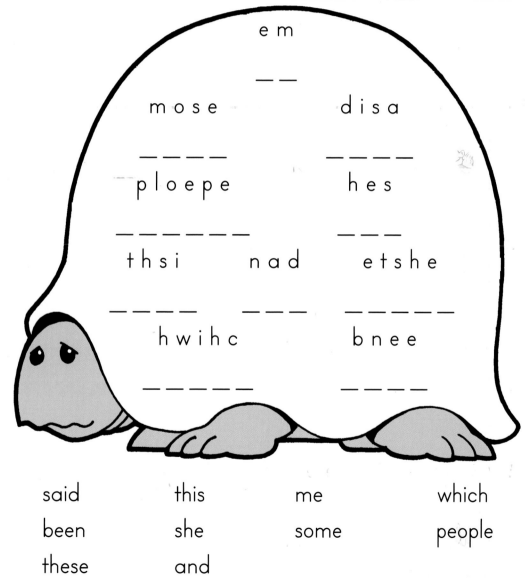

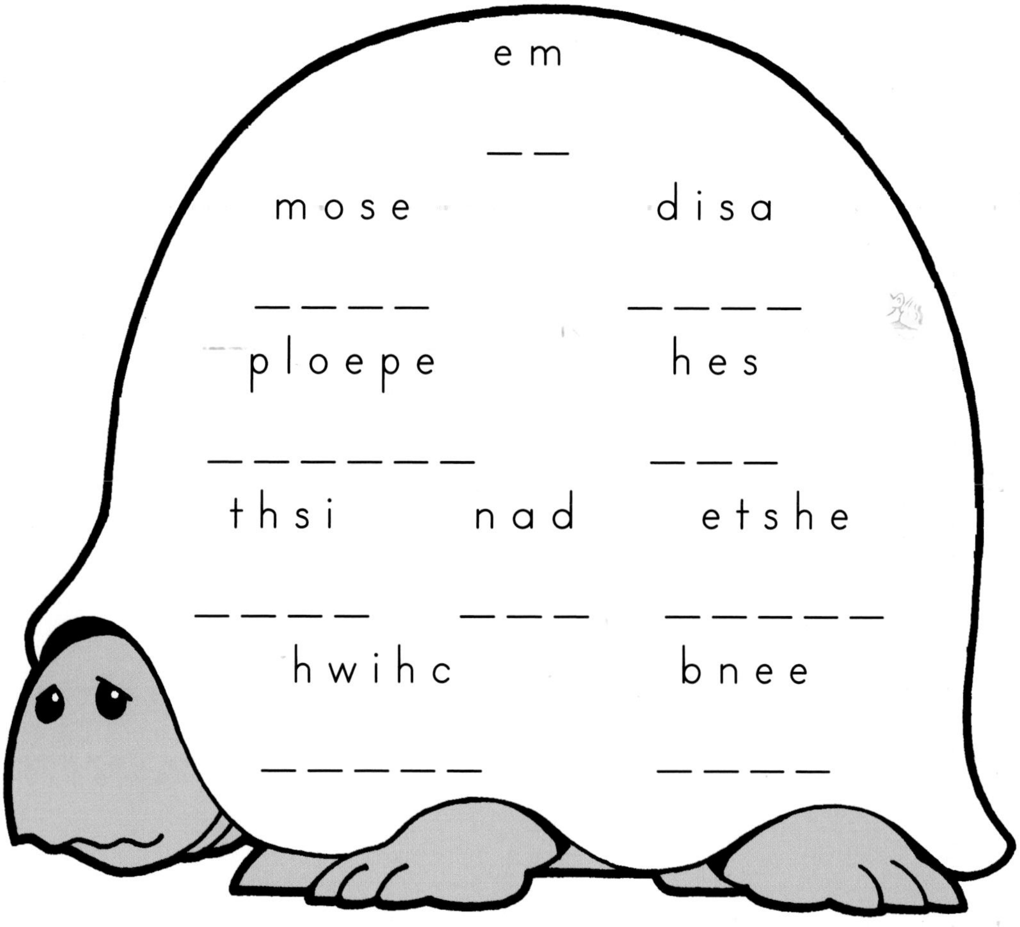

said	this	me	which
been	she	some	people
these	and		

Animal ABC Order

Directions: Put these words in alphabetical order.

1.

cat dog
lizard bird

____
____
____
____

2.

lion giraffe
tiger elephant

____
____
____
____

3.

pig cow
horse sheep

____
____
____
____

4.

fish crab
octopus shark

____
____
____
____

Same Letter ABC Order

Directions: Put these words in alphabetical order.

1.	**2.**
doll ____________	gum ____________
dance ____________	gate ____________
drive ____________	glue ____________
dinosaur ____________	goat ____________
deer ____________	grape ____________
3.	**4.**
melt ____________	snake ____________
monkey ____________	sail ____________
milk ____________	slide ____________
math ____________	soft ____________
mud ____________	smell ____________

Controlled Rr Words

Directions: Say the name for each picture. Print its name under it. Use the list of words to help you.

tractor	turkey	corn
bird	shark	yarn

1.

2.

3.

4.

5.

6.

Identifying Digraphs

Directions: Read the word in the first column. Write the digraph in the second column. Fill in the bubble in the third column to show if the digraph is heard at the beginning, in the middle, or at the end of the word.

Digraphs			
ch	sh	th	wh

Word	Digraph	Position in Word Beginning	Middle	End
1. cherry	ch	●	○	○
2. match		○	○	○
3. father		○	○	○
4. mouth		○	○	○
5. wash		○	○	○
6. lunch		○	○	○
7. sheep		○	○	○
8. teacher		○	○	○
9. whale		○	○	○

Describe It

Directions: Write a word that describes each picture below. Use the words in the Word Bank to help you.

Word Bank		
hot	three	smelly
quiet	cute	big

1. 

4. 

2. 

5. 

3. 

6. 

More Than One

Directions: Write a singular noun for the first picture. Make the noun plural to match the second picture.

	Singular		Plural
Example: 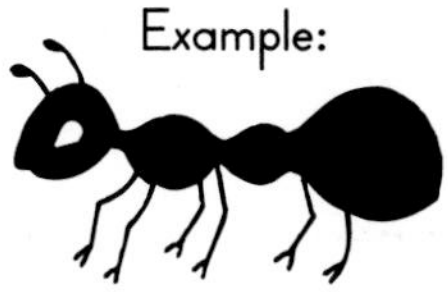	ant		ants
1. 			
2. 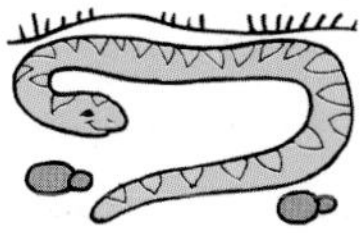		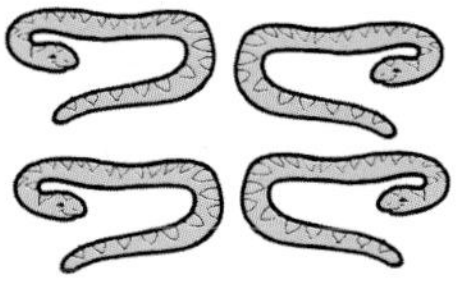	
3. 			
4. 			
5. 			
6. 			

First Words

Directions: Practice capitalizing the first word in each sentence by writing it on the line.

1. ________ mom took me shopping.
   my

2. ________ we play now?
   can

3. ________ like to eat cookies.
   i

4. ________ are going to the movies.
   we

5. ________ helped me bake a cake.
   she

6. ________ are eggs in the nest.
   there

7. ________ you coming with us?
   are

End It Right

Directions: Read each sentence below. Write the correct punctuation mark at the end of the sentence.

1. Does your class have a pet

2. My class has a pet lizard

3. His name is Tiny Tim

4. One day the lizard escaped

5. We looked all over the classroom for him

6. Do you know how hard it is to find something so small

7. We looked and looked

8. Then Sandy yelled, "There he is "

9. We put him back in his cage

10. We were so happy

Connect the Dots

Directions: Count by connecting the dots in number order from 1–50.

Connect the Dots

Directions: Count by connecting the dots in number order from 50–100.

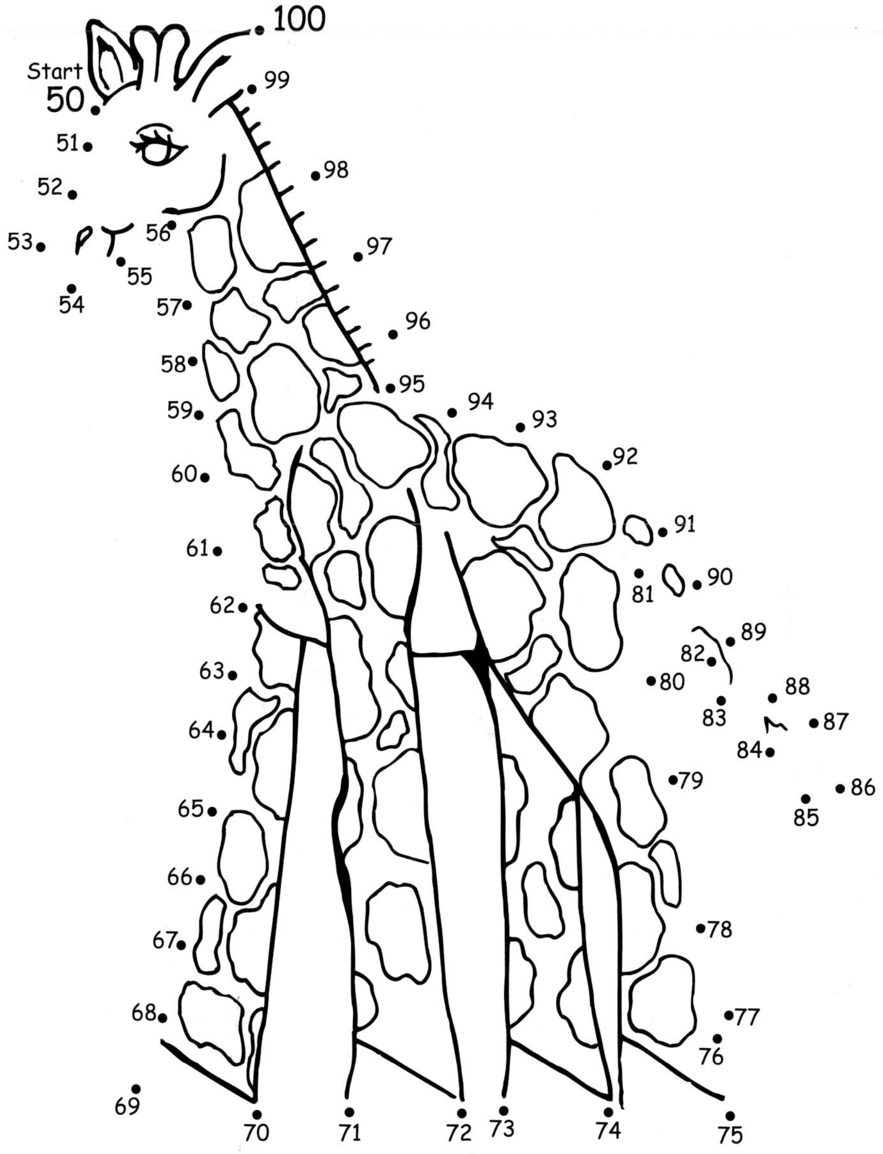

Count, Write, Name

Directions: Count the number of pictures. Write the number name. Use the Word Bank to help you.

Word Bank

one	two	three	four	five
six	seven	eight	nine	ten

1. 

2. 

3. 

4. 

5. 

Pizza, Pizza

Directions: Count the dots. Color the puzzle.

1 = red	**2 = brown**	**3 = yellow**	**4 = blue**

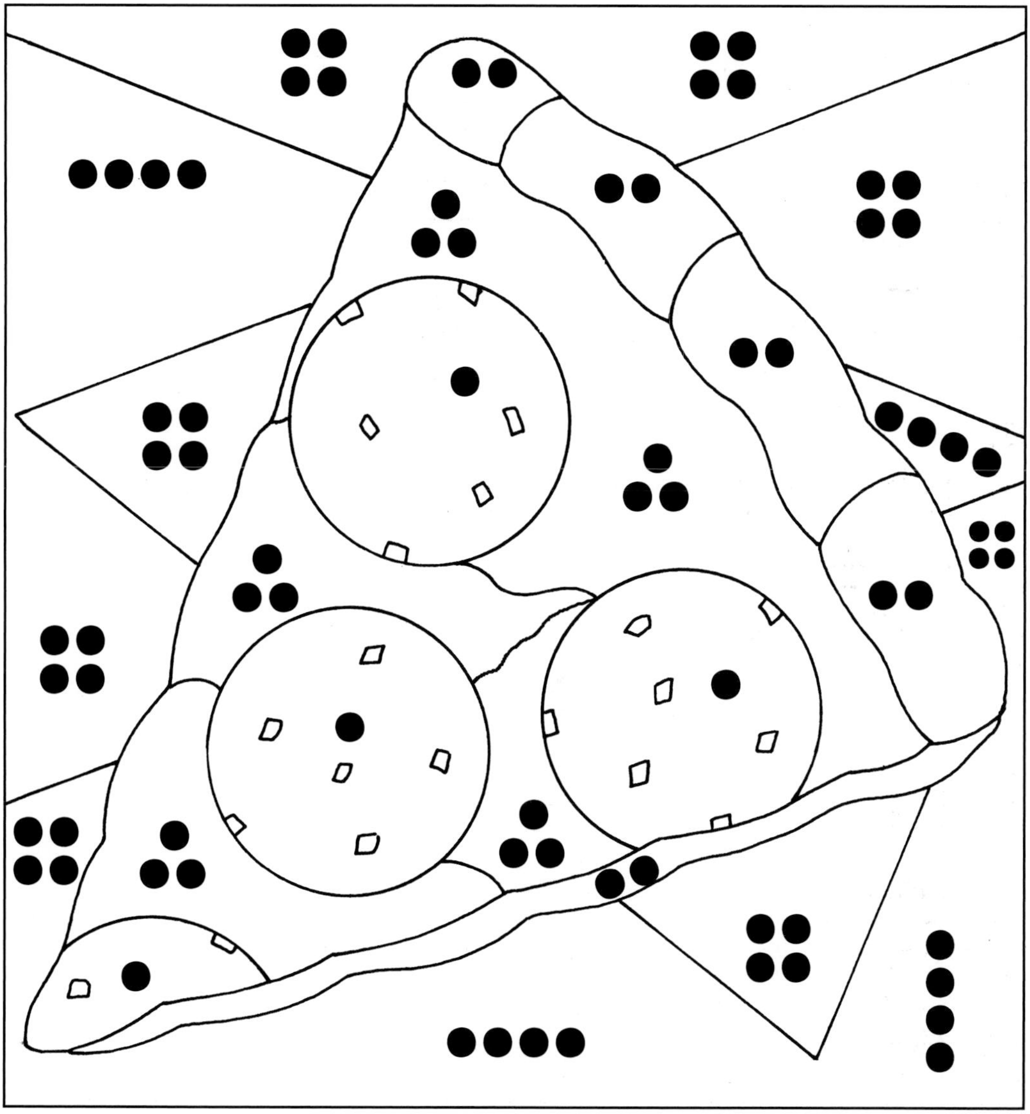

Coloring Fun

Color 3 stars yellow.

Color 2 balls red.

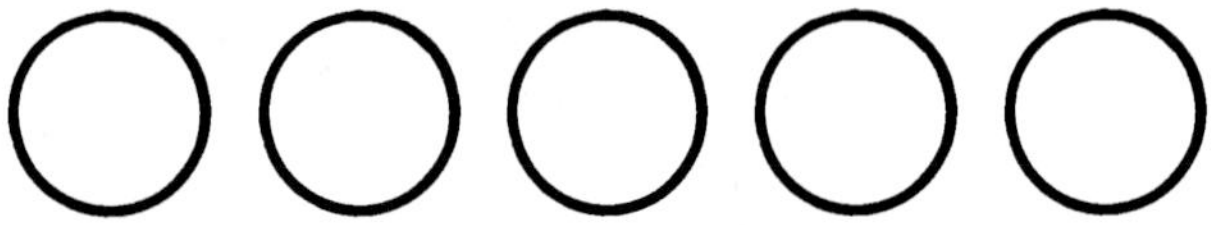

Color 1 bell blue.

Color 3 tops yellow.

Color 4 apples red.

Color 5 hats blue.

1. How many things are yellow? ____________________

2. How many things are red? ______________________

3. How many things are blue? _____________________

Everything Counts

Directions: Count and write the number of space things in the picture. Then color the pictures.

Counting by 2s

Directions: Color the numbers you say when counting by **2s**.

1	2	3	4	5	6	7	8	9	10
11	12	13	14	15	16	17	18	19	20
21	22	23	24	25	26	27	28	29	30
31	32	33	34	35	36	37	38	39	40
41	42	43	44	45	46	47	48	49	50
51	52	53	54	55	56	57	58	59	60
61	62	63	64	65	66	67	68	69	70
71	72	73	74	75	76	77	78	79	80
81	82	83	84	85	86	87	88	89	90
91	92	93	94	95	96	97	98	99	100

Counting by 5s

Directions: Help Max get home by counting by **5s**.

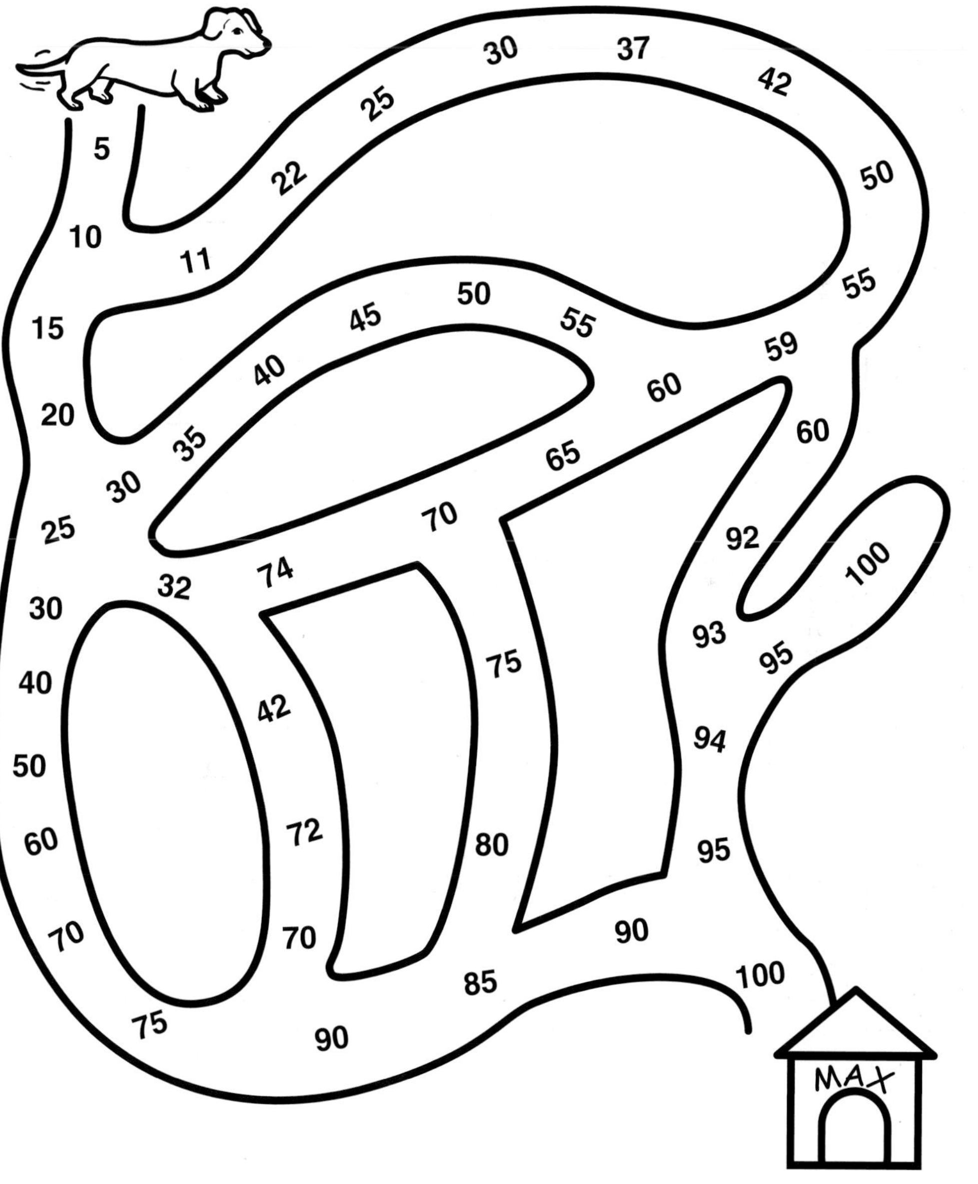

Counting by 10s

Directions: Count by **10s** to complete the dot-to-dot.

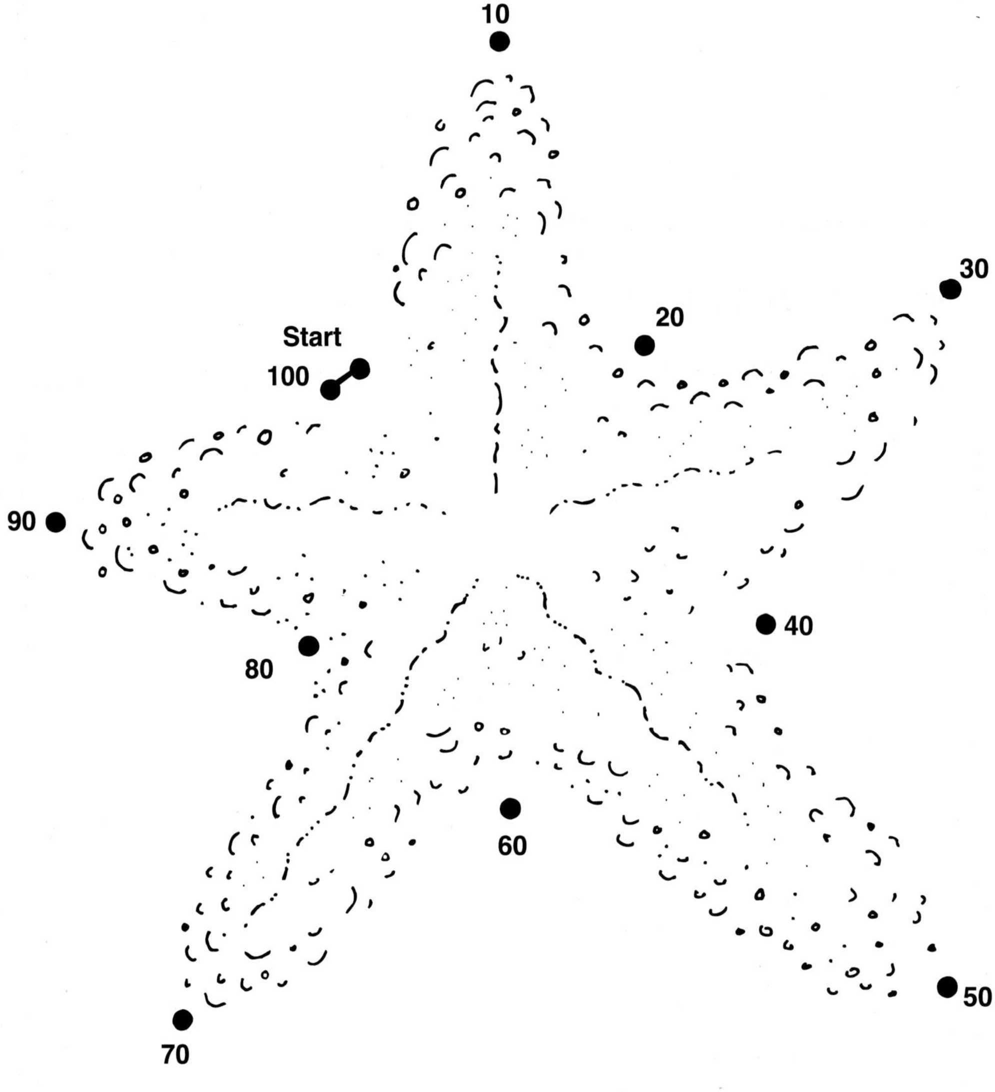

Before, After, Between

Directions: Write the number that comes before.

1. ________ 16	**4.** ________ 35
2. ________ 29	**5.** ________ 72
3. ________ 67	**6.** ________ 53

Directions: Write the number that comes after.

7. 19 ________	**10.** 38 ________
8. 93 ________	**11.** 84 ________
9. 62 ________	**12.** 55 ________

Directions: Write the number that comes between.

13. 23 ______ 25	**16.** 41 ______ 43
14. 56 ______ 58	**17.** 75 ______ 77
15. 94 ______ 96	**18.** 87 ______ 89

Sequencing Numbers

Directions: Place the numbers on the berries in order from least to greatest.

1.

______ ______ ______ ______ ______

2.

______ ______ ______ ______ ______

3.

______ ______ ______ ______ ______

4.

______ ______ ______ ______ ______

Odd and Even

Directions: Decide which numbers are odd and even. Color the puzzle.

odd = red	even = blue

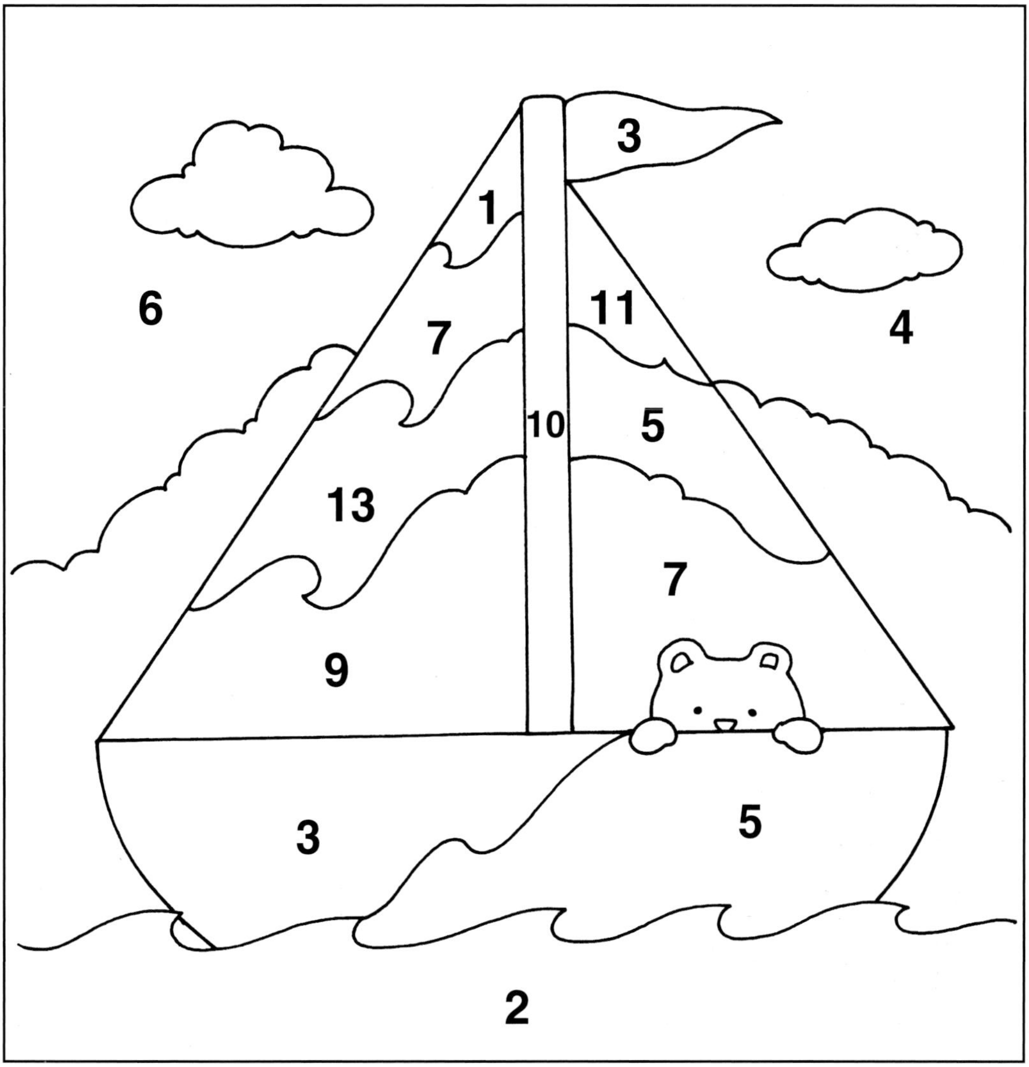

Show Addition

Directions: Write a number sentence to go with each picture.

1. 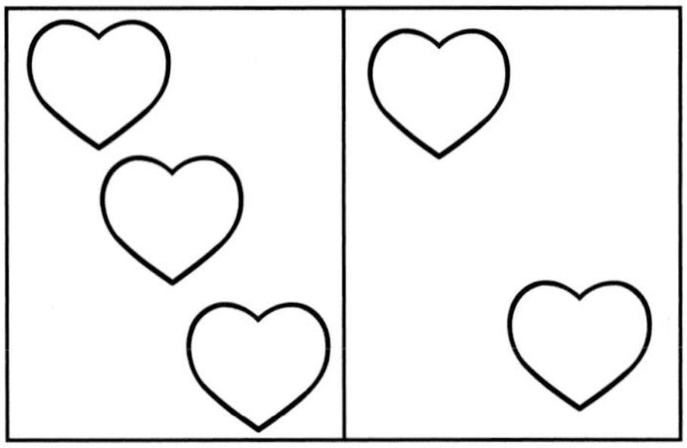

3 + 2 = 5

2. 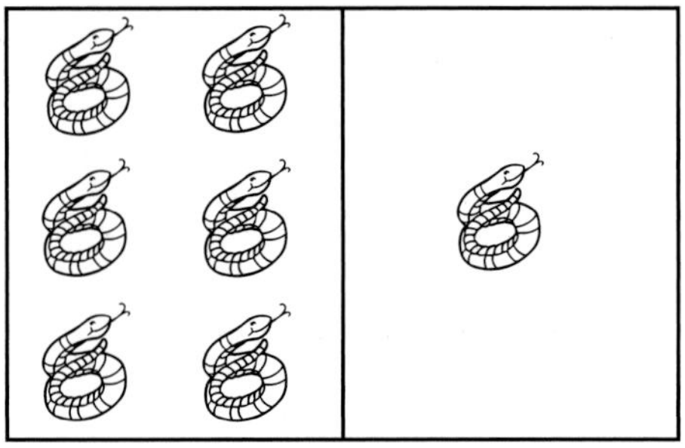

____ + ____ = ____

3. 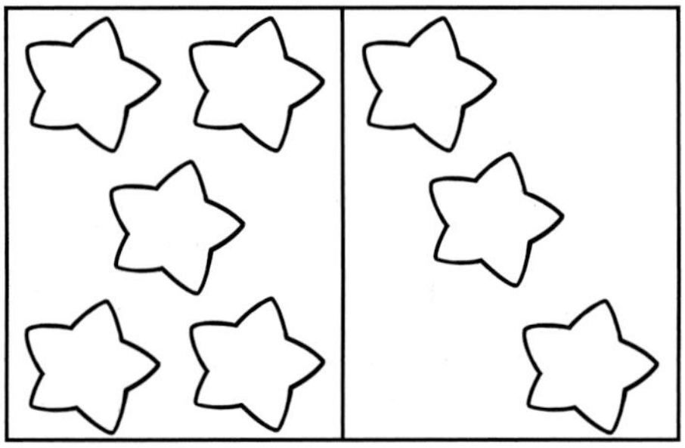

____ + ____ = ____

4. 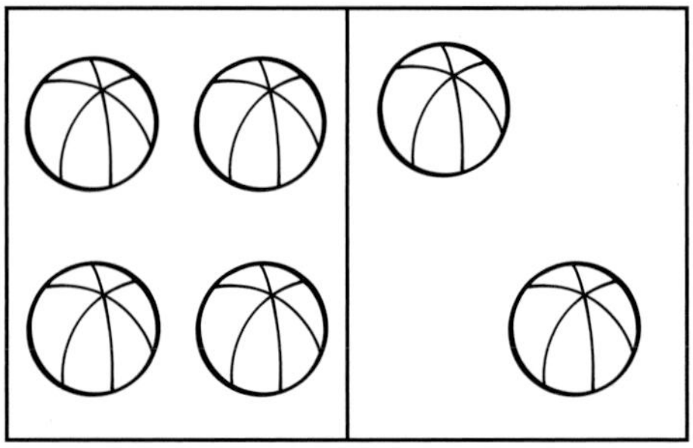

____ + ____ = ____

5. 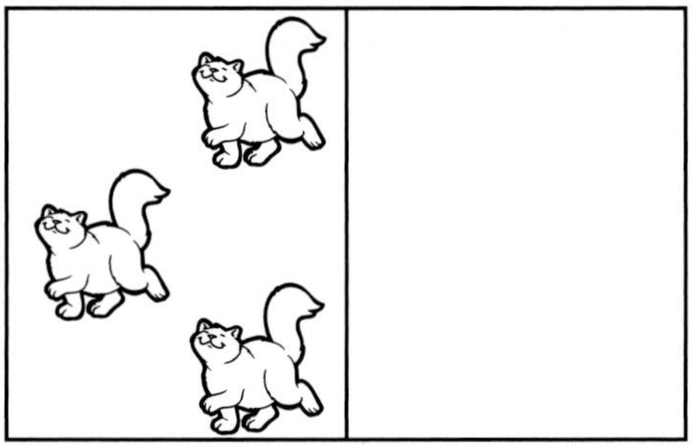

____ + ____ = ____

6. 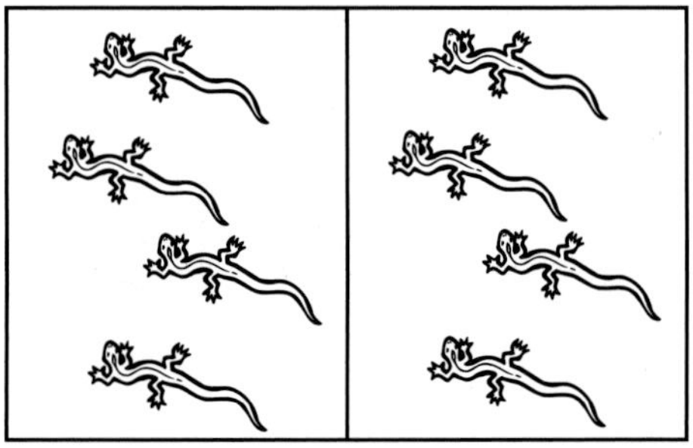

____ + ____ = ____

Books of Nine

Directions: Find the total on each book. Color each book that equals 9.

1. $\begin{array}{r} 5 \\ +\ 4 \\ \hline \end{array}$

2. $\begin{array}{r} 6 \\ +\ 3 \\ \hline \end{array}$

3. $\begin{array}{r} 2 \\ +\ 2 \\ \hline \end{array}$

4. $\begin{array}{r} 4 \\ +\ 5 \\ \hline \end{array}$

5. $\begin{array}{r} 5 \\ +\ 2 \\ \hline \end{array}$

6. $\begin{array}{r} 2 \\ +\ 7 \\ \hline \end{array}$

7. $\begin{array}{r} 1 \\ +\ 8 \\ \hline \end{array}$

8. $\begin{array}{r} 1 \\ +\ 4 \\ \hline \end{array}$

9. $\begin{array}{r} 0 \\ +\ 9 \\ \hline \end{array}$

Adding Palm Trees

Directions: Add the numbers on each tree. Add the top two numbers first. Then add the bottom number to the sum of the first numbers.

Sailing into Addition

Directions: What a great day to go sailing! Solve the problems on each sailboat, and you will go far!

1.

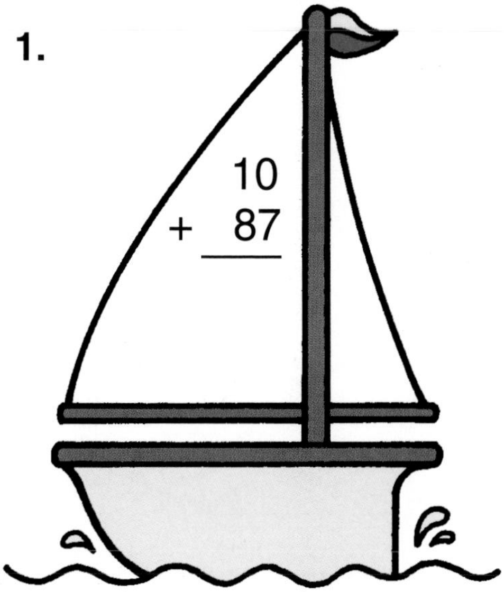

$$\begin{array}{r} 10 \\ +\ 87 \\ \hline \end{array}$$

2.

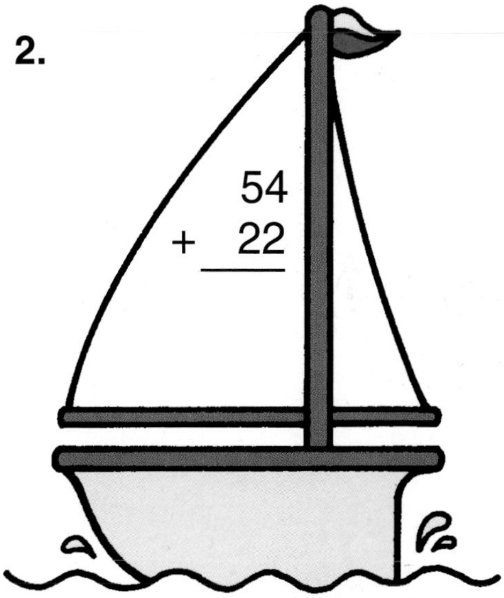

$$\begin{array}{r} 54 \\ +\ 22 \\ \hline \end{array}$$

3.

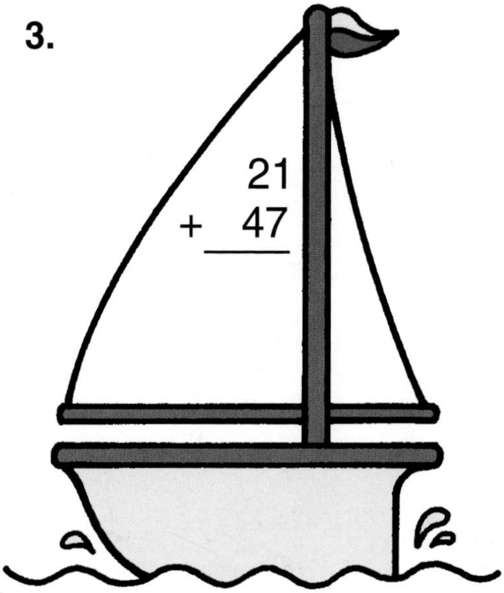

$$\begin{array}{r} 21 \\ +\ 47 \\ \hline \end{array}$$

4.

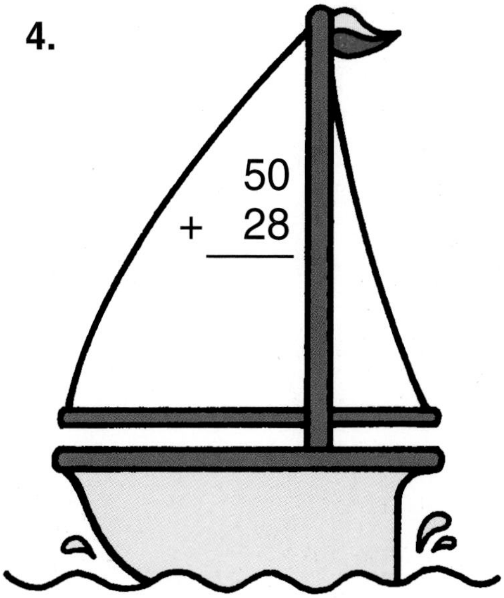

$$\begin{array}{r} 50 \\ +\ 28 \\ \hline \end{array}$$

Subtraction Garden

Directions: Solve each problem. Color each flower according to the color code.

0 = pink	3 = orange
1 = blue	4 = yellow
2 = red	

1.

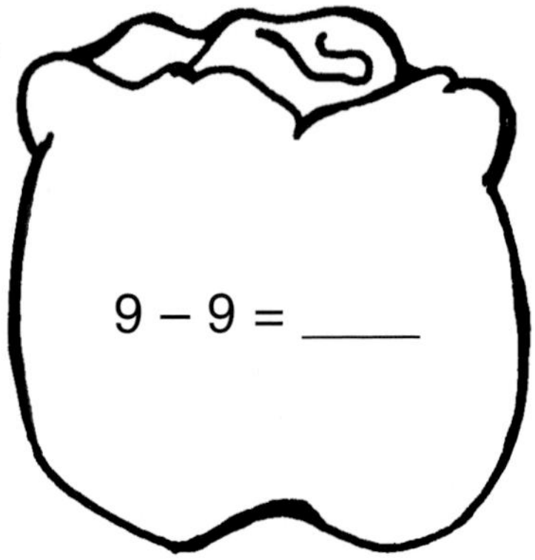

2.

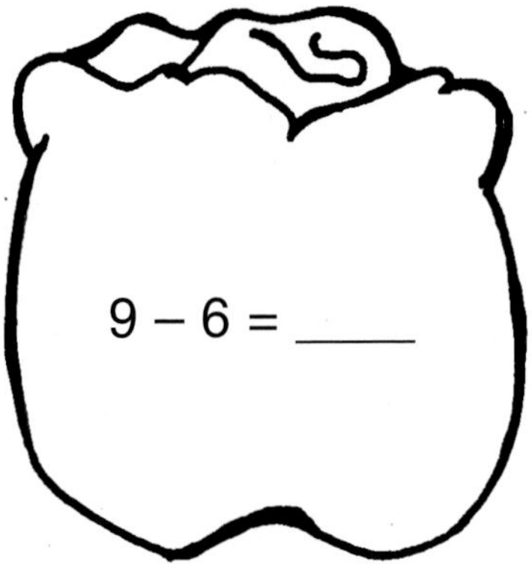

3.

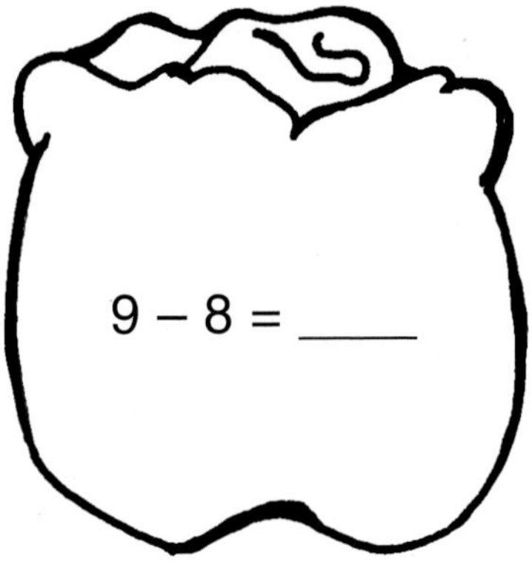

4.

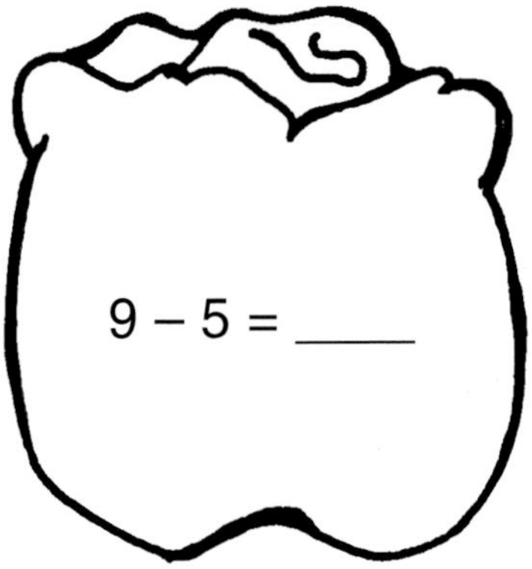

5.

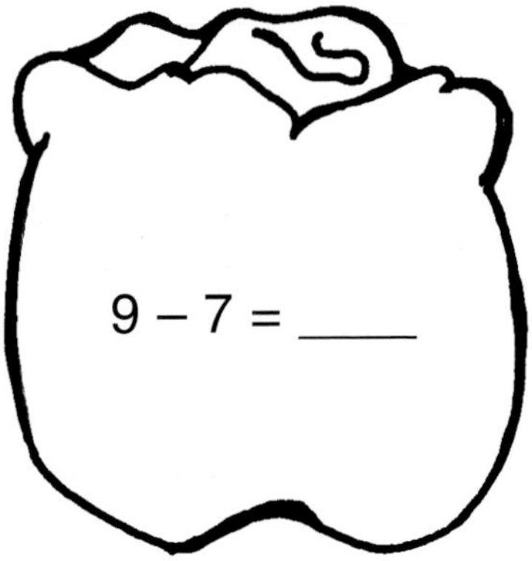

Dog Bones!

Directions: Draw a line to match each equation to its answer.

9 – 2 = ____

7 – 4 = ____

10 – 9 = ____

6 – 6 = ____

3 – 1 = ____

Through the Rain Forest

Directions: Solve each subtraction problem along the rain forest path. How fast can you get to the end?

Finish Line

Directions: Color the cars. Then, write the color of the car to show the place in which each will finish the race.

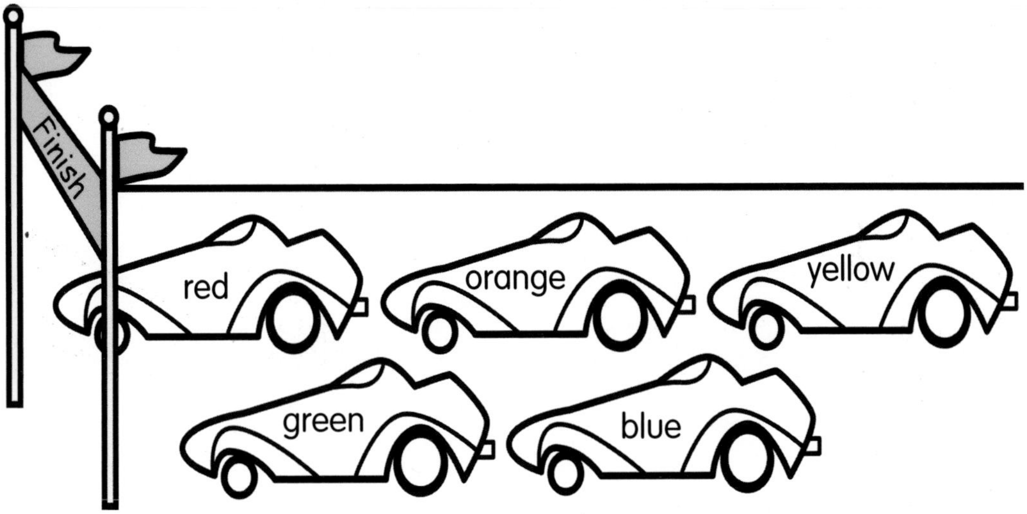

1. First ____________ **4.** Second ____________

2. Third ____________ **5.** Last ____________

3. Fourth ____________

6. What color is the car before the green car? ____________

7. What color is the car after the blue car? ____________

More or Less?

Directions: Write the numerals that show the number of things in each group. Color the group which is more in each row.

< is the symbol for "less than"

> is the symbol for "greater than"

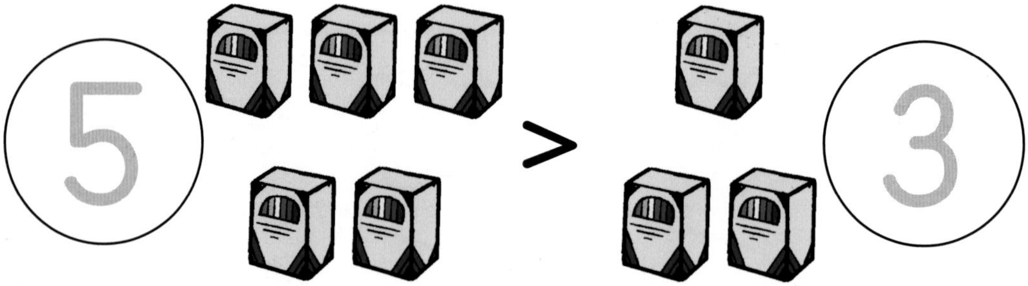

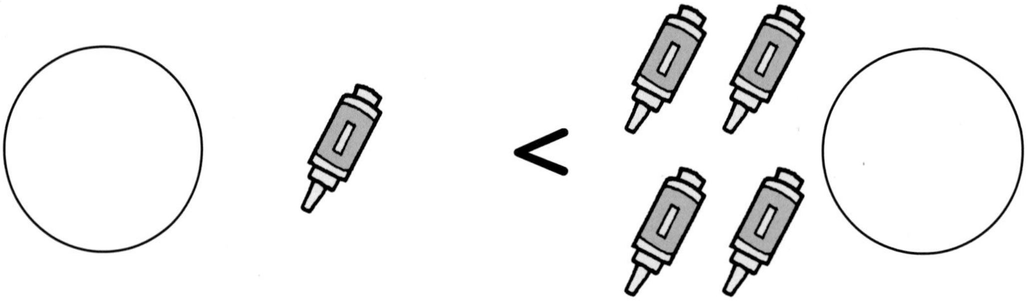

Directions: Write the correct "less than" (<) or "greater than" (>) symbol between the two numbers.

10 ◯ 8   2 ◯ 0   35 ◯ 14

64 ◯ 51   9 ◯ 11   79 ◯ 97

Pay For It

Directions: Color in the coins that could be used to pay for each item. (There may be more than one combination of coins that will work.)

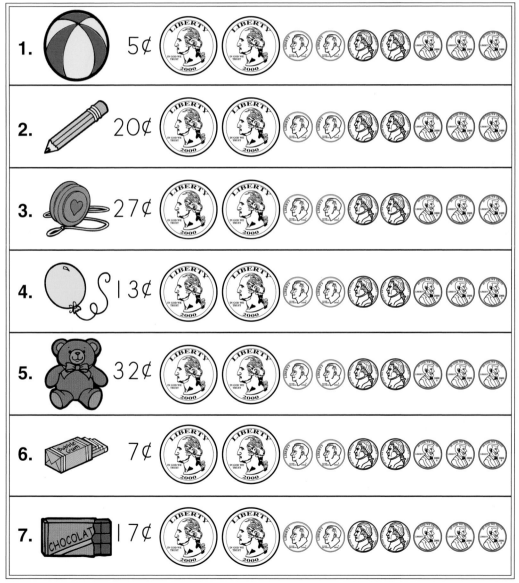

1.		5¢	
2.		20¢	
3.		27¢	
4.	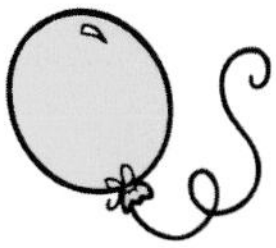	13¢	
5.		32¢	
6.		7¢	
7.		17¢	

Word Problems

Directions: Read each word problem. In the box, write the answer to the question.

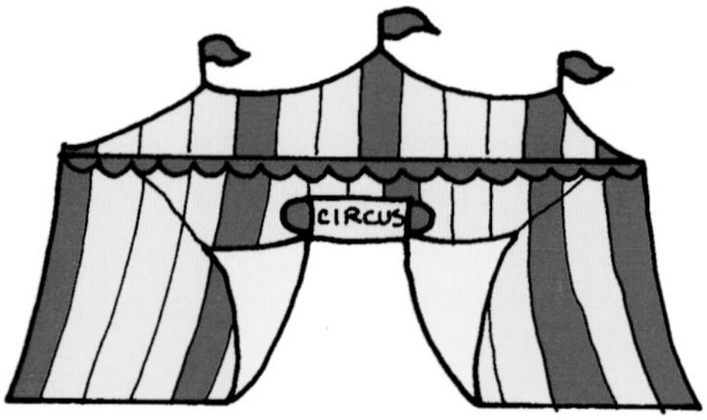

At the circus, Kenny saw 16 tigers, 14 horses, and 22 monkeys. How many animals did he see in all?

When Sandra went to the tidepools, she counted 28 starfish, 32 fish, and 46 shells. How many things did she see in all?

During one month, Jared ate 27 sandwiches, 23 apples, and 52 cookies. How many things did he eat in all?

Emily did 19 addition problems and 33 subtraction problems at school. At home, her mother gave her 21 more. How many problems did she solve in all?

Fish Bowl

Directions: Tally the objects in the fish bowl. Then, create a bar graph of the tallied information. The first one is done for you.

Item	Tally Marks
	|

Item	1	2	3	4	5	6	7	8

Days of the Week

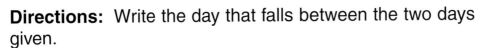

Directions: Write the day that falls between the two days given.

1. Sunday ______________ Tuesday

2. Thursday ______________ Saturday

3. Monday ______________ Wednesday

4. Friday ______________ Sunday

5. Wednesday ______________ Friday

6. Tuesday ______________ Thursday

7. Saturday ______________ Monday

Months of the Year

Directions: Write the month that falls between the two months given.

1. January ____________________ March
2. June ____________________ August
3. October ____________________ December
4. February ____________________ April
5. July ____________________ September
6. September ____________________ November
7. March ____________________ May
8. August ____________________ October
9. April ____________________ June
10. November ____________________ January
11. May ____________________ July
12. December ____________________ February

Best Friends

Directions: Read the story below. Answer the questions at the bottom of the page. Use complete sentences.

Best Friends

Martha and Janis are best friends. Every afternoon, the girls do their homework together. They munch on their favorite snack, popcorn. After they finish their homework, Martha and Janis go to the park. Martha takes her skates. Janis brings her scooter. They enjoy going to the park. It is good to have a best friend.

1. Who are the best friends? ______________________

____

2. What do the girls do in the afternoon? ____________

____

3. Where do the girls go when they are done with their homework?__________________________________

____

Penguins

Directions: Read the passage below. Answer the questions at the bottom of the page by filling in the correct bubble.

Penguins

Penguins are unusual birds. They have feathers, but they cannot fly. They are very good at swimming. In fact, penguins spend most of their time swimming. The water is where penguins find their food. They really enjoy eating fish, squid, and krill. There are not many birds like the penguin!

1. What is a penguin's body covering?

(a) fur (b) feathers (c) scales

2. What are penguins good at doing?

(a) sliding (b) swimming (c) walking

3. What do penguins like to eat?

(a) fish (b) insects (c) plants

Using Inference

Directions: Read each short story. Fill in the bubbles to show the best answer to the questions.

1. Bob wears a wig. He puts on big shoes and silly clothes. Bob paints his face with make up. Then he goes to work. What is Bob's job?

ⓐ fireman ⓑ clown ⓒ bus driver

2. Sue could hear meowing. She walked over to the tree and looked up. What was in the tree?

ⓐ a bird ⓑ a dog ⓒ a cat

3. Mark drew a shape on his paper. He did not lift his pencil at all. The shape has no straight lines. What shape did Mark draw?

ⓐ square ⓑ circle ⓒ triangle

4. Mary went with her mom to visit family. They visited her mom's mom. Who did Mary see?

ⓐ her sister ⓑ her uncle ⓒ her grandma

Practice and Learn

WORKBOOK

Math Puzzles & Games

Slithering By

Directions: Name each number. Color the puzzle.

zero = green   one = yellow   two = blue

Colorful Gumballs

Directions: Name each number. Color the puzzle.

three = red	four = orange	five = yellow	six = green

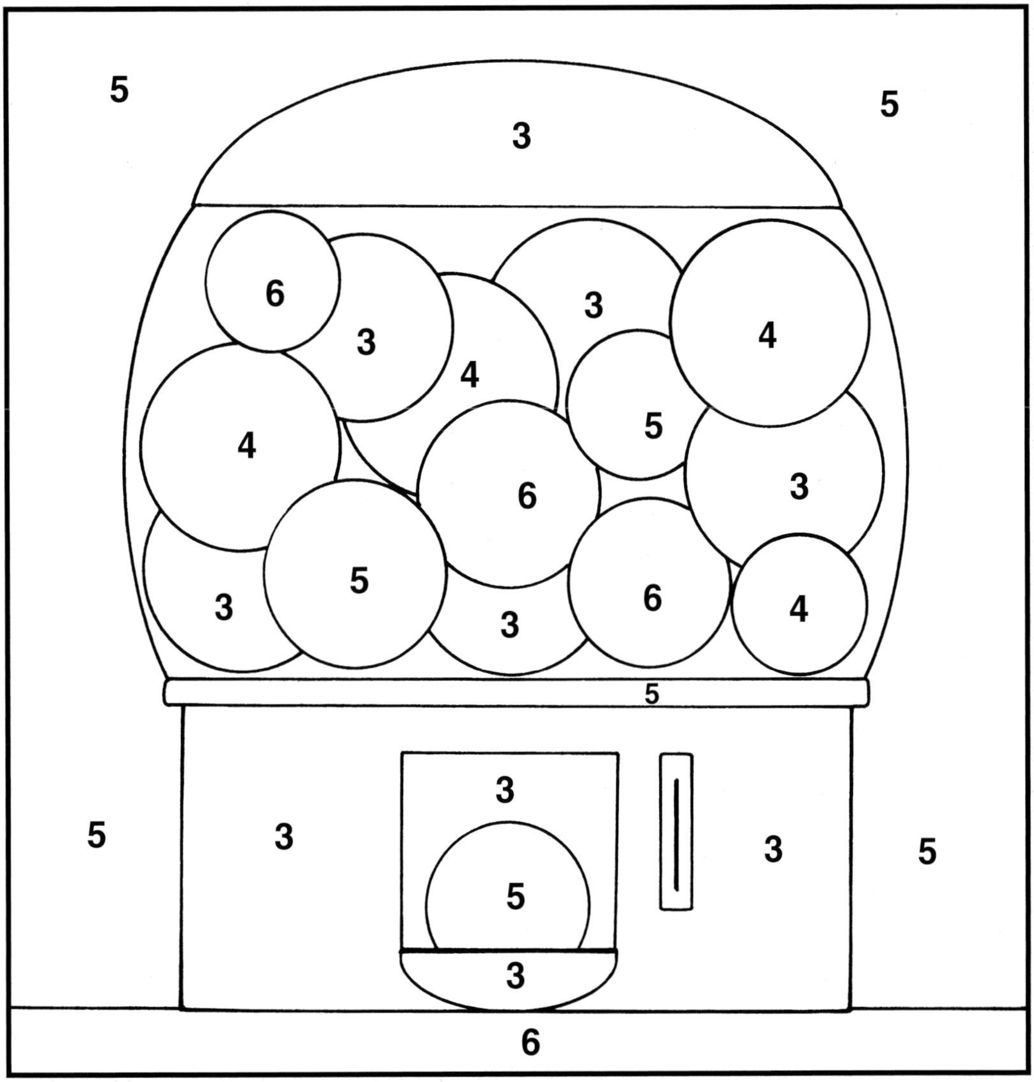

Howdy!

Directions: Count the dots. Color the puzzle.

4 = yellow	**5 = brown**	**6 = red**	**7 = green**

Turtle Time

Directions: Count the dots. Color the puzzle.

7 = brown	**8 = green**	**9 = yellow**	**10 = blue**

Grandma's Quilt

Directions: Name each number. Color the puzzle.

seven = purple	**eight = blue**	**nine = green**	**ten = red**

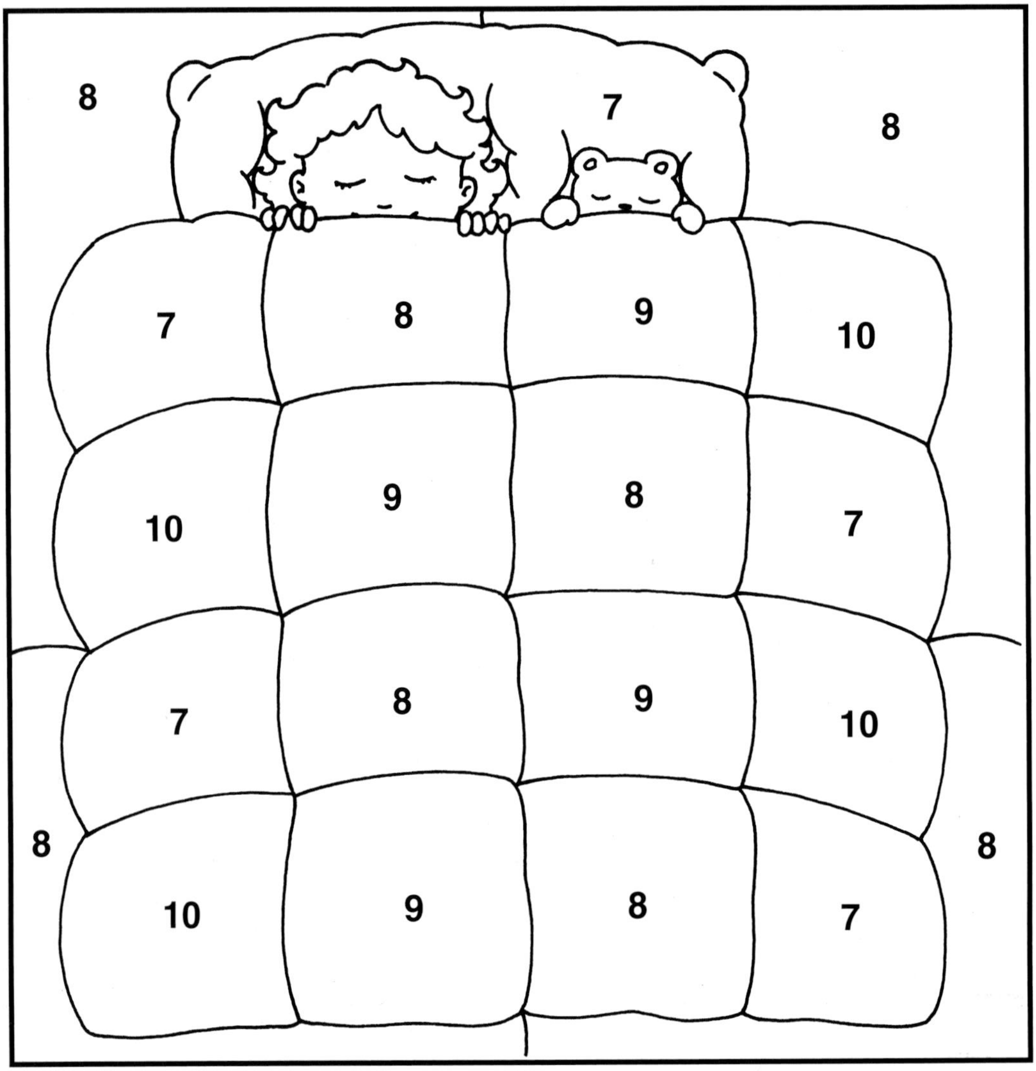

Color by Number

Directions: Color this picture using the color key in the box.

1 = yellow	**3 = blue**	**5 = green**	**7 = pink**	**9 = gray**
2 = red	**4 = orange**	**6 = purple**	**8 = brown**	**10 = black**

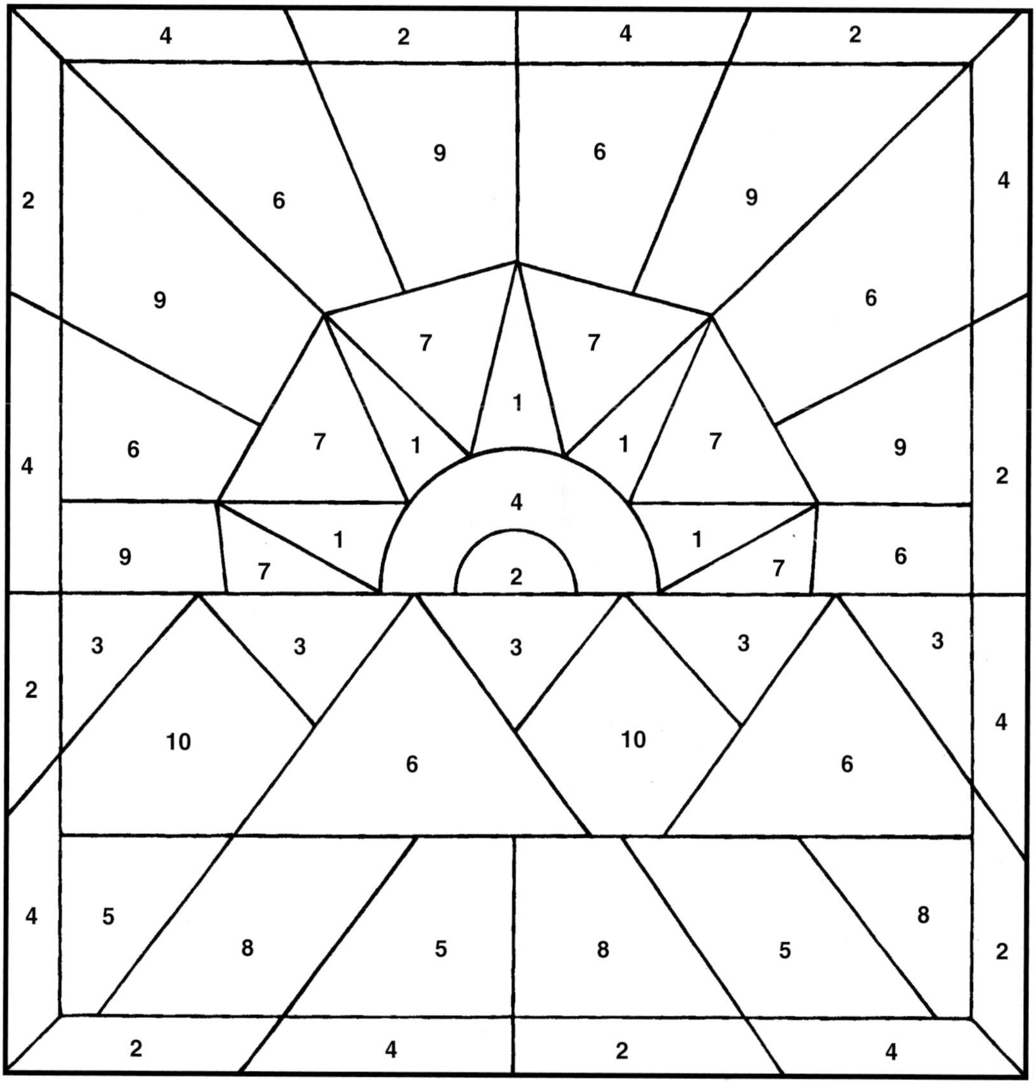

Give Me a 1, 2, 3!

Directions: Read each number word. Color the puzzle.

0 = purple	**1 = red**	**2 = blue**	**3 = gray**

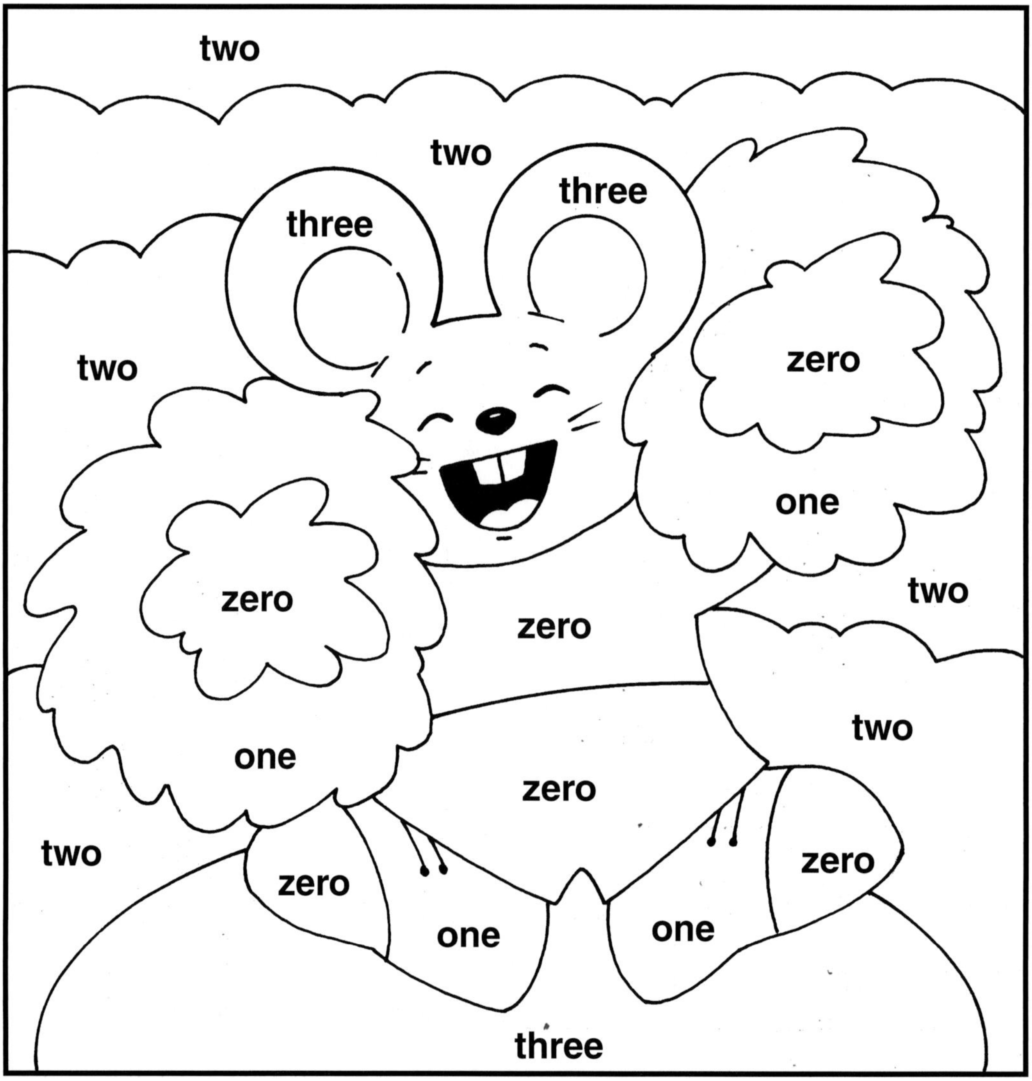

Numbers of the Sea

Directions: Read each number word. Color the puzzle.

4 = blue	5 = green	6 = purple

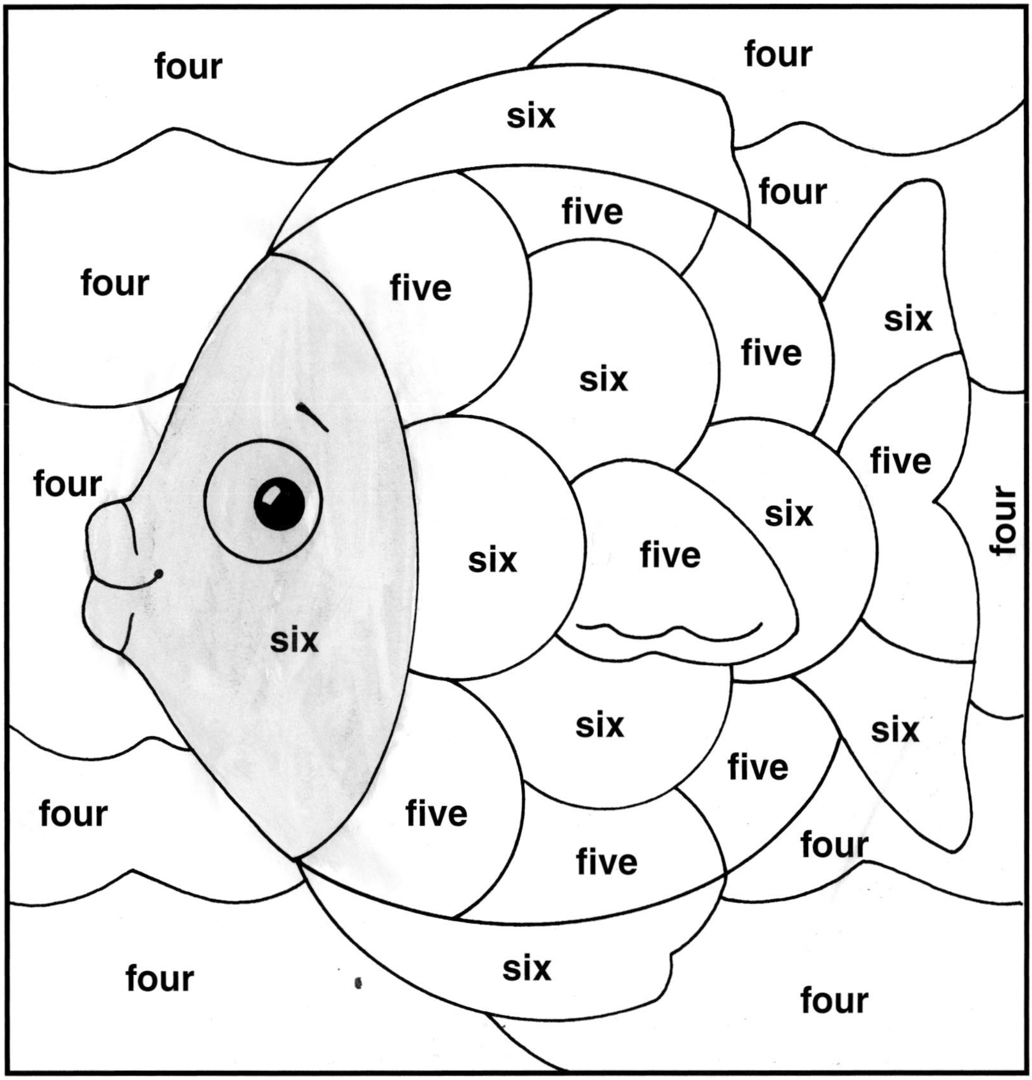

Come Fly Away with Me

Directions: Read each number word. Color the puzzle.

7 = red	**8 = brown**	**9 = blue**	**10 = green**

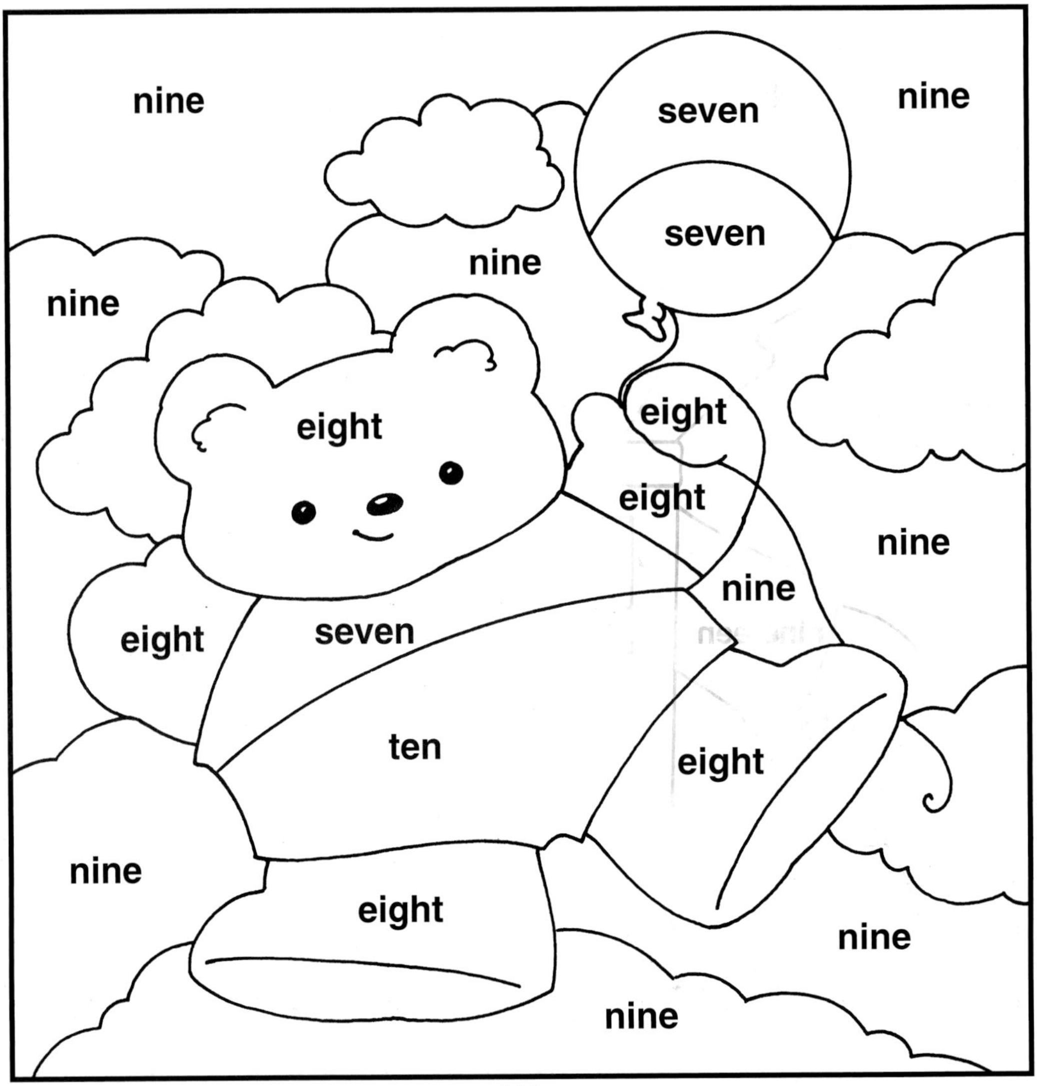

Robbie Robot

Directions: Read each number word. Color the puzzle.

17 = gray	18 = red	19 = blue	20 = green

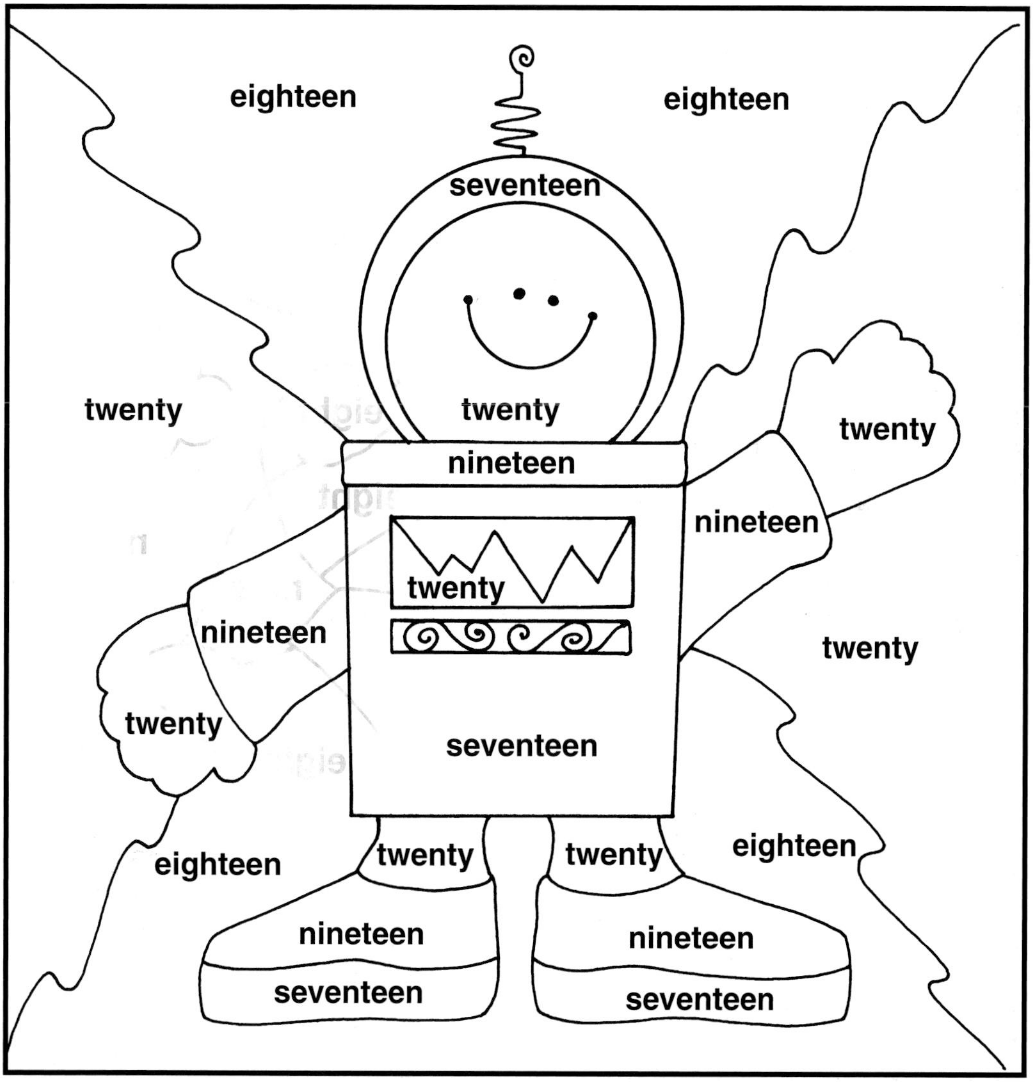

Toucan Tom

Directions: Write the missing numbers. Color the puzzle.

0 = blue	**1 = green**	**2 = purple**	**3 = red**	**4 = orange**

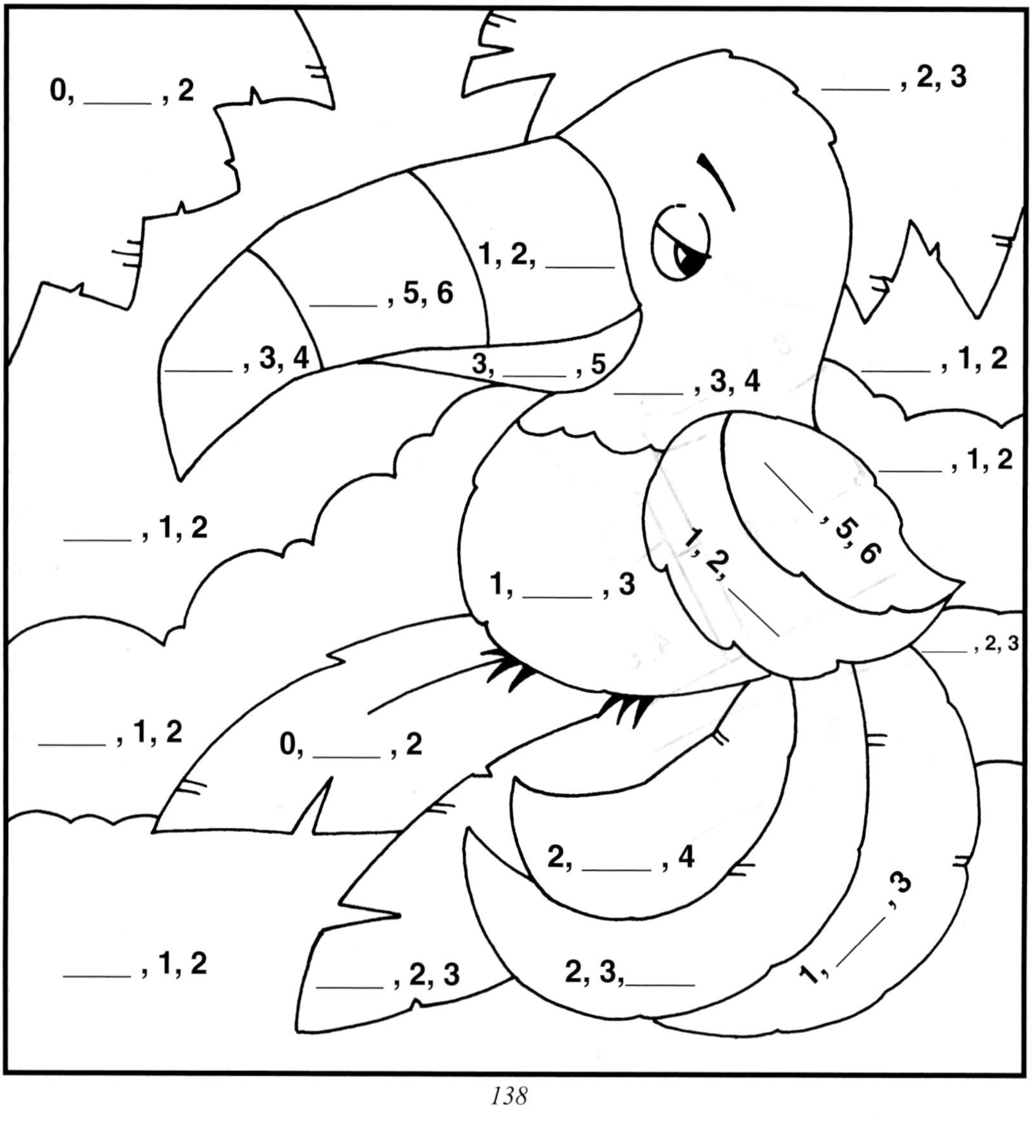

Box Full of Colors

Directions: Write the missing numbers. Color the puzzle.

5 = red	**6 = orange**	**7 = yellow**	**8 = brown**	**9 = green**

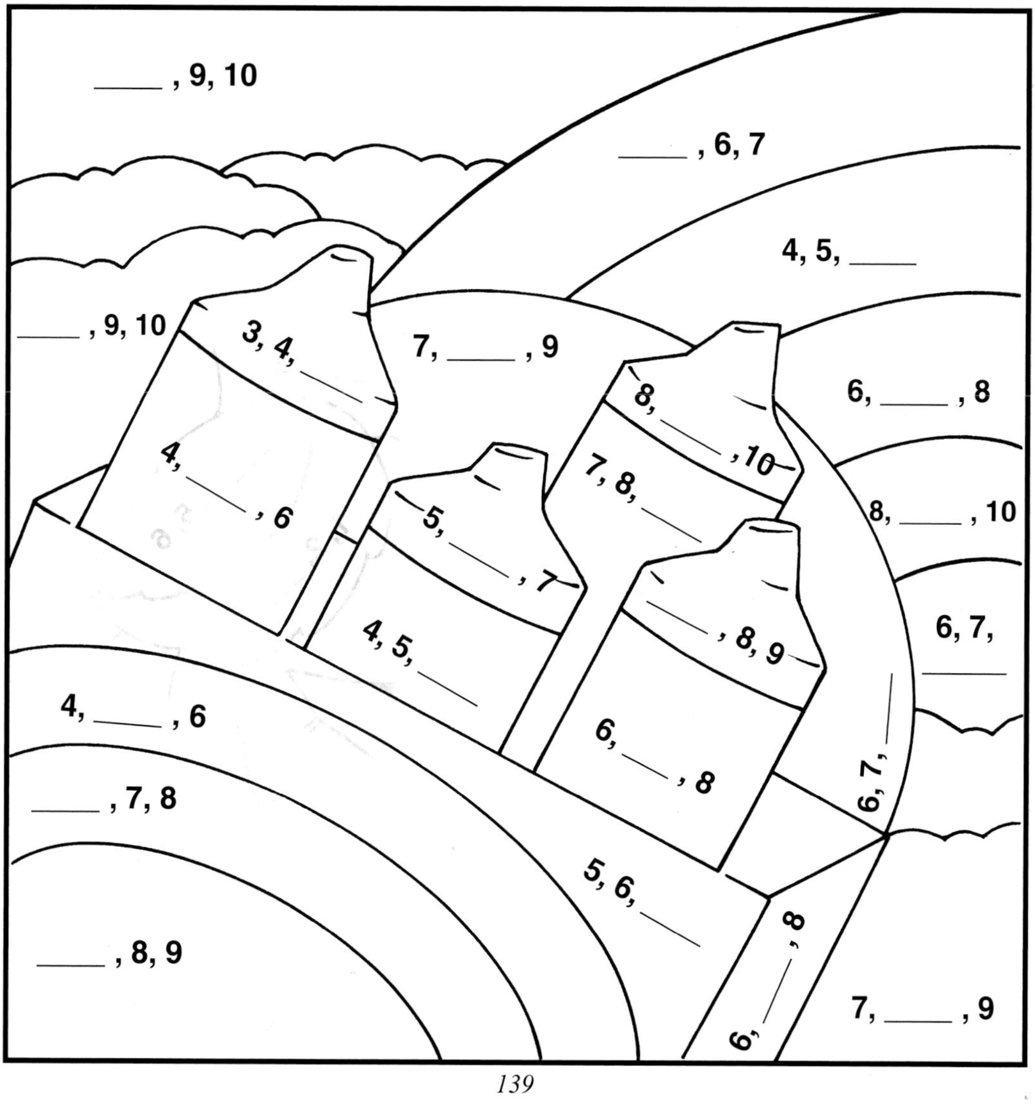

Rat-A-Tat-Tat

Directions: Write the missing numbers. Color the puzzle.

15 = orange	17 = purple	19 = blue
16 = brown	18 = red	20 = yellow

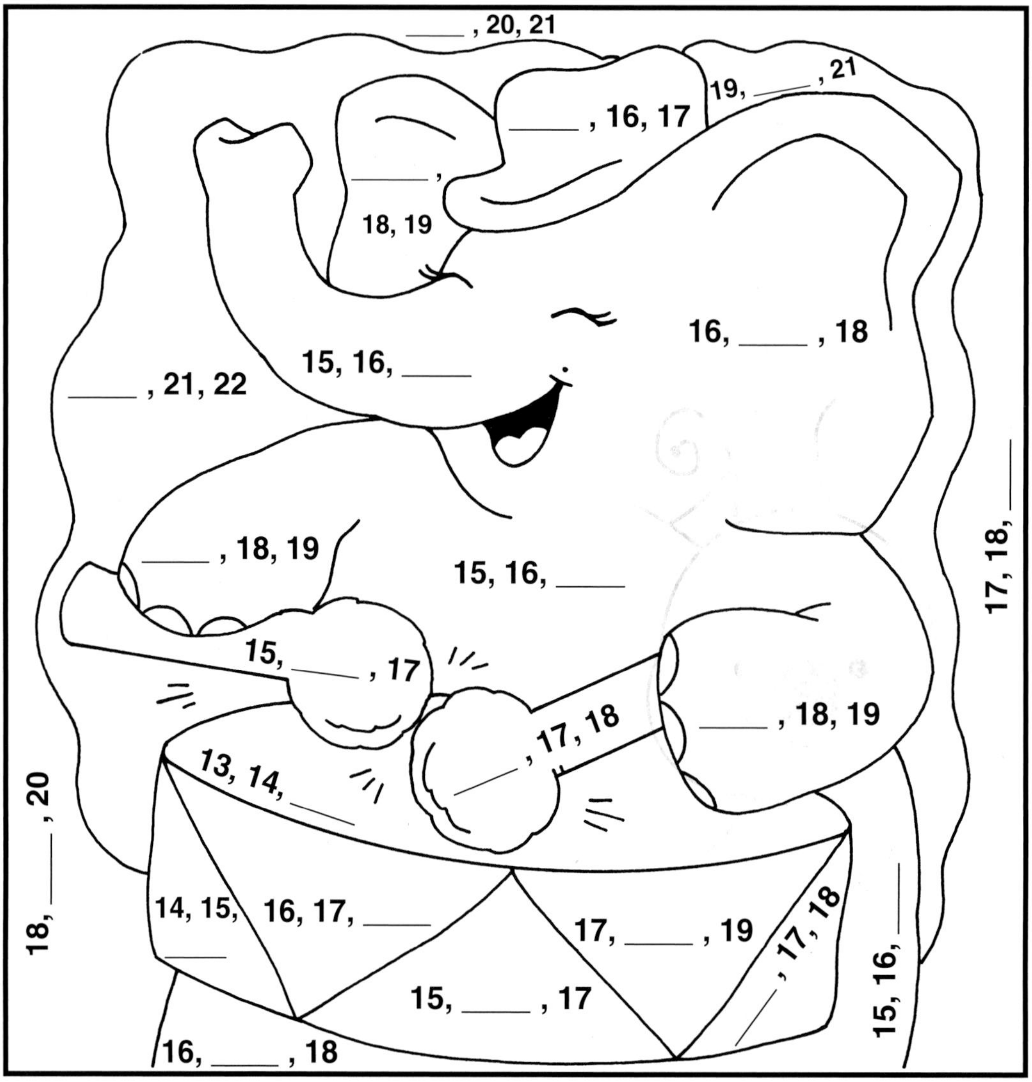

Busy as a Bee

Directions: Solve each addition problem. Color the puzzle.

0 = yellow	1 = black	2 = blue	3 = green

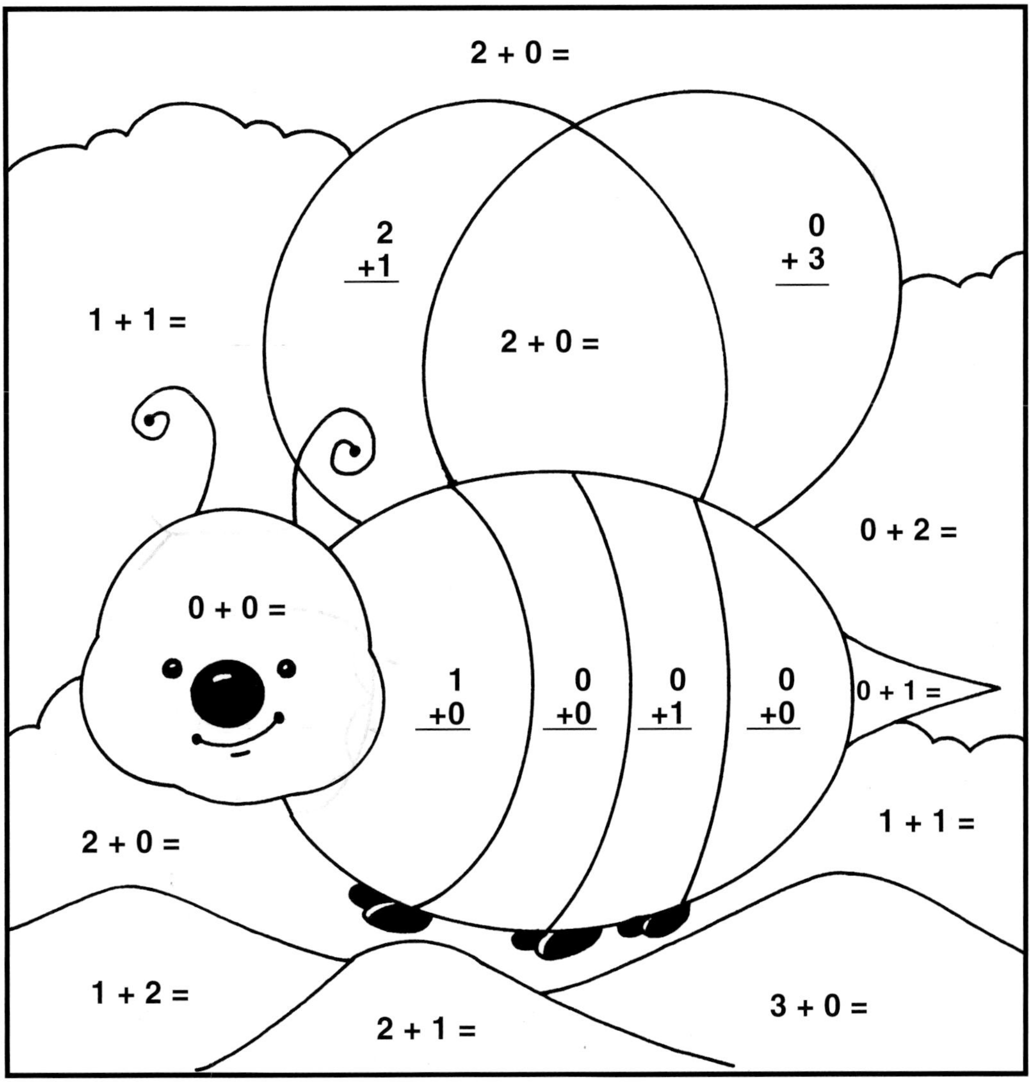

Home Sweet Home

Directions: Solve each addition problem. Color the puzzle.

4 = brown	**5 = orange**	**6 = green**

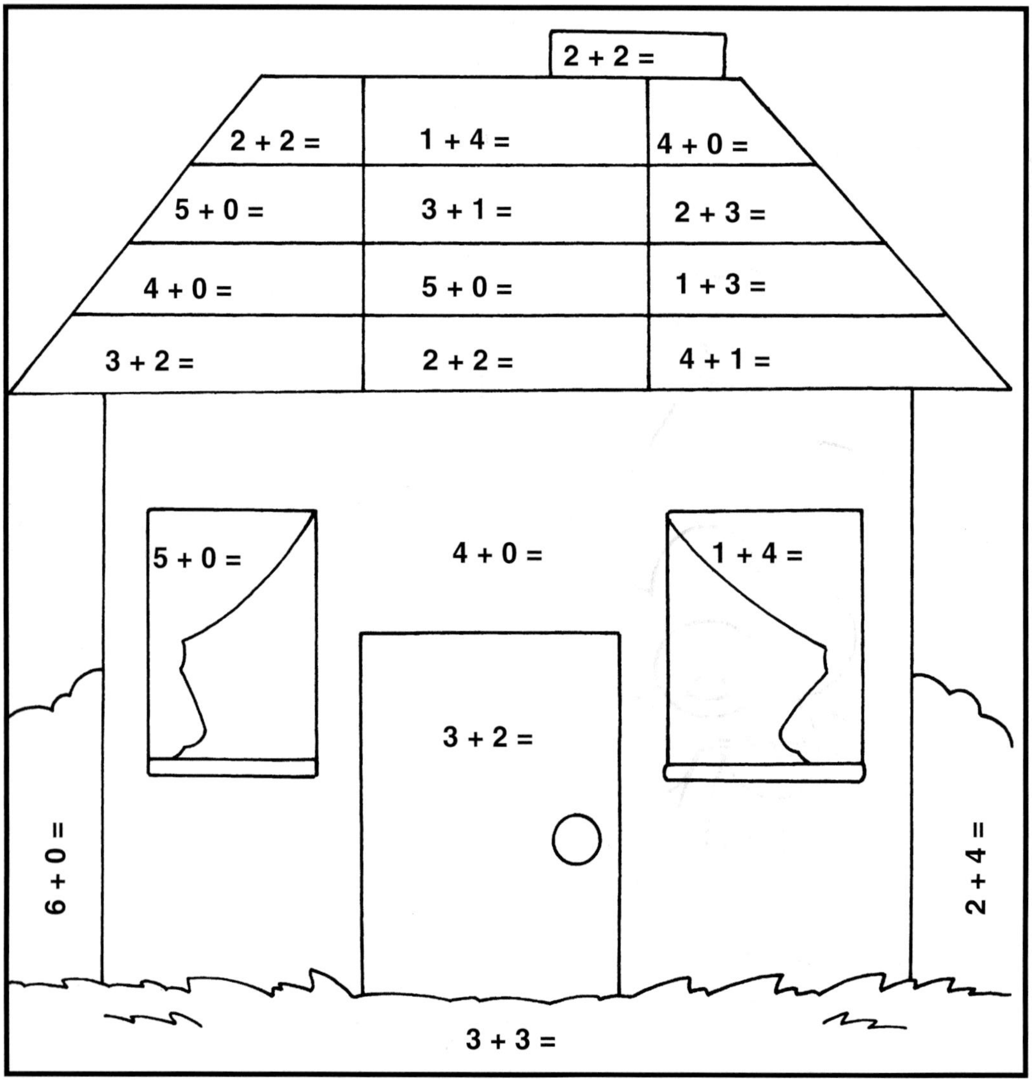

Fluttering By

Directions: Solve each addition problem. Color the puzzle.

7 = orange	8 = yellow	9 = green	10 = blue

Over the Rainbow

Directions: Solve each subtraction problem. Color the puzzle.

0 = red	**1 = orange**	**2 = yellow**	**3 = blue**

Blooming Buds

Directions: Solve each subtraction problem. Color the puzzle.

4 = green	**5 = orange**	**6 = purple**	**7 = yellow**

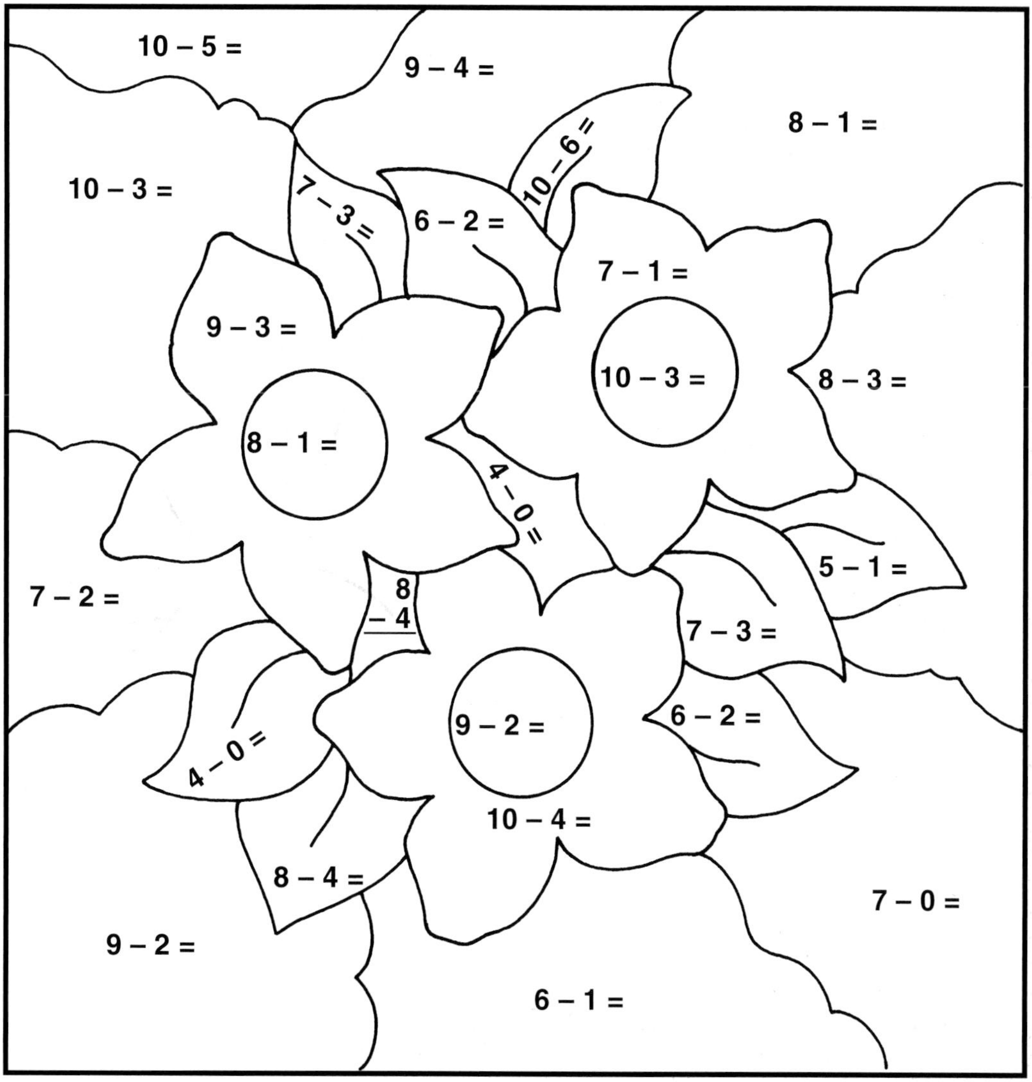

Camping Out

Directions: Solve each subtraction problem. Color the puzzle.

8 = yellow	**9 = brown**	**10 = red**	**11 = green**

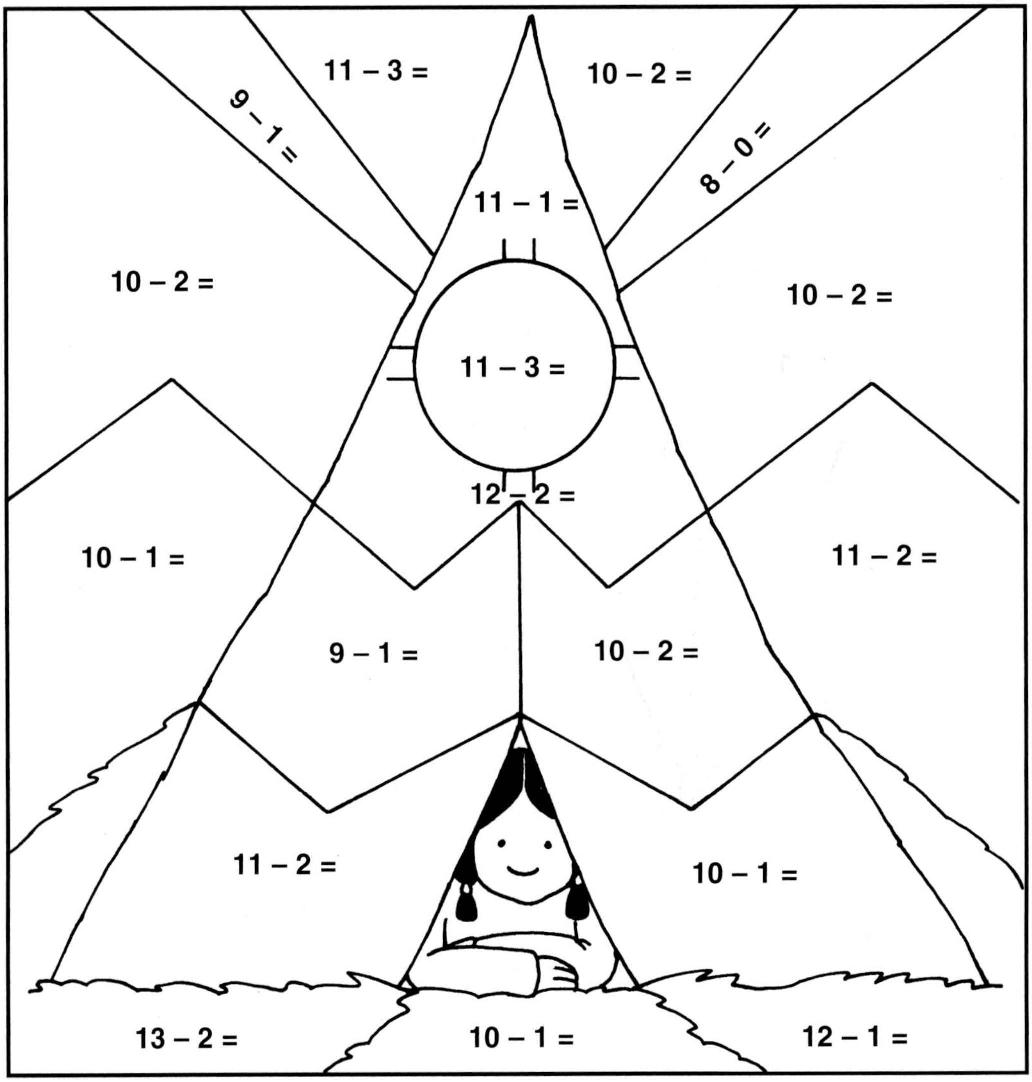

Stripes for Dad

Directions: Solve each subtraction problem. Color the puzzle.

12 = purple   13 = green   14 = blue

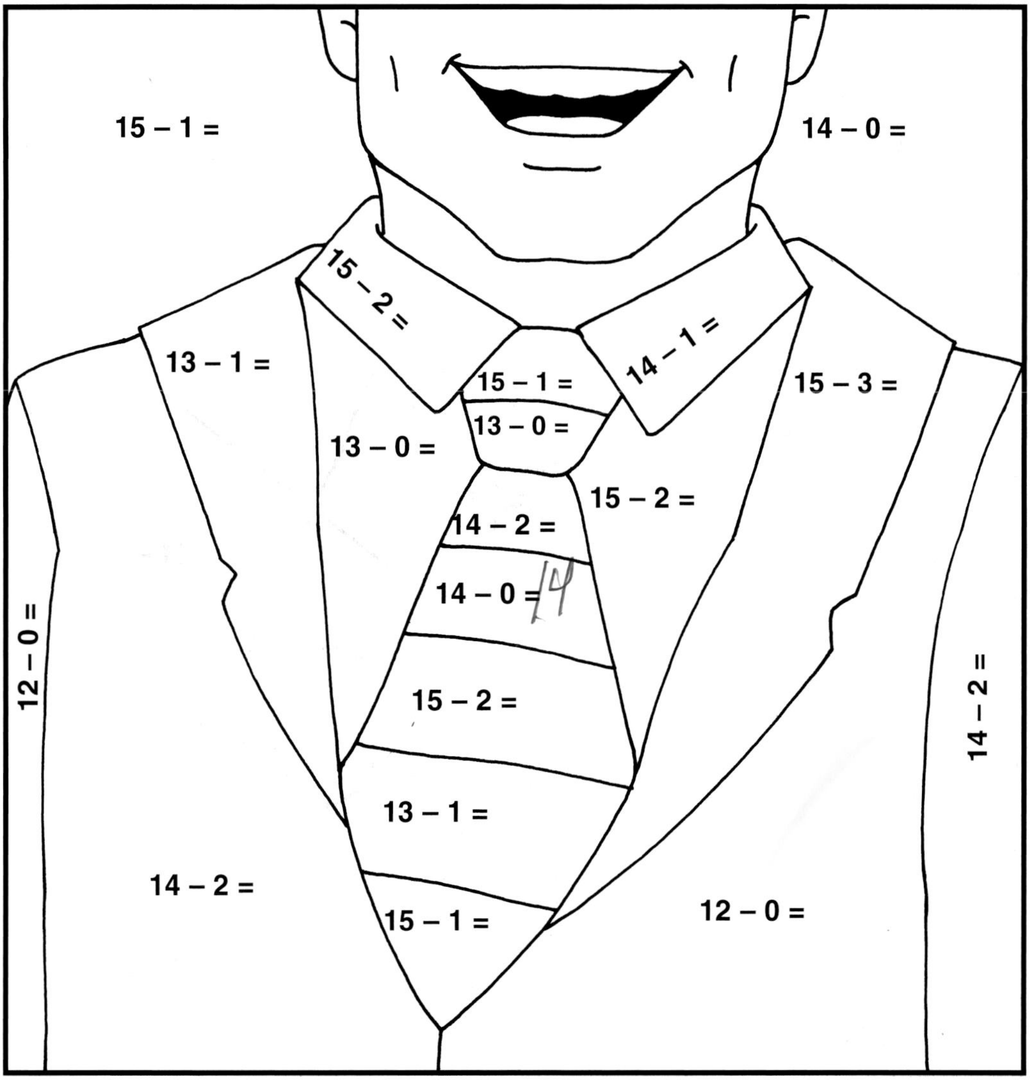

Odd and Even

Directions: Decide which numbers are odd and even. Color the puzzle.

odd = red	even = blue

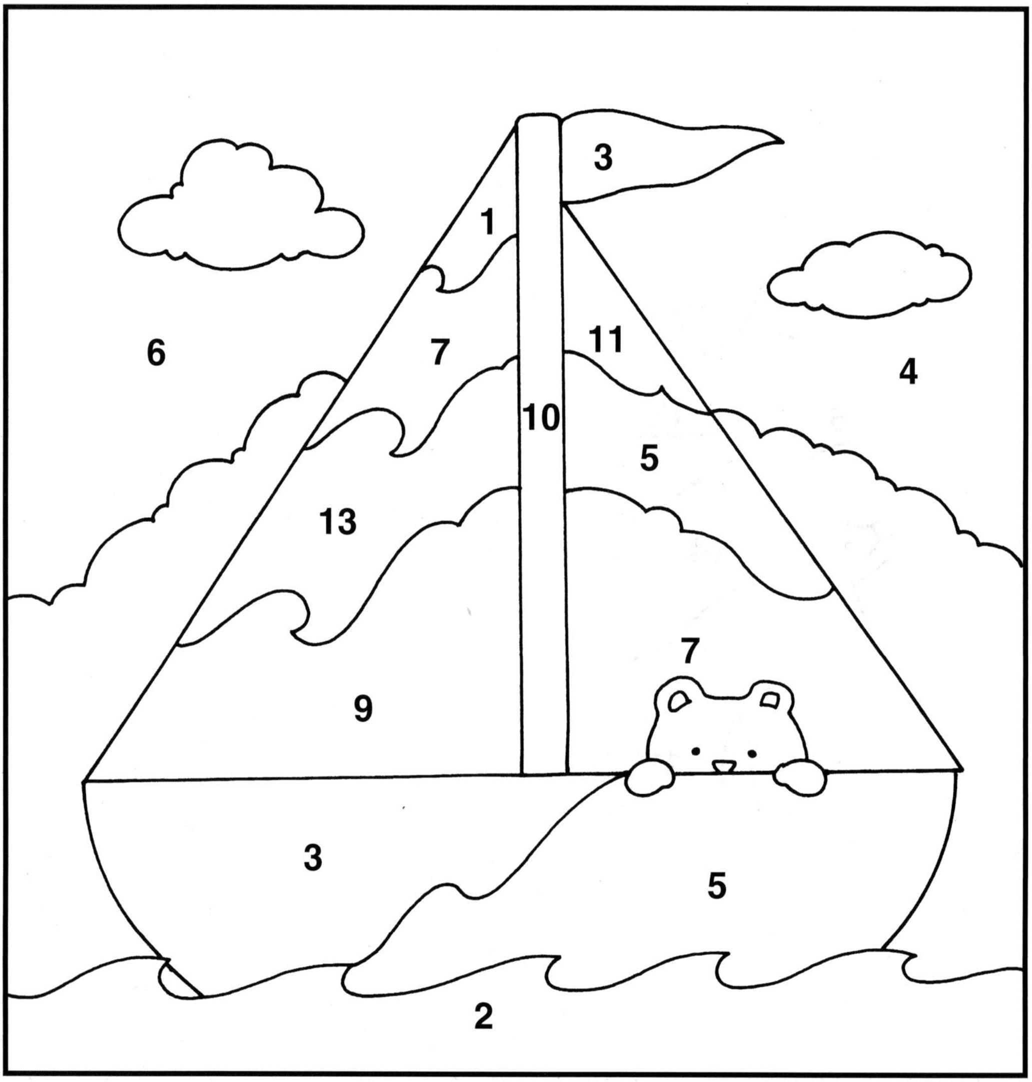

The Opposite Twins

Directions: Decide which numbers are odd and even. Color the puzzle.

odd = yellow **even = orange**

By the 2's

Directions: Complete each number pattern. Color the puzzle.

2 = yellow	**4 = purple**	**6 = blue**	**8 = green**	**10 = red**

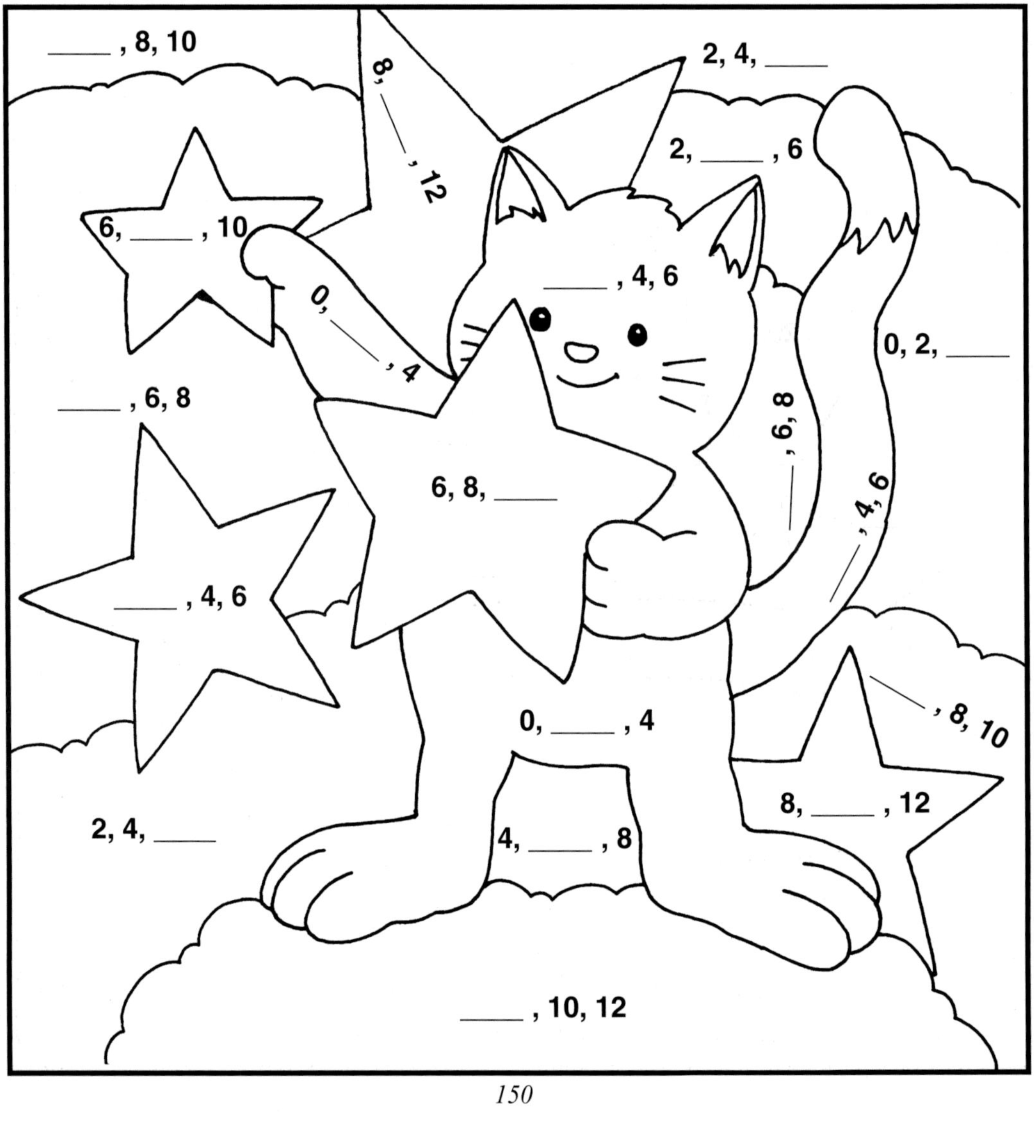

It's Heavy!

Directions: Complete each number pattern. Color the puzzle.

5 = red **10 = blue** **15 = green** **20 = purple** **25 = brown**

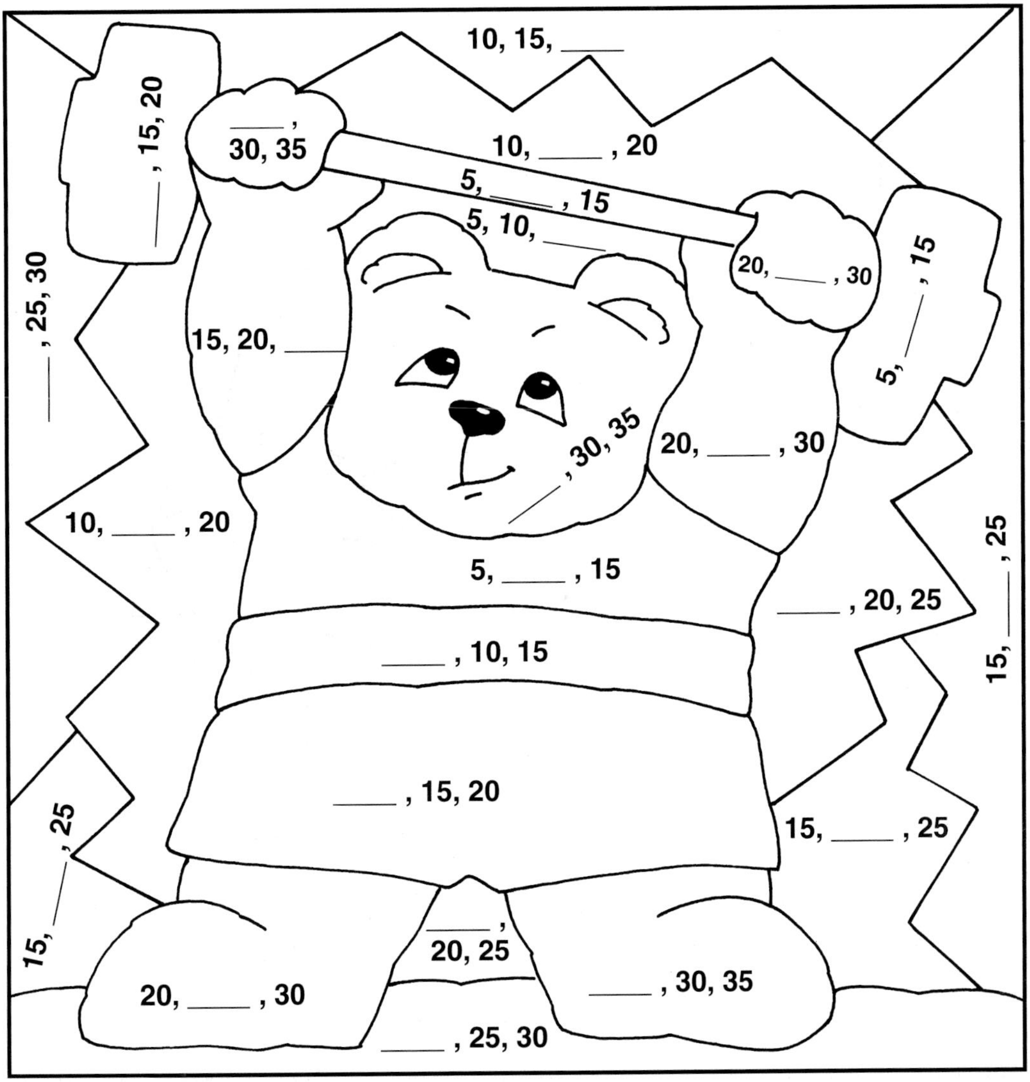

Give a Cheer!

Directions: Complete each number pattern. Color the puzzle.

10 = red	**20 = brown**	**30 = green**	**40 = orange**

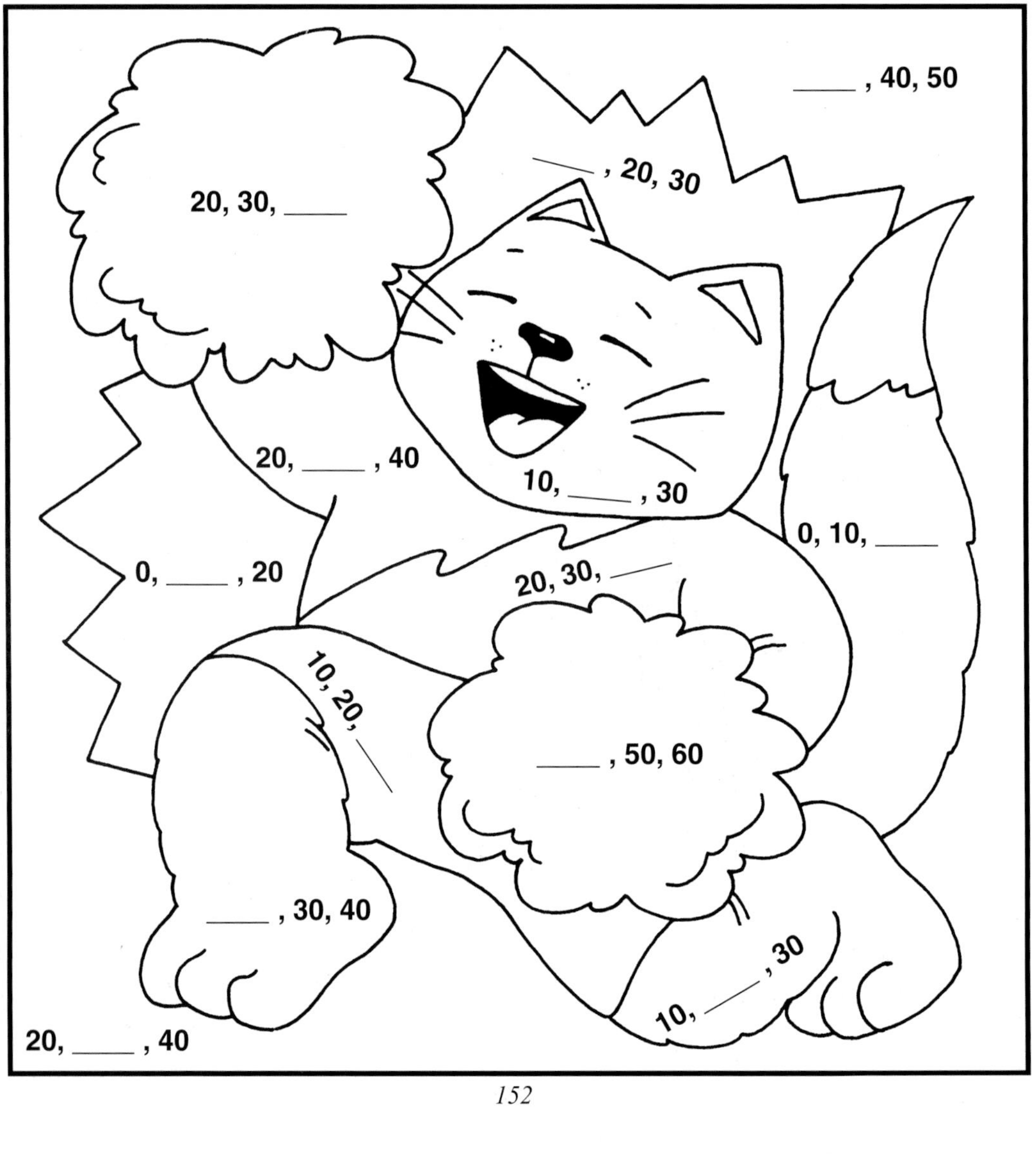

On the Island

Directions: Complete each number pattern. Decide how you are counting. Color the puzzle.

Counting by 1 = blue	**Counting by 2 = green**
Counting by 5 = yellow	**Counting by 10 = brown**

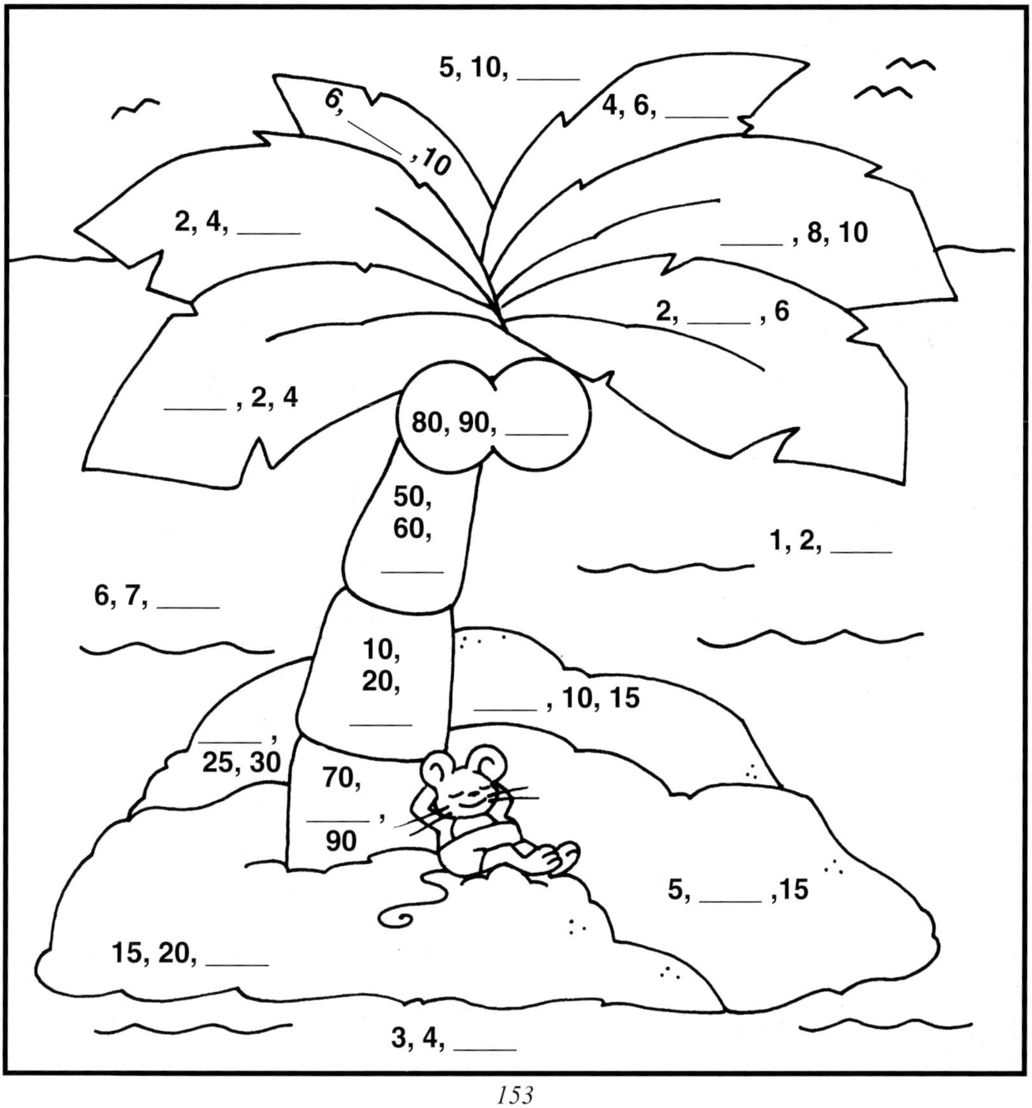

Blast Off!

Directions: Solve each problem. Color the puzzle.

5 = blue	**6 = red**	**7 = gray**	**8 = purple**

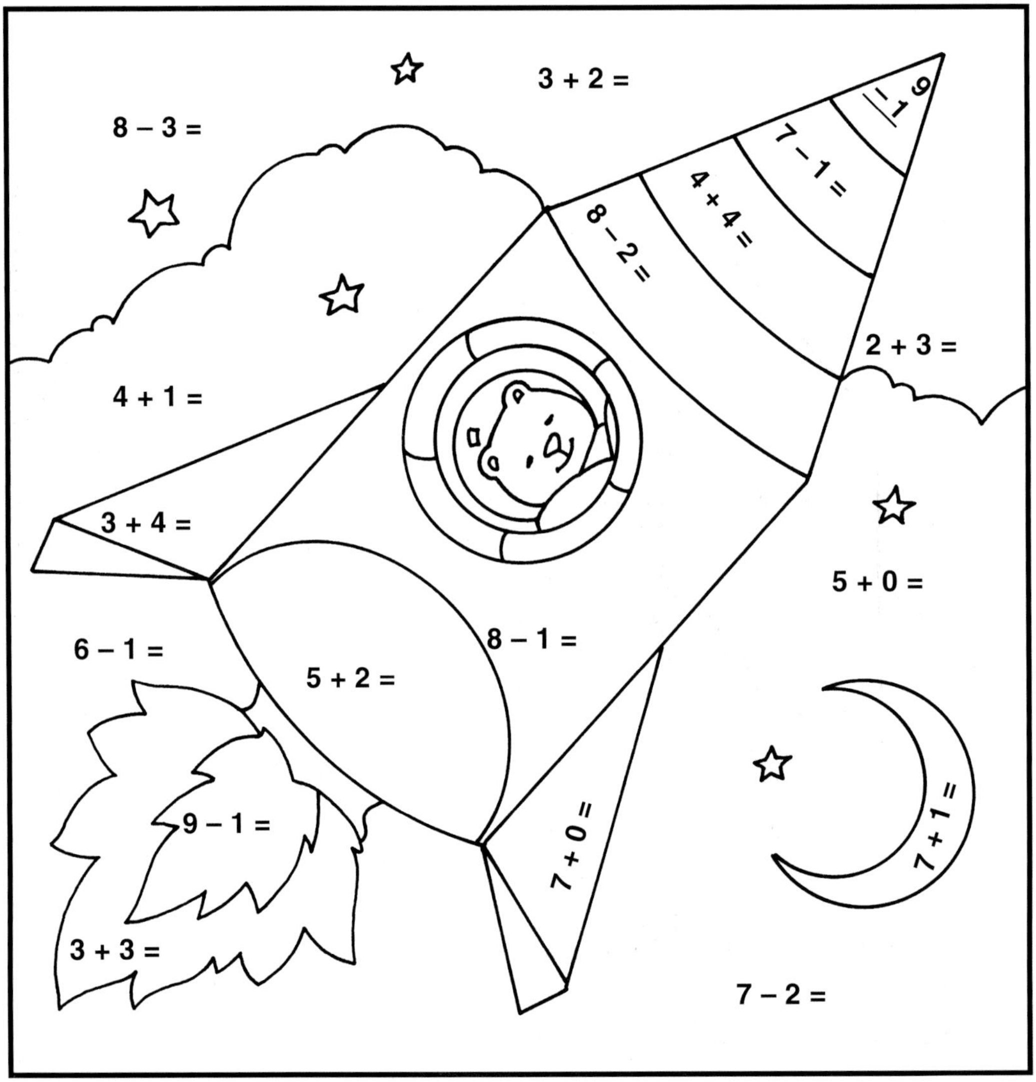

At the Barn

Directions: Solve each problem. Color the puzzle.

9 = brown	**10 = yellow**	**11 = red**	**12 = pink**

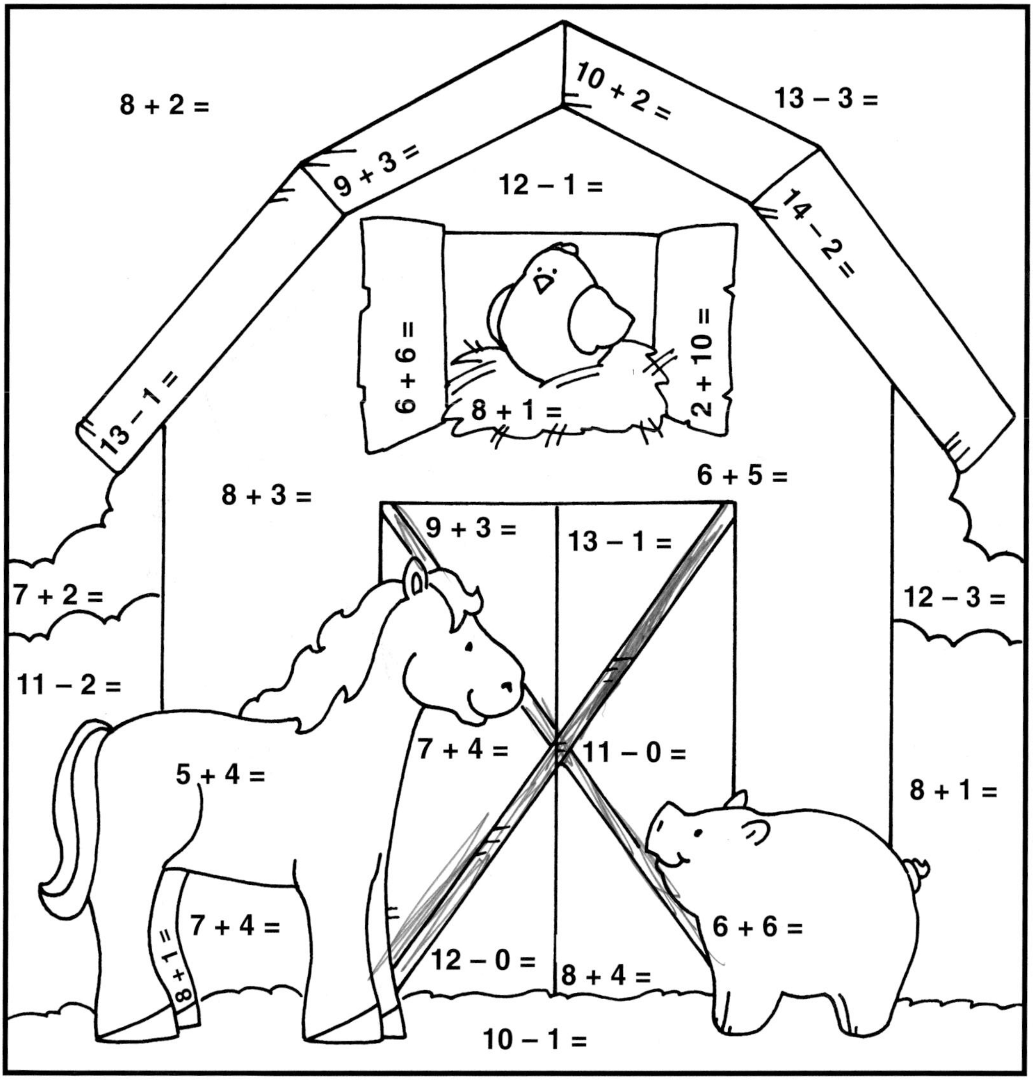

Pennies, Nickels, and Dimes

Directions: Determine the value of each coin. Color the puzzle.

1¢ = pink	5¢ = green	10¢ = blue

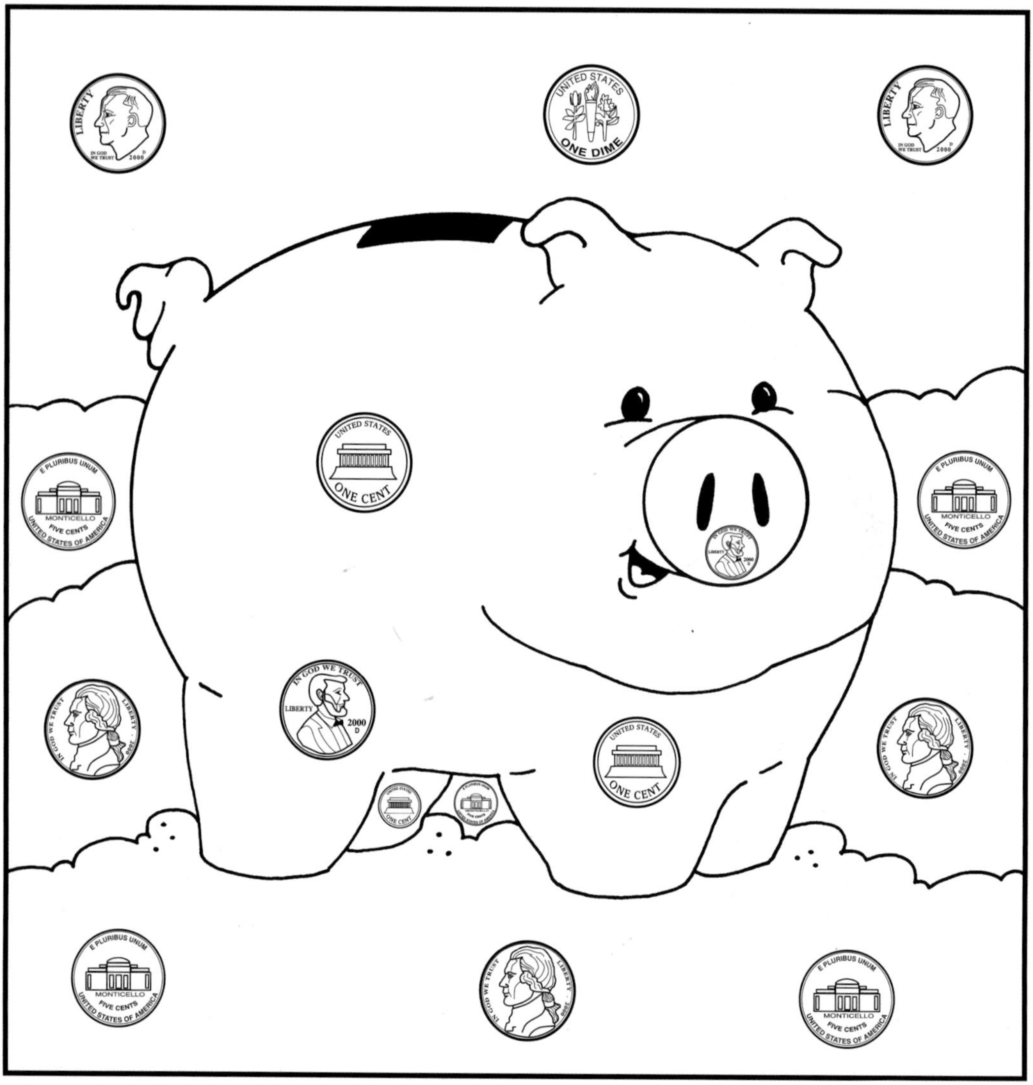

Money on the Flag

Directions: Determine the value of each coin. Color the puzzle.

1¢ = black	**5¢ = blue**	**10¢ = white**	**25¢ = red**

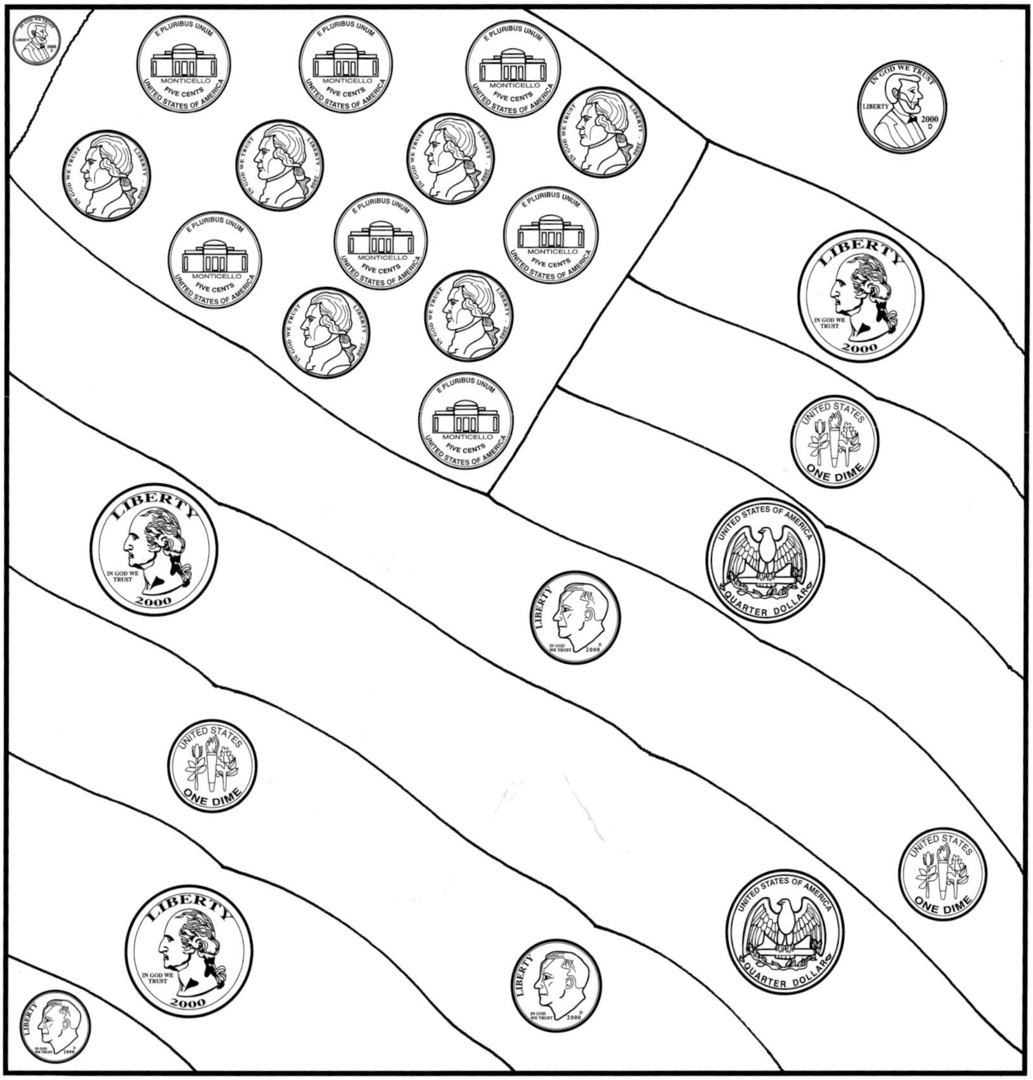

Crazy Canisters

Directions: All of Charlie's canisters fell off the counter. Can you help put them in number order from the greatest to the least? Write the answers on the lines below.

1. ______________________
2. ______________________
3. ______________________
4. ______________________
5. ______________________
6. ______________________
7. ______________________

Amazing Numbers

Directions: Follow the numbers 1 through 20 to get the bear cub to its mother.

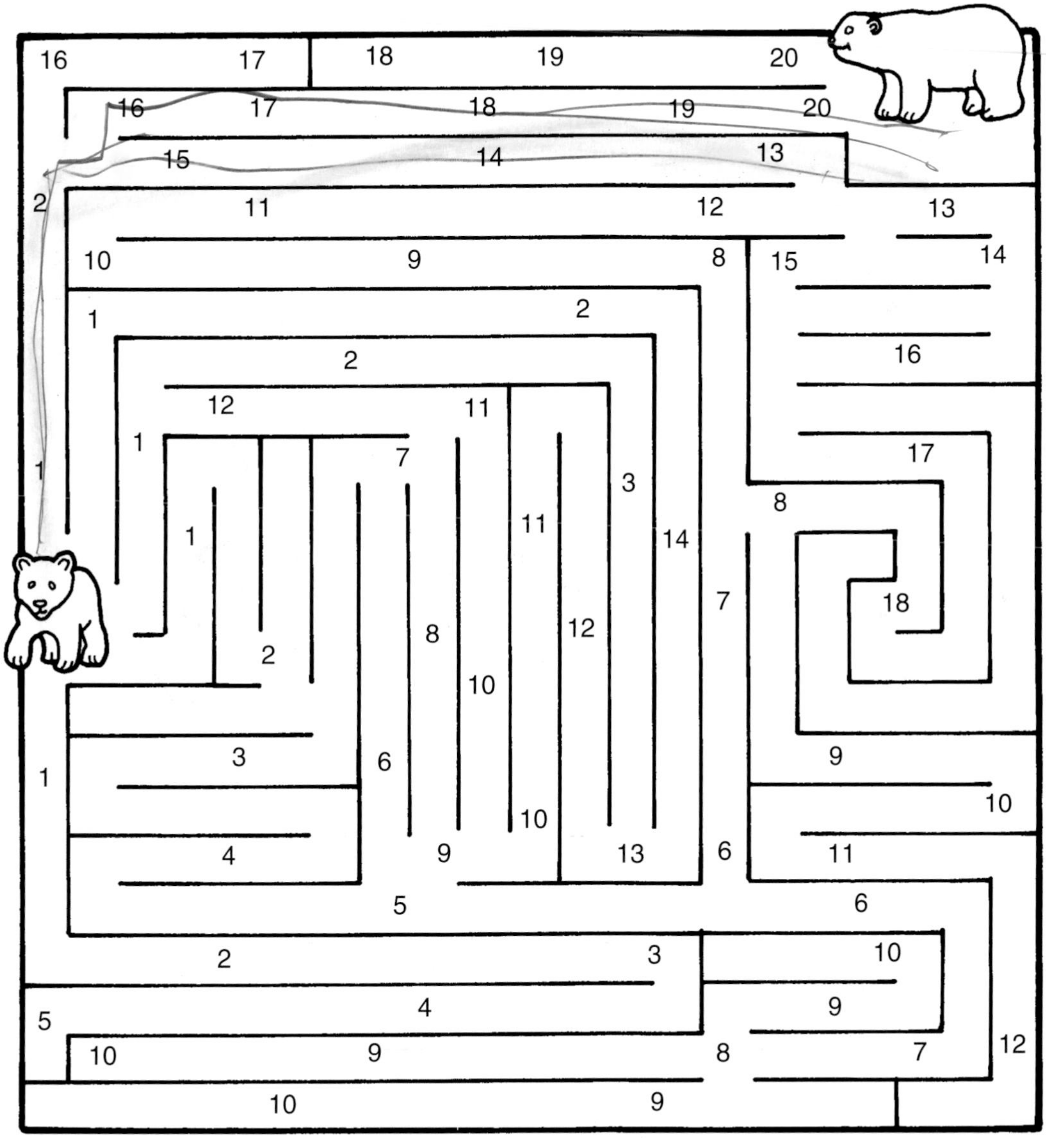

What's in the Box?

Directions: Guess what is in the box. Find the sums. Then write the letter in each box that matches each sum. Read the word you spell and draw a picture of it in the box.

5	6	7	8	9
r	g	a	o	f

3	4	1	6	2
+4	+5	+4	+2	+4
7				
a				

Math Boxes

Directions: Circle the math sentences that equal the number at the top.

5	7	8
5 + 0	3 + 4	5 + 3
4 + 3	7 + 0	1 + 7
1 + 4	6 + 1	0 + 8
0 + 5	3 + 3	4 + 3

4	6	2
10 – 6	6 – 0	5 – 1
9 – 2	5 – 3	2 – 0
7 – 3	10 – 4	4 – 2
4 – 0	9 – 3	9 – 7

A Purse Full of Money

Directions: One of these purses is filled with money. To find the lucky purse, write the total for each addition problem. Then follow the directions below.

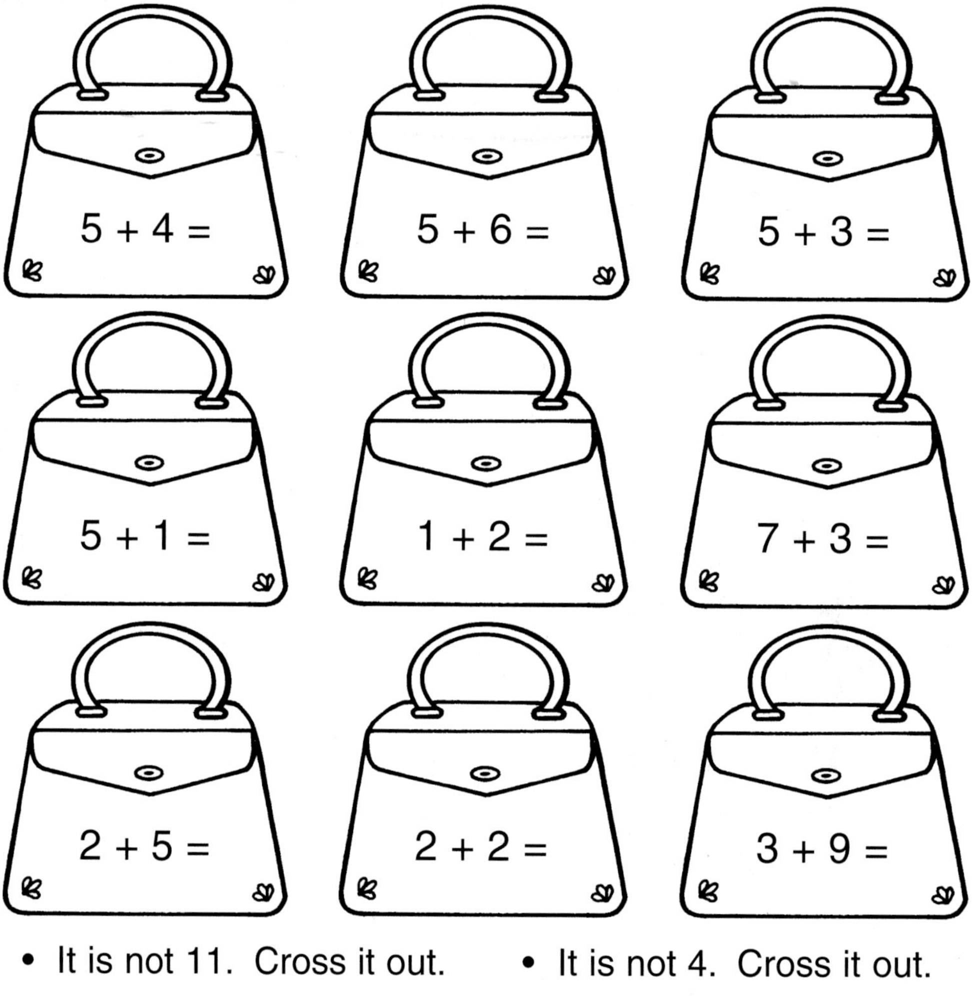

- It is not 11. Cross it out.
- It is not 8. Cross it out.
- It is not 9. Cross it out.
- It is not 12. Cross it out.
- It is not 4. Cross it out.
- It is not 3. Cross it out.
- It is not 6. Cross it out.
- It is not 7. Cross it out.

Fishbowl Addition

Directions: Find the sums. Color the picture.

9 = orange	10 = brown	11 = blue	12 = yellow

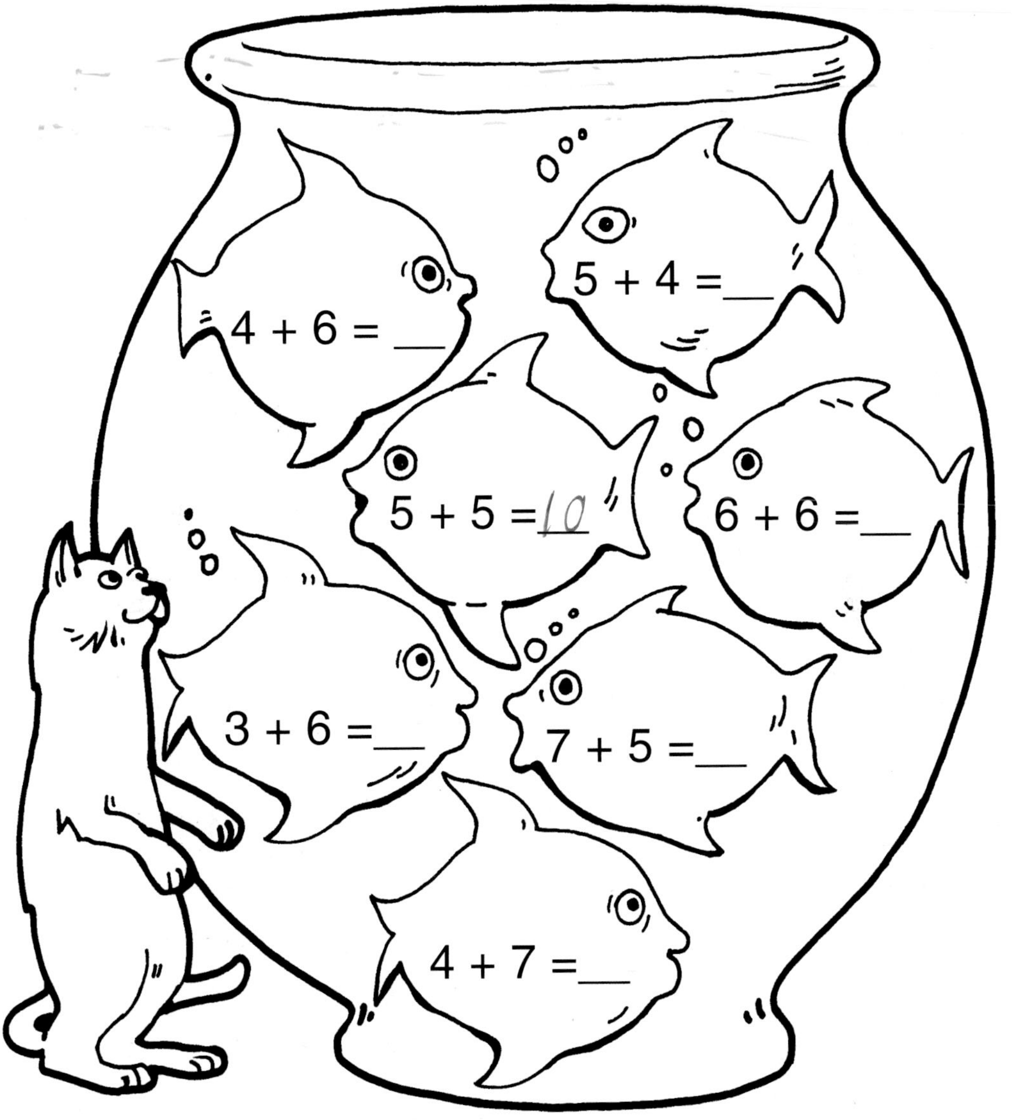

The Big Peanut Search

Directions: Edgar Elephant can't remember where he put his peanuts. Can you help him find them? Find the sum of each number pair. Write the code letter of each answer on the correct line.

0 + 0 = _____ = **A**	5 + 5 = _____ = **P**
3 + 4 = _____ = **D**	2 + 1 = _____ = **R**
1 + 3 = _____ = **E**	1 + 0 = _____ = **S**
5 + 6 = _____ = **N**	2 + 3 = _____ = **T**
5 + 1 = _____ = **I**	2 + 6 = _____ = **U**
6 + 3 = _____ = **O**	4 + 8 = _____ = **H**
0 + 2 = _____ = **L**	

____ ____ ____   ____ ____ ____ ____ ____ ____ ____
5 12 4   10 4 0 11 8 5 1

____ ____ ____   ____ ____   ____ ____ ____
0 3 4   6 11   5 12 4

____ ____ ____ ____ ____,   ____ ____ ____.
2 6 9 11 1   7 4 11

Getting the Eggs Home

Directions: To find the path through the maze, color and connect the number pairs that equal 12.

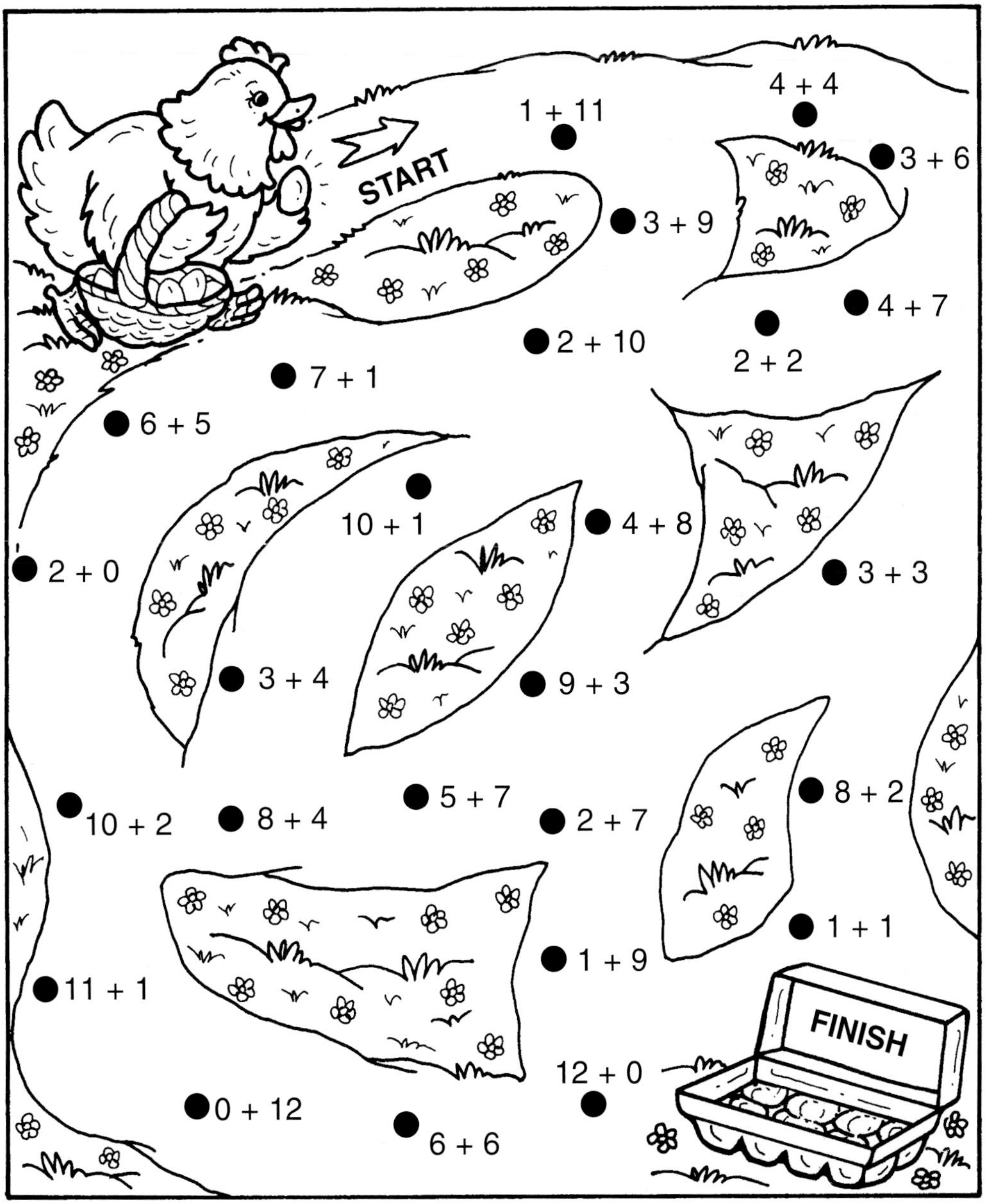

Stompin' Boots

Directions: Juan and his buddies plan to buy these boots for hiking. Before they can take them home, they have to solve the math problems on each boot. Write the number in each box that will make each number sentence correct. The first one has been done for you.

1.

2.

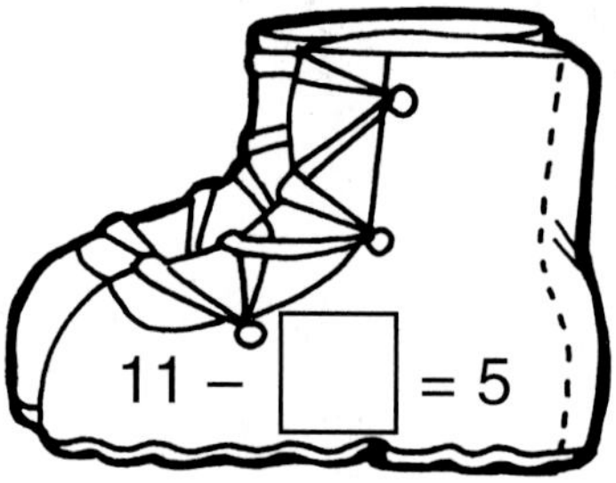

3.

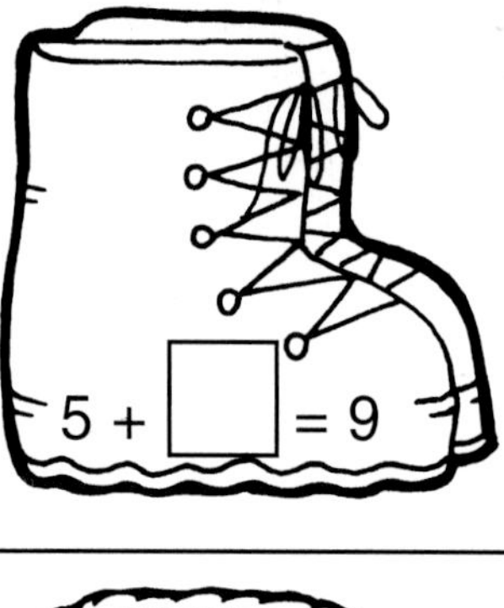

4.

5.

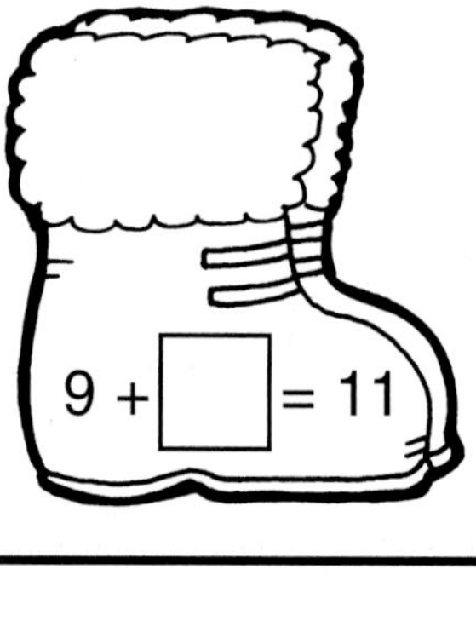

6.

Can You Dew It?

Directions: Look at the picture below. Count each of the items listed and put the number next to the word. Use these numbers to add or subtract the math problems that follow.

____ children ____ raindrops ____ umbrellas

____ puddles ____ rain boots ____ raincoats

Add or subtract. Use the numbers above to help you.

1. **Add**	2. **Subtract**	3. **Add**
______ children	______ raindrops	______ umbrellas
+ ______ rain boots	− ______ puddles	+ ______ raincoats
________	________	________

Places, Everyone

Directions: Label the place each person occupies in line. Then, answer the questions at the bottom of the page.

1.  Matt ________

2.  Sue ________

3.  Mary ________

4.  Daniel ________

5.  Andrew ________

6.  Max ________

first	second	third	fourth	fifth	sixth

7. Who is before Matt? ____________________

8. Who is after Max? ____________________

9. Who is at the end of the line? ____________________

Math Wizard

Directions: Fill in the blank boxes as you follow the path. If the operation says add, add the two numbers together. If it says subtract, take away the second number and fill in the answer box. The first answer box has been done for you. Get to the end of the path as fast as you can.

	Start ⇨	5	−	2	=	3	+	1	=
4	+		=	3	−		=	2	+
=									
	−	1	=		−	2	=		+
									1
	=	1	+		=	4	+		=
−									
2	=		−	3	=		Finish!		

The Circus

Directions: Answer the questions. Color the picture.

1. How many clowns are there?____________________

2. How many elephants are there?____________________

3. How many horses are there?____________________

4. How many saddles are there?____________________

5. How many shoes are there?____________________

Math Review

Directions: Look at the Venn diagram. Answer the questions.

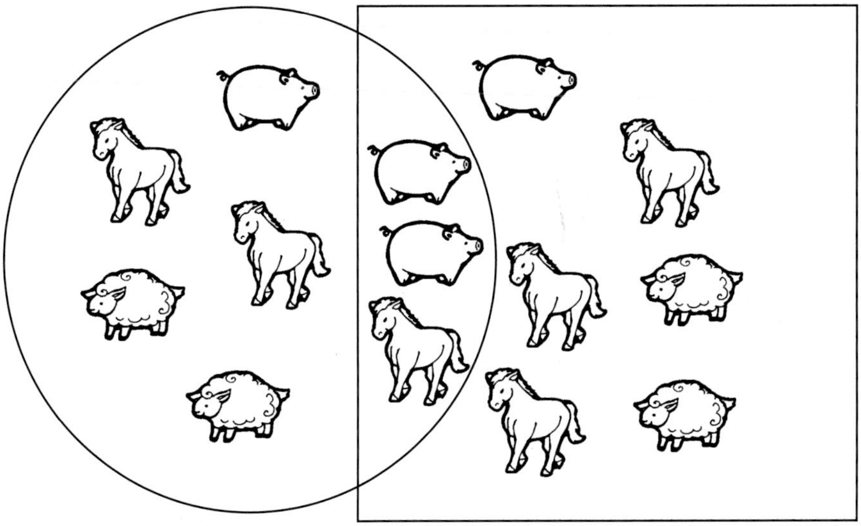

1. How many pigs are in the square? 1 ____________

2. How many sheep are in the circle? 2 ____________

3. How many horses are in the square, but not in the circle?

   3 ____________

4. Which farm animal is not in both the square and the circle?

   None ____________

5. Use the numbers 3, 5, and 8 to make two addition problems and 2 subtraction problems.

   ______ + ______ = ______   ______ − ______ = ______

   ______ + ______ = ______   ______ − ______ = ______

Ten, More or Less

Directions: Find ten more and ten less than the number given. The first one has been done for you.

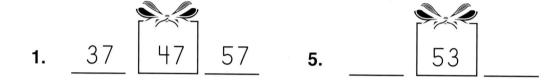

1. 37 | 47 | 57

5. ____ | 53 | ____

2. ____ | 82 | ____

6. ____ | 41 | ____

3. ____ | 36 | ____

7. ____ | 74 | ____

4. ____ | 79 | ____

8. ____ | 68 | ____

Fish Tank Count

Directions: Count each type of plant or animal in the fish tank. Write the correct number next to each object.

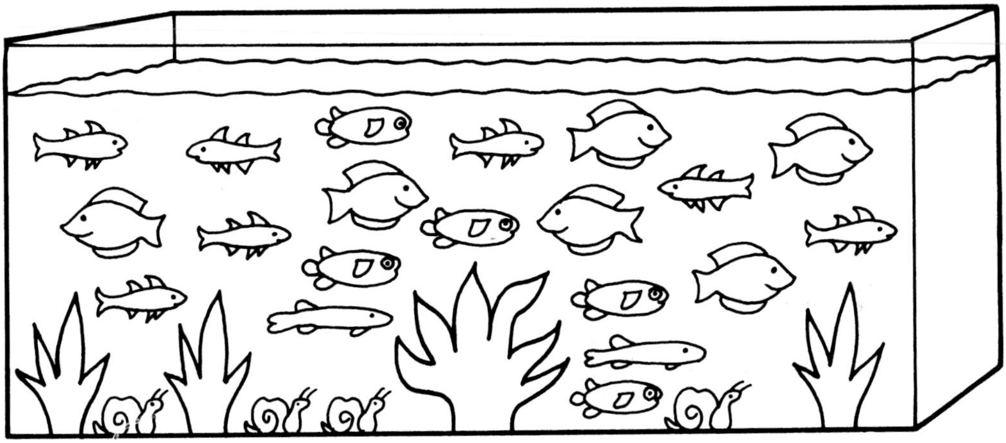

1.  3

2.  2

3.  1

4. 

5. 

6. 

7. 

8. 

Who's Driving 20?

Directions: Add each group of numbers on the cars below. The funniest clown is driving the car whose sum equals 20. Which car is that clown driving? Color that car.

Car 1

Car 2

Car 3

Car 4

Car 5

Car 6

Shapes All Over

Directions: Shapes are hidden everywhere below. Can you find the correct number of each shape?

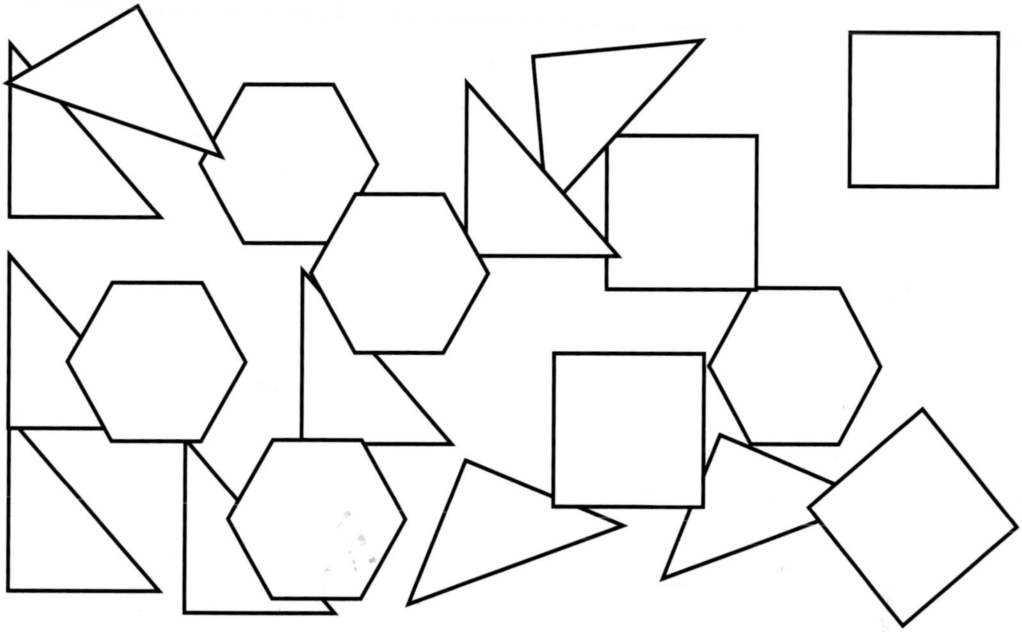

1. How many triangles? ______________

2. How many hexagons? ______________

3. How many squares? ______________

On Target

Directions: Use the target board below to solve the problems.

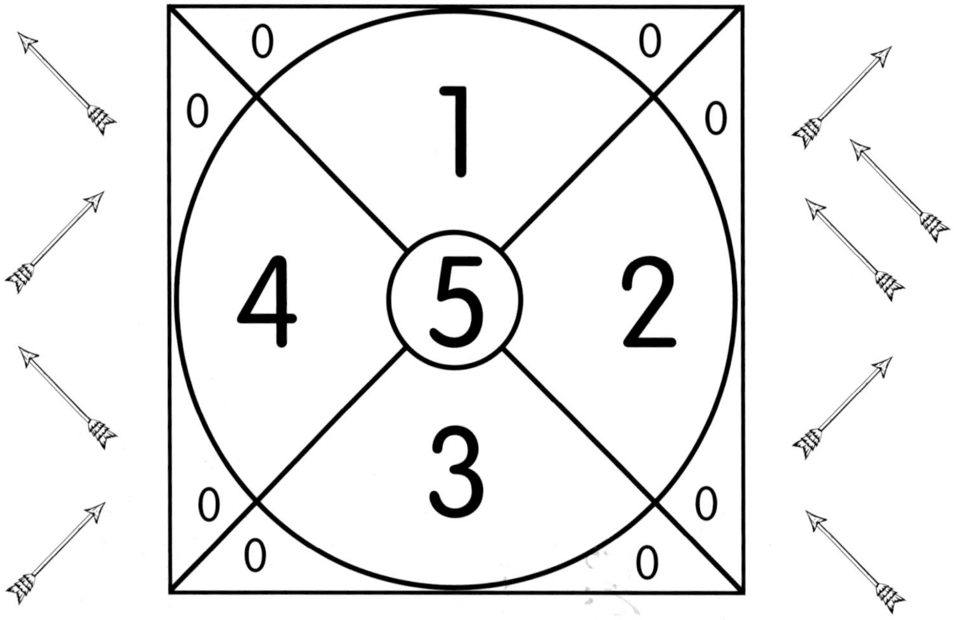

1. Julie shot two arrows for a total of 8 points. The first arrow hit a 5. What was the other number that Julie hit?

Julie hit a _______________.

2. Keith shot two arrows for a total of 4 points. Both arrows hit the same number. What were the numbers Keith hit?

Keith hit a ____ and a ____.

3. Pete shot two arrows for a total of 5 points. The first arrow hit a 4. What was the other number that Pete hit?

Pete hit a _______________.

4. Sally shot two arrows for a total of 2 points. What numbers did Sally hit?

Sally hit a ____ and a ____.

Number Gumball Machine

Directions: Color the gumballs using the color code.

1 – 20 = Red	61 – 80 = Green	81 – 100 = Yellow
21 – 40 = Orange	41 – 60 = Blue	

Counting Body Parts

Directions: Skip count in order to solve the problems. The first one has been done for you.

 **1.** How many eyes on 7 boys? 2 + 2 + 2 + 2 + 2 + 2 + 2 ___14___	 **2.** How many elbows on 4 men? ________	 **3.** How many faces on 7 people? ________
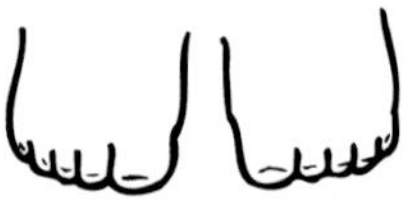 **4.** How many toes on 5 babies? ________	 **5.** How many fingers on 6 girls? ________	 **6.** How many feet on 3 brothers? ________
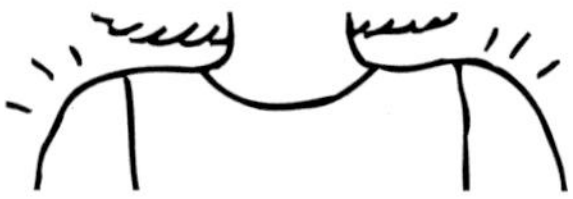 **7.** How many shoulders on 2 teachers? ________	 **8.** How many ears on 4 fathers? ________	 **9.** How many noses on 9 women? ________

Farm Squabble

Directions: Uncle Ted's animals got loose! Can you fill in the graph below to help him count his animals?

Graph the animals below.

	1	2	3	4	5	6
pigs						
cows						
sheep						
chickens						
dogs						

1. What animal does he have the most of? ____________________

2. How many more sheep does he have than dogs? ____________

Word Problems

1. Jennifer bought 12 books. During the summer, she read 5 books. How many books does she still need to read?

Jennifer needs to read ________ more books.

---

2. In a field, there are 14 white cows and 7 black cows. There are 4 horses in a pen. How many cows are there in all?

A. 18 **B.** 21 **C.** 25

---

3. Margo brought 20 cookies to a party. Linda brought 10 cookies to the party. How many cookies did Margo and Linda bring in all?

Margo and Linda brought _________ cookies in all.

---

4. Hannah has 16 stuffed animals on a shelf. She gave away 4 stuffed animals. How many stuffed animals does Hannah have left on the shelf?

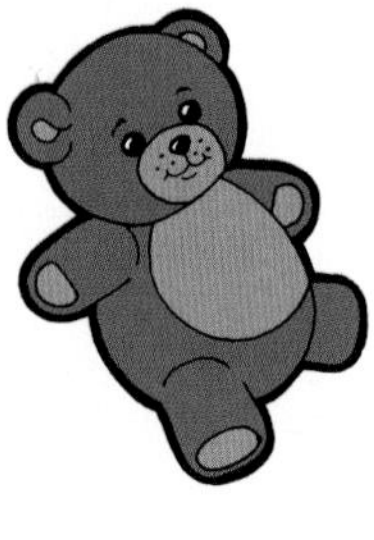

A. 20 **B.** 18 **C.** 12

More Word Problems

1. Peggy has 5 . Mattie has 7 . What number sentence tells how many  Peggy and Mattie have in all? (Circle the correct letter.)

A. 7 – 5 = 2 **B.** 7 + 5 = 11 **C.** 5 + 7 = 12

---

2. Two children plan to share 6 cookies. Circle to show how each child can get an equal share of the cookies.

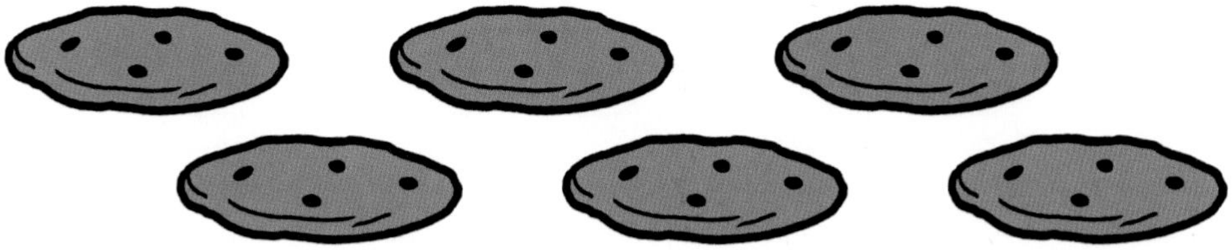

---

3. James has 6 blue cubes, 6 orange cubes, and 6 green cubes. How many cubes does James have in all? (Circle the correct letter.)

A. 6 **B.** 12 **C.** 18

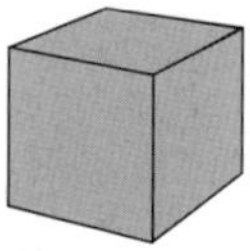

---

4. Three friends plan to share 9 pencils. Circle to show how each friend can get an equal number of pencils.

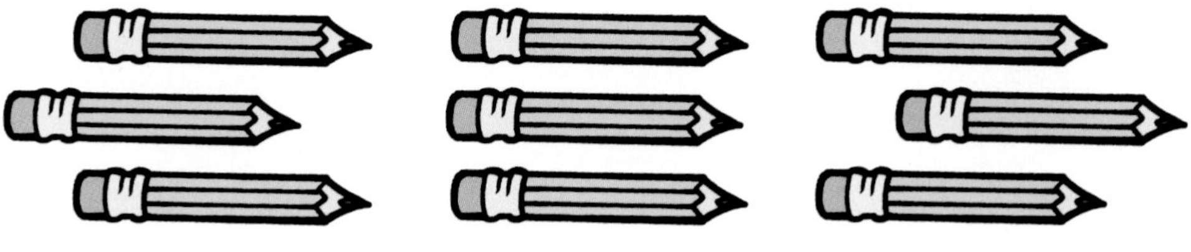

Quick Quizzes

1. Yolanda picked seven roses yesterday. Today, Yolanda picked twelve roses. How many more roses did Yolanda pick today?

_________ roses

2. Write a story problem for the number sentence below.

4 – 2 = ?

____

____

____

3. At a beach, Jim found 6 large shells and 4 small shells. How many shells did he find in all?

_________ shells

4. Look at the shape equation. Which answer shows the number sentence that matches? (Circle the correct letter.)

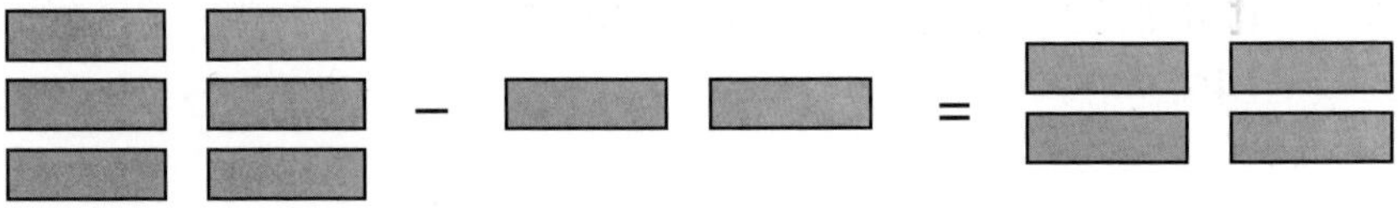

A. 8 + 2 = 10

B. 6 + 2 = 8

C. 6 – 2 = 4

D. 4 – 2 = 2

More Quick Quizzes

1. How much money is shown below? (Write your answer on the line.)

__________ cents

2. Write the word for each number.

7 ▲ ▲ ▲ ▲ ▲ ▲ ▲ ____________________

9 ● ● ● ● ● ● ● ● ● ____________________

6 □ □ □ □ □ □ ____________________

3. Write the number that comes after each number below.

4, ________, 6, ________, 8, ________, 10, ________

4. Look at the tally marks. How much is shown? (Circle the correct letter.)

A. 23 **B.** 24 **C.** 25

Apples and Oranges

1. Sammy has 4 apples and 6 oranges. Sue has 7 apples. How many apples do Sammy and Sue have in all?

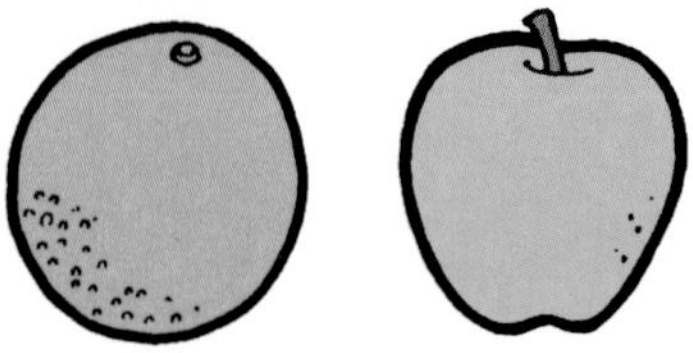

_________ apples

2. Each pail of sand makes 1 castle. How many castles will 4 pails of sand make?

_________ castles

3. Find the answer to each problem. (Circle the correct letter.)

15 – 8 =	
A.	9
B.	8
C.	7

23 – 7 =	
A.	16
B.	17
C.	28

19 – 7 =	
A.	11
B.	12
C.	13

4. Jim hit 3 home runs. Mike hit 4 more home runs than Jim. How many home runs did Mike hit?

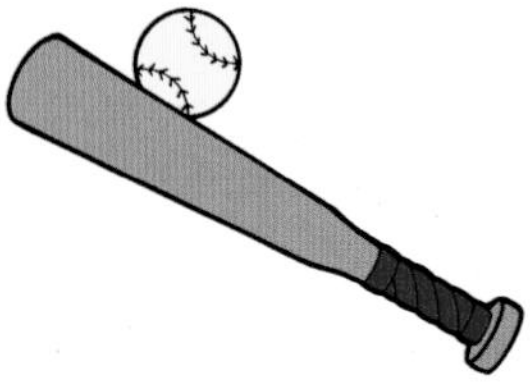

Mike hit _________ home runs.

Clocks and Shapes

1. Which shape is the same size and shape as the shaded figure? (Circle the correct letter.)

A. **B.** **C.**

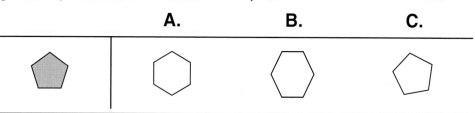

2. Look at the two clocks. Mark 10 minutes later on the second clock.

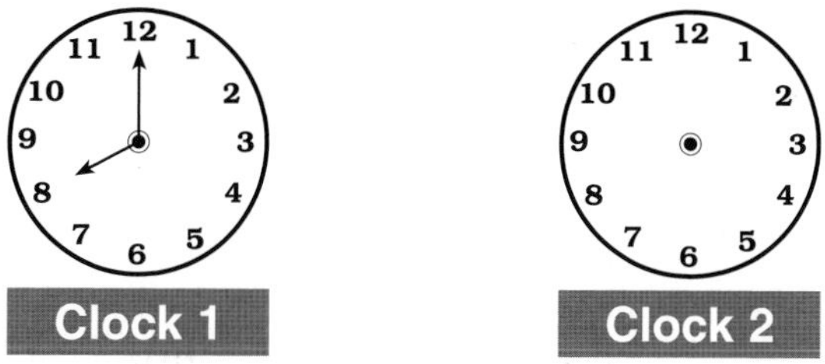

3. Circle the rectangles below.

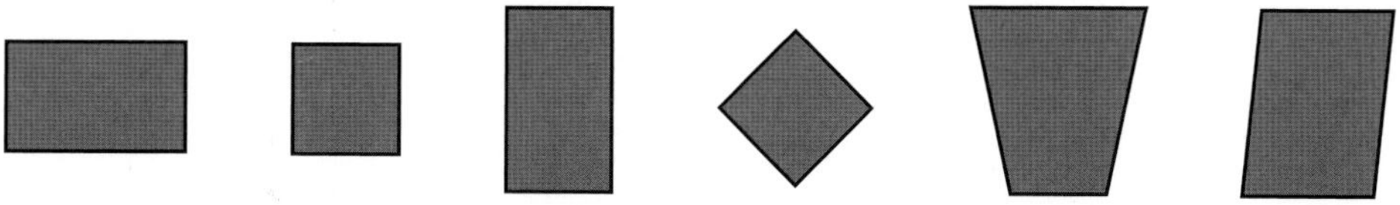

4. Read the time on the clocks. Show 10 minutes later on all four clocks.

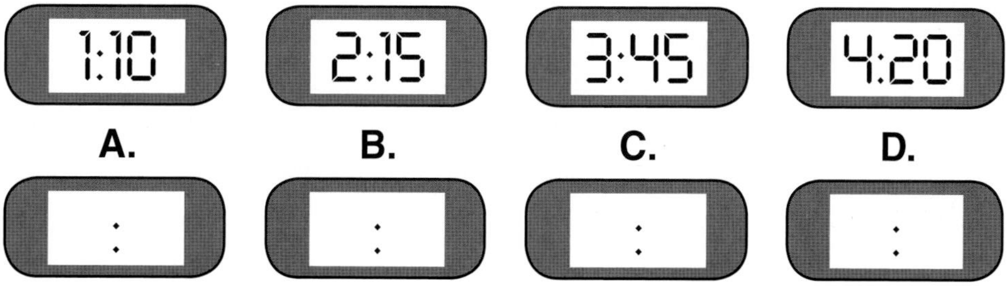

Answer Key

Pages 128–157
Make sure the pictures have been filled in according to the color keys given on each page.

Page 158
1. 99
2. 93
3. 85
4. 77
5. 38
6. 21
7. 20

Page 159

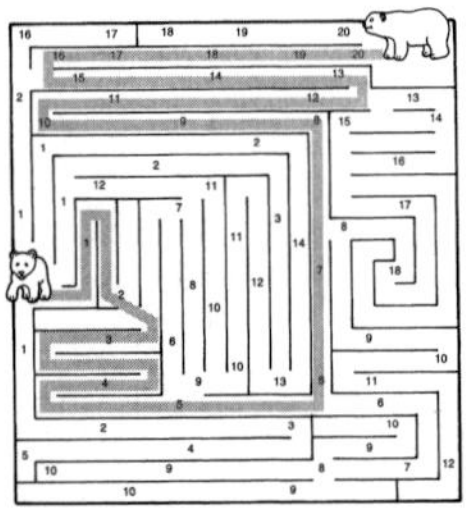

Page 160
a frog

Page 161
5: 5 + 0, 1 + 4, 0 + 5
7: 3 + 4, 7 + 0, 6 + 1
8: 5 + 3, 1 + 7, 0 + 8
4: 10 – 6, 7 – 3, 4 – 0
6: 6 – 0, 10 – 4, 9 – 3
2: 2 – 0, 4 – 2, 9 – 7

Page 162
The purse with "7 + 3" has the money.

Page 163
The fish should be colored according to the color key.

Page 164
The peanuts are in the lion's den.

Page 165

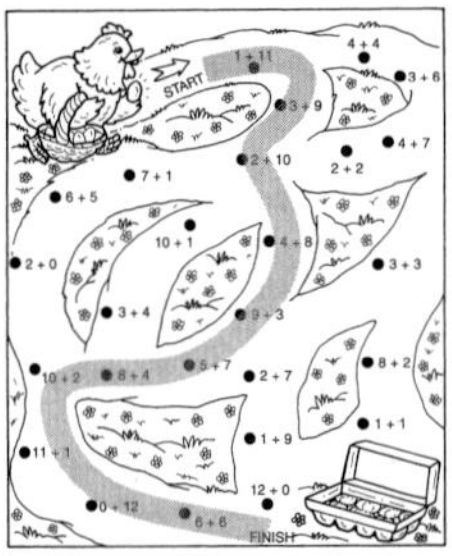

Page 166
1. 5
2. 6
3. 4
4. 10
5. 2
6. 8

Page 167
7 children, 6 puddles, 10 raindrops, 14 rain boots, 5 umbrellas, 4 raincoats
1. 7 + 14 = 21
2. 10 – 6 = 4
3. 5 + 4 = 9

Page 168
1. Matt, fourth
2. Sue, fifth
3. Mary, second
4. Daniel, sixth
5. Andrew, third
6. Max, first
7. Andrew (also, Max and Mary)
8. Mary (also everyone else)
9. Daniel

Page 169
missing boxes: 4, 6, 3, 7, 6, 4, 5, 9, 10, 8, 5

Page 170
1. 3 clowns
2. 3 elephants
3. 4 horses
4. 6 saddles
5. 10 shoes

Page 171
1. 3 pigs
2. 2 sheep
3. 3 horses
4. sheep
5. 3 + 5 = 8, 5 + 3 = 8, 8 – 5 = 3, 8 – 3 = 5

Page 172
1. 37, 57
2. 72, 92
3. 26, 46
4. 69, 89
5. 43, 63
6. 31, 51
7. 64, 84
8. 58, 78

Page 173
1. 3
2. 2
3. 1
4. 0
5. 6
6. 4
7. 7
8. 5

Page 174
Car 1: 17
Car 2: 18
Car 3: 20
Car 4: 17
Car 5: 25
Car 6: 13

Page 175
triangles: 10
hexagons: 5
squares: 4

Page 176
1. 3
2. 2, 2
3. 1
4. 1, 1

Page 177
The picture should be colored according to the color key.

Page 178
1. 14
2. 8
3. 7
4. 50
5. 60
6. 6
7. 4
8. 8
9. 9

Page 179
pigs, 3
cows, 4
sheep, 6
chickens, 5
dogs, 2
1. sheep
2. 4

Page 180
1. 7
2. 21
3. 30
4. 12

Page 181
1. C
2. 3 each
3. c
4. 3 each

Page 182
1. 5
2. Answers will vary.
3. 10
4. C

Page 183
1. 4
2. seven, nine, six
3. 5, 7, 9, 11
4. B

Page 184
1. 11 apples
2. 4 castles
3. C, A, B
4. 7 home runs

Page 185
1. C
2. Clock should read 8:10.
3. There are two rectangles.
4. A. 1:20; B. 2:25; C. 3:55; D. 4:30

Practice and Learn
WORKBOOK

Reading Comprehension

Baking a Cake

Directions: Look at the picture. Read the story.

I baked a cake in my oven. I ate the cake. It tasted good.

Directions: Read the questions. Circle the correct pictures.

1. What was baked?  

2. Where was it baked?  

3. Who ate the cake?  

In the Garden

Directions: Look at the picture. Read the story.

Joey mows the grass. He uses the hose to water the plants. Joey is a good gardener.

Directions: Read the questions. Circle the correct pictures.

1. What does Joey mow?

2. What does Joey water?

My Pet Dog

Directions: Look at the picture. Read the story.

My dog can fetch an egg from a hen. The hen may peck, but my pet can run like a jet!

Directions: Fill in the missing word in each sentence.

1. The ________________ can fetch an egg.

2. The ________________ can run like a jet.

Jack and Jill

Directions: Look at the picture. Read the poem.

Jack and Jill
  Went up a hill
To fetch a pail of water;
Jack fell down
  And broke his crown,
And Jill came tumbling
  after.

Directions: Answer the questions.

1. Who went up a hill?

____

2. What happened to Jack?

____

____

A Bath

Directions: Look at the picture. Read the story.

I scrub myself in the tub. A bug looks at me.
I splash on the rug. The bug jumps in the tub.

Directions: Fill in the missing word in each sentence.

1. The person is in the __________.

2. The __________ jumps in the tub.

Bedtime

Directions: Read the story.

At bedtime, my father reads a story to me and tucks me in my covers. Then we tell each other about our day. He says that he is proud of me. I always have sweet dreams!

Directions: Answer the questions.

1. What is the first thing the father does?

2. What does the child tell the father?

3. How does the child sleep?

Giraffes

Directions: Read the passage below. Answer the questions at the bottom of the page by filling in the correct bubbles.

Giraffes live on the grasslands of Africa. They are known for their long legs and necks. Giraffes are so tall that they feed on leaves at the tops of trees. Giraffes use their long tongues to pull the leaves off the trees. In order for giraffes to get water, they have to spread their front legs apart and bend way down low. Although giraffes have few enemies, they are always on the lookout for danger. They have good eyesight and hearing to help them.

1. What are giraffes known for?

ⓐ their patterns
ⓑ their long legs and necks
ⓒ their good eyesight

2. What does the word *feed* mean in this passage?

ⓐ eat ⓑ seed ⓒ collect

3. How do giraffes get leaves?

ⓐ from a caregiver
ⓑ collect them on the ground
ⓒ pull them off the trees

4. Why do giraffes have to spread their legs when drinking water?

ⓐ their height
ⓑ to look for danger
ⓒ to reach the leaves

Penguins

Directions: Read the passage below. Answer the questions at the bottom of the page by filling in the correct bubbles.

Penguins are unusual birds. They have feathers, but they cannot fly. They are very good at swimming. In fact, penguins spend most of their time swimming. The water is where penguins find their food. They really enjoy eating fish, squid, and krill. There are not many birds like the penguin!

1. What is a penguin's body covering?

ⓐ fur ⓑ feathers ⓒ scales

2. What do penguins like to eat?

ⓐ fish ⓑ insects ⓒ plants

3. What is the main idea of the paragraph?

ⓐ Penguins are good swimmers.

ⓑ Penguins find their food in water.

ⓒ Penguins are unusual birds.

An Odd Fish

A seahorse does not swim like other fish do. It moves through the water like a rocking horse. Its head looks like a horse's head. It uses its long **snout** to suck up food.

The seahorse has a hard body that feels like bones. It can wrap its tail around a piece of seaweed. It hides there so that sea turtles and sharks do not find it.

A male seahorse gives birth to the babies! The female puts her eggs into his pouch. He carries the eggs for six weeks. Then the little babies pop out and swim away.

An Odd Fish *(cont.)*

Directions: Fill in the bubble next to the right answer.

1. A seahorse's head looks like

ⓐ a horse's.

ⓑ seaweed.

2. What happens last?

ⓐ The male carries the eggs.

ⓑ The babies swim away.

3. What makes a seahorse different from other fish?

ⓐ It swims in a different way.

ⓑ It is a horse, not a fish.

4. A snout is

ⓐ an ear.

ⓑ a nose and mouth.

5. Why does the seahorse hide from sea turtles and sharks?

ⓐ They want to eat the seahorse.

ⓑ They are playing hide and seek.

A Whale of a Time

Dolphins are little whales. But most whales are big. The blue whale is the **largest** animal on Earth.

Whales live in the sea. They swim in groups. They make sounds to "talk." All whales have a hole on top of their heads. They do not stay under the water all of the time. They need to come up for air. When they go back under the water, the hole shuts.

Whales are mammals, just like us. They are smart. They can learn tricks. You may see a dolphin at a sea park. They are fun to watch!

A Whale of a Time *(cont.)*

Directions: Fill in the bubble next to the right answer.

1. Most whales are

ⓐ big.

ⓑ small.

2. What happens first?

ⓐ The whale does a trick.

ⓑ The man teaches the whale a trick.

3. How is a whale different from a fish?

ⓐ All fish live in fresh water.

ⓑ A fish is not a mammal.

4. What word means the same as *largest*?

ⓐ biggest

ⓑ weakest

5. What trick might a sea park whale do?

ⓐ jump through a hoop

ⓑ sing a song

Plants Are Important

All plants need water, air, and light. Plants do not eat. They use the light from the sun to make their own food. That is why a plant always grows towards the sun. Plants make the food in their leaves. Then they store the food in their stems and roots. They use this food on **gloomy** days when the sun is covered by clouds.

If there were no plants, there would be no life on Earth. Plants start every food chain. An animal eats the plant. Or it eats the seeds or fruit of the plant. Then another animal eats that animal. Some animals eat both plants and animals.

Plants Are Important *(cont.)*

Directions: Fill in the bubble next to the right answer.

1. Plants cannot

ⓐ eat food.

ⓑ use food.

2. What happens first?

ⓐ A plant uses food from its roots.

ⓑ A plant makes food from the sun.

3. Where do plants get water?

ⓐ the ground

ⓑ the store

4. *Gloomy* means

ⓐ dark.

ⓑ bright.

5. Picture a bush growing in the shade of a tree. How does it look?

ⓐ Most of the bush's branches are growing towards the shade.

ⓑ Most of the bush's branches are growing away from the shade.

Water

You know that there is more water than land on Earth. But did you know that there are two kinds of water? There is fresh water, and there is salt water. There is much more salt water than fresh water on Earth. Salt water is in the sea. We cannot drink it. It would make us ill. But most sea animals must stay in salt water. If they are put in fresh water, they die.

Lakes and rivers hold fresh water. Rain, snow, and ice are **forms** of fresh water. Many animals and all plants and people need fresh water. Without water there could be no life on Earth.

Water *(cont.)*

Directions: Fill in the bubble next to the right answer.

1. What kind of water can people drink?

ⓐ salt water

ⓑ fresh water

2. What happens last?

ⓐ A person gets sick.

ⓑ A person drinks salt water.

3. Why do freshwater animals have to stay in fresh water?

ⓐ because salt water is different and not good for them

ⓑ because there isn't enough salt water for them

4. The word *forms* means

ⓐ kinds.

ⓑ spots.

5. What happens when snow melts?

ⓐ It turns into salt water.

ⓑ It turns into fresh water.

Air

Air is all around us. We cannot see it. But it takes up space. It takes up space inside of a balloon. When the balloon pops, the air **rushes** out.

When air moves outside, we call it wind. Warm air goes up. Cold air goes down. Wind, warm air, and cold air make our weather change.

We must take care to keep our air clean. We need to breathe air. All plants and animals do. Even fish breathe air. Their gills take air out of the water.

Air *(cont.)*

Directions: Fill in the bubble next to the right answer.

1. What needs air?

ⓐ just animals

ⓑ both plants and animals

2. What happens last?

ⓐ The balloon hits something sharp.

ⓑ The air goes out of the balloon.

3. When the wind blows,

ⓐ warm and cold air move around outdoors.

ⓑ no rain can fall.

4. *Rushes* means

ⓐ moves slowly.

ⓑ moves quickly.

5. Why do we need clean air?

ⓐ If we breathe dirty air, it may make us sick.

ⓑ Clean air costs less than dirty air.

The Great Lakes

The five Great Lakes are very big. They can be seen from space! The lakes hold a lot of fresh water. One is Lake Superior. It is the second-biggest lake in the world.

The lakes are between America and Canada. On one side of four lakes is America. On the other side is Canada. But this is not true for one lake. Lake Michigan is inside the U.S.

The Great Lakes are **linked**. A ship can move from one to the other. Many ships go from lake to lake. They bring things to people. These ships may even go out to the sea. Then they can go to other countries.

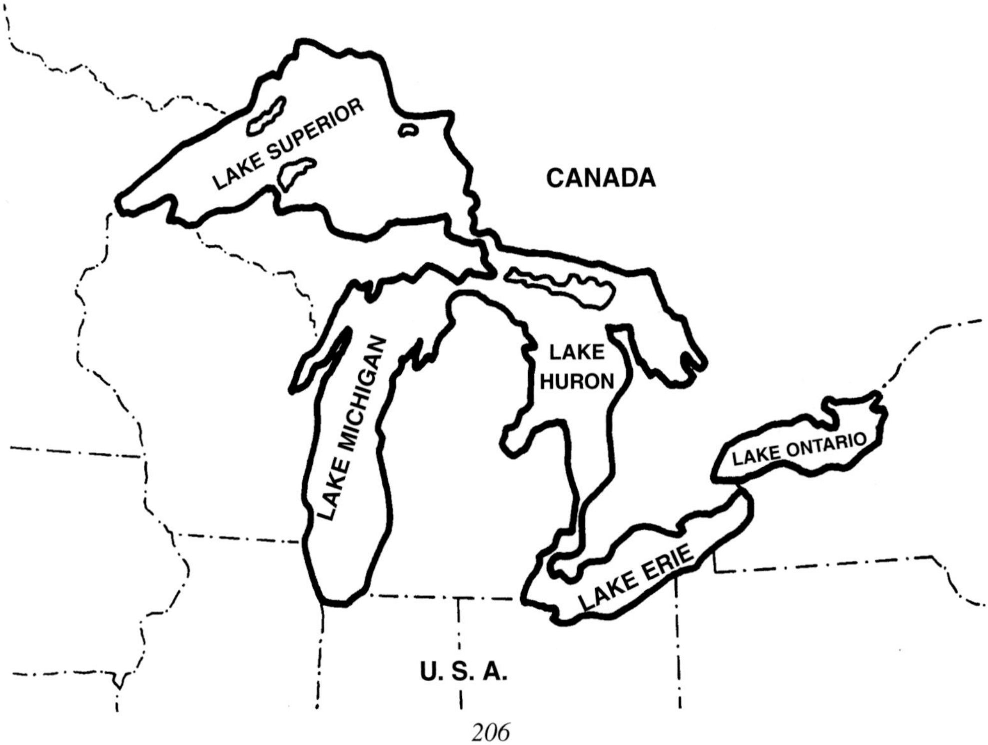

The Great Lakes *(cont.)*

Directions: Fill in the bubble next to the right answer.

1. What is the second-biggest lake in the world?

ⓐ Lake Erie

ⓑ Lake Superior

2. What two countries share the Great Lakes?

ⓐ America and Canada

ⓑ America and Mexico

3. Can a ship from the sea reach the Great Lakes?

ⓐ no

ⓑ yes

4. *Linked* means

ⓐ stacked.

ⓑ joined.

5. Picture a ship bringing things to people in the Great Lakes. What is the ship made of?

ⓐ paper

ⓑ metal

The Desert

A desert is hot and dry. Very little rain falls. Wind blows the sand. This forms dunes. Each day the sun heats up the desert. Then at night the desert gets very cold!

Many kinds of animals and plants live in a desert. Most animals sleep in the day. They come out at night to hunt. Some animals, like the camel, store water in their bodies. They can go for weeks without a drink. Cactus plants store water, too. Their sharp **needles** keep the animals from taking it.

Few people live in the desert. They need more water than they can find there.

The Desert *(cont.)*

Directions: Fill in the bubble next to the right answer.

1. What kind of plant can store water?

ⓐ a cactus

ⓑ grass

2. Is the desert hot at all times?

ⓐ no

ⓑ yes

3. Why do some plants and animals store water?

ⓐ because it snows in the desert

ⓑ because it is dry in the desert

4. Why are most desert animals awake at night?

ⓐ They cannot see during the day.

ⓑ It is cool enough to come out then.

5. Picture a desert during the day. What do you see?

ⓐ lots of animals

ⓑ lots of sand

Don't Play with Fire

Be careful near fire. Clothes and paper burn easily. Keep away from hot stoves and grills. Never play with matches or a lighter.

If you ever catch on fire, do not run! Drop to the ground. Roll around until the fire goes out. Then get help. Burns are bad. You must see a doctor right away.

Have a smoke **alarm** in your home. If you hear it, get out! Fire can move fast. Smoke can, too. Smoke rises, so stay low. Try not to breathe smoke. If you cannot reach a door, go out a window.

Stay back. Firefighters will put out the fire.

Don't Play with Fire *(cont.)*

Directions: Fill in the bubble next to the right answer.

1. What catches fire easily?

ⓐ green grass

ⓑ paper

2. If you hear a smoke alarm, what should you do first?

ⓐ Call the firefighters.

ⓑ Get out of the house.

3. The word *alarm* means

ⓐ a noise that warns.

ⓑ the sound of a horn.

4. Why shouldn't you run if you catch on fire?

ⓐ Running is too hard to do.

ⓑ Running would not put out the fire.

5. Picture a house on fire. What is coming out of its windows?

ⓐ smoke

ⓑ bugs

The Fourth of July

We see fireworks on the Fourth of July. There are **parades**. Most people have the day off. Why? It is America's birthday.

At one time a king ruled America. He lived across the sea. The people did not like this. They wanted to make their own laws. They wanted to be free. So they told the king. It was July 4, 1776.

The king got mad. He sent men to fight. When the war was over, America was free.

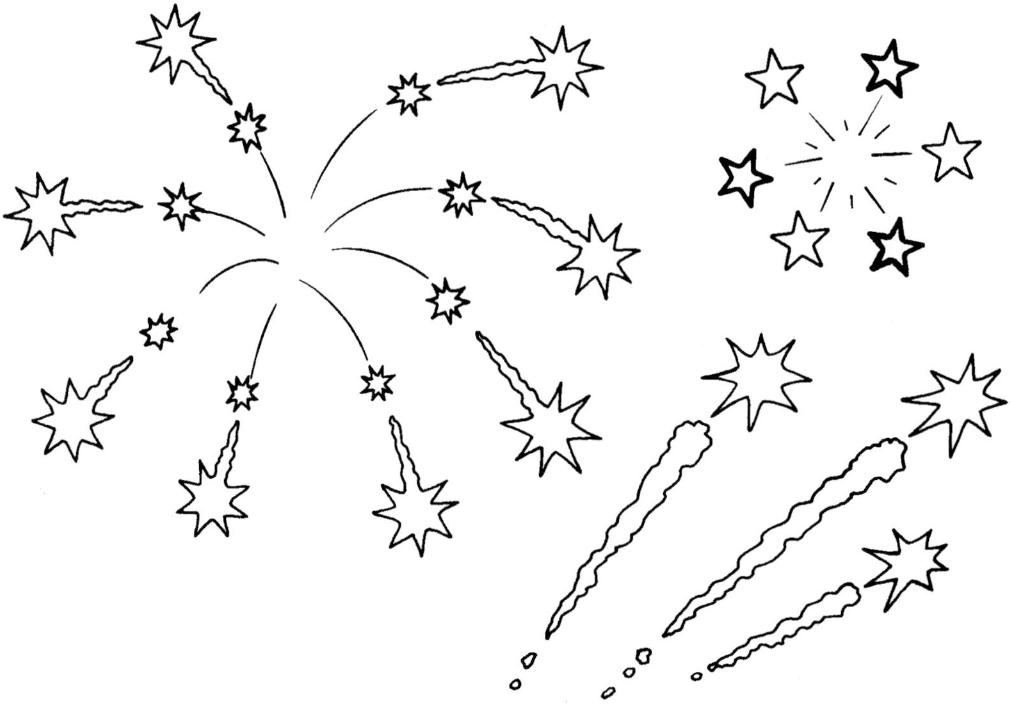

The Fourth of July *(cont.)*

Directions: Fill in the bubble next to the right answer.

1. On July 4, 1776,

ⓐ a king started to rule America.

ⓑ the people told the king that they were free.

2. What happened first?

ⓐ The people had parades and fireworks on July 4th.

ⓑ The people fought to be free.

3. America's birthday is July 4th because

ⓐ that is the day that the king lost the war.

ⓑ that is the day that the people said they were free.

4. During *parades*

ⓐ bands play music.

ⓑ people run.

5. What would have happened if America lost the fight?

ⓐ The people would have made their own laws.

ⓑ The king would have stayed the ruler.

The First Thanksgiving

In 1620 the Pilgrims left England. They wanted their own land. They sailed in a ship called the *Mayflower*. When they reached America, they named their new home Plymouth.

The first winter was hard. There wasn't much to eat. Half of the people died. In the spring, Native Americans found them. They gave the Pilgrims corn seeds. They told them where to fish and dig for clams.

By that fall the people had lots of food. They had a big **feast**. They asked the Native Americans to come. They ate for three days! It was the first Thanksgiving.

The First Thanksgiving *(cont.)*

Directions: Fill in the bubble next to the right answer.

1. What was the name of the ship the Pilgrims sailed on?

ⓐ *Plymouth*

ⓑ *Mayflower*

2. What happened last?

ⓐ The people almost starved to death.

ⓑ The people met the Native Americans.

3. Did it help the Pilgrims when the Native Americans gave them corn seeds?

ⓐ Yes, because then the Pilgrims had a crop of corn.

ⓑ No, because the Pilgrims didn't know what to do with them.

4. The word *feast* means

ⓐ meal.

ⓑ wedding.

5. Why did the Pilgrims ask the Native Americans to come?

ⓐ because the Native Americans had given them help

ⓑ because they wanted to stop the war with the Native Americans

Keeping You Safe

Many people work to keep you safe. Your doctor wants to keep you well. When you are sick, your doctor may give you pills so you will get better.

The police make sure that no one breaks into your home. They keep watch so that no one hurts you.

Firefighters put out fires. If your home catches on fire, they come. They spray water from hoses. The fire will go out. Your home may be saved.

Ambulance workers hurry to you if you are hurt badly. They take care of you. They rush you to the **hospital**. They can save your life.

Keeping You Safe *(cont.)*

Directions: Fill in the bubble next to the right answer.

1. What do ambulance workers do?

ⓐ They take hurt or very sick people to a hospital.

ⓑ They use hoses to fight fires.

2. What happens last?

ⓐ A person calls the ambulance.

ⓑ The hurt child goes away in the ambulance.

4. A *hospital* is

ⓐ where the firefighters work.

ⓑ where doctors help people who are hurt.

5. Who do you call if someone broke into your home?

ⓐ the police

ⓑ the doctor

6. Picture a doctor's office. Who else works there?

ⓐ nurses

ⓑ police

The First Clothes

Long, long ago people had no clothes. They lived in warm places. They did not need clothes. But the people followed animals. So over time they moved to colder places. They did not like the cold. So after they killed an animal they put its skin around them. It was like a **blanket**. Then they felt warmer.

Over time they learned to make needles from bird bones. They made thread from strong grass. They cut the animal skins with sharp rocks or bones. Then they sewed the pieces together into the first clothes. The clothes kept the people warm.

The First Clothes *(cont.)*

Directions: Fill in the bubble next to the right answer.

1. What did the early people use for needles?

ⓐ bird bones

ⓑ strong grasses

2. What happened first?

ⓐ People used animal skins to stay warm.

ⓑ People did not wear clothes.

3. A *blanket* is

ⓐ clothes.

ⓑ something we cover up with.

4. Why did the people make animal skins into clothes?

ⓐ They did not know what else to do with the animal skins.

ⓑ The clothes stayed on better than the animal-skin blanket did.

5. Picture a person wearing some of the first clothes. What do you see on the clothes?

ⓐ fur

ⓑ buttons

The Dodos

Dodo birds had only one home. They lived on an island in the Indian Ocean. When **sailors** found their island, the birds were in big trouble. These birds could not fly. They were easy to catch. So the men ate them.

Pigs came on the ships. Sometimes the men could not catch them. Then the pigs stayed on the island. The pigs ate all of the dodo birds' eggs.

In 1680 the last dodo bird died. There are none of these birds left on Earth.

The Dodos *(cont.)*

Directions: Fill in the bubble next to the right answer.

1. Which animal died out?

ⓐ dodo birds

ⓑ pigs

2. What happened last?

ⓐ Sailors found the island.

ⓑ Pigs were loose on the island.

3. What made the dodo birds easy to catch?

ⓐ They could not fly.

ⓑ They could not run.

4. *Sailors* are

ⓐ the people who keep animals safe.

ⓑ the people who work on ships.

6. Picture a dodo bird's nest from long ago. Where is it?

ⓐ on the ground

ⓑ high up in a tree

Chewing the Cud

A deer is afraid when it is in an open field. It thinks that other animals might attack it. So it tears off big pieces of leaves and branches from bushes. But it does not chew them. It **swallows** them whole!

This food gets stored in a special part of the deer's stomach. When the deer is back in the woods, it feels safer. Then it brings up the stored food, or cud. The deer chews the cud. Chewing the cud breaks the food into little pieces. Then the deer's body can use it.

Chewing the Cud *(cont.)*

Directions: Fill in the bubble next to the right answer.

1. What is in cud?

ⓐ leaves and bark

ⓑ meat

2. What happens last?

ⓐ The deer grabs branches and leaves from a field.

ⓑ The deer chews the cud.

3. Why does the deer chew cud?

ⓐ to break its food into small pieces its body can use

ⓑ to keep its teeth from getting too long

4. *Swallows* means

ⓐ smells.

ⓑ gulps.

5. Which animal would a deer be afraid of?

ⓐ a wolf

ⓑ a rabbit

Our Sun and Moon

The sun is a big star. It gives heat and light to Earth. The sun is always shining. During our night, it shines on the other side of the world. The sun is there on cloudy days. The clouds hide it.

The moon has no light of its own. It **reflects** the sun's light. The moon seems to change shape. But it does not. The whole moon is still there. We just see less of it when part of the moon is in the Earth's shadow.

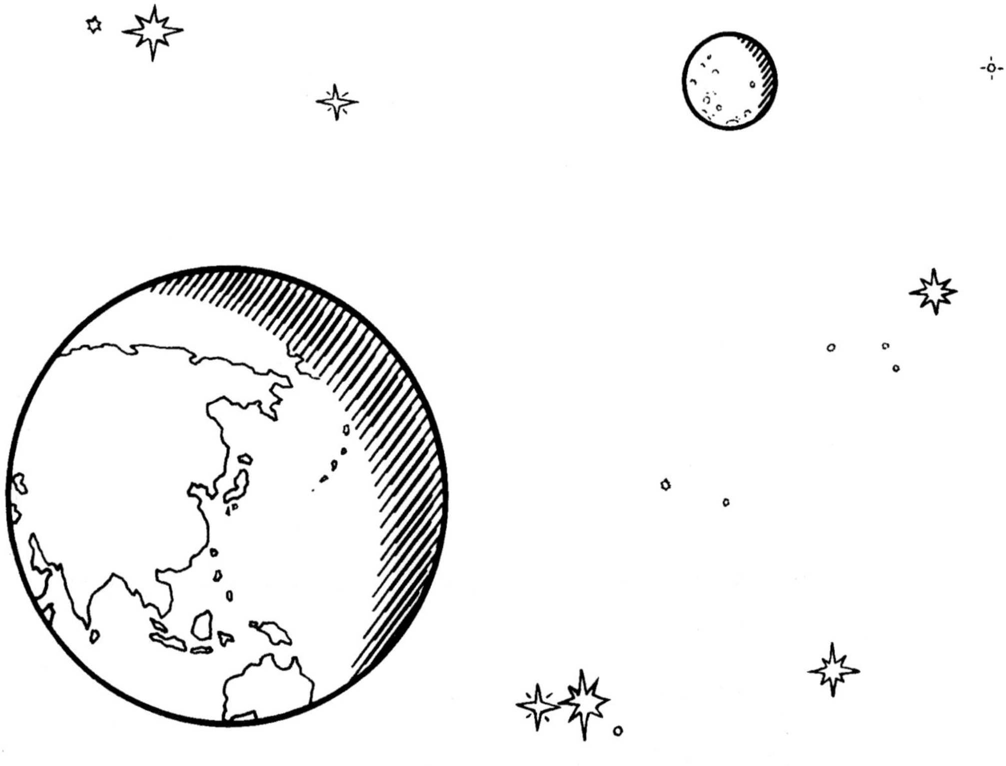

Our Sun and Moon *(cont.)*

Directions: Fill in the bubble next to the right answer.

1. Which looks like it changes shape?

ⓐ Earth

ⓑ the moon

2. What happens at the start of our day?

ⓐ The sun comes up.

ⓑ The sun goes down.

3. What would Earth be like without the sun?

ⓐ It would be hot and bright.

ⓑ It would be cold and dark.

4. *Reflects* means

ⓐ drinks up.

ⓑ throws back.

5. What happens when the moon is completely in the Earth's shadow?

ⓐ We can not see the moon at all.

ⓑ We have a full, round moon.

Native American Games and Toys

Have you ever played cat's cradle? That string game comes from Native Americans. Have you ever seen a lacrosse game? The players catch and throw a ball with nets on poles. That was a Native American game, too.

Native American boys and girls played other games, as well. They hid a small rock in a shoe and took turns guessing which shoe it was in. They made marks on flat stones. They used them as dice in **games of chance**.

The children played with toys. Little girls had dolls made of corncobs. Small boys had bows and arrows. They shot at logs. Older boys shot at moving hoops.

Native-American Games and Toys *(cont.)*

Directions: Fill in the bubble next to the right answer.

1. What were the Native American girls' dolls made with?

ⓐ flat stones

ⓑ corncobs

2. How are today's toys different from the Native American toys?

ⓐ No one plays with dolls or bows anymore.

ⓑ Their toys were made of things found outside.

3. *Games of chance* are

ⓐ games you win by luck.

ⓑ games you win by skill.

4. Why did boys use bows and arrows?

ⓐ because they didn't like the other games

ⓑ because when they grew up, it would help them to hunt

5. Picture Native American children long ago. What are they doing?

ⓐ playing with stones and sticks

ⓑ pulling a wagon with toys in it

Stars

When you look up in the sky at night, what do you see? If it is a clear night, you will see stars. Stars are all of the little lights you see in the sky. There are many, many stars. There are so many that no one can count them all!

Stars are not all the same. Some are big. Some are small. Some give more light than others do. The sun is a star. It isn't the biggest one. But it is **closer** to our Earth than the others. That's why we see it so well.

Stars (cont.)

Directions: Fill in the bubble next to the right answer.

1. In the night sky there are many

ⓐ moons.

ⓑ stars.

2. What happens first?

ⓐ You see the stars in the sky.

ⓑ The sun goes down.

3. What does the sun send to Earth?

ⓐ light

ⓑ storms

4. *Closer* means

ⓐ nearer.

ⓑ bigger.

5. Picture a night when you can see many stars. What is *not* in the sky?

ⓐ the moon

ⓑ thick clouds

Becoming Farmers

Long, long ago people did not know how to grow food. So they looked for fruits and nuts. They hunted and ate animals. The animals moved around. So the people had to move around, too. At night they looked for a cave to stay in. When they couldn't find one, they often got cold and wet.

Then people found out that if they put seeds in the ground, plants would grow. Then they could eat the plants or their seeds. This let the people stay in one place. They made homes and grew **crops**. They stored up food, too. They lived longer.

Becoming Farmers *(cont.)*

Directions: Fill in the bubble next to the right answer.

1. After people became farmers, they

ⓐ had a longer life than when they moved with the animals.

ⓑ had a shorter life than when they moved with the animals.

2. What happened first?

ⓐ People stayed in one place.

ⓑ People went where the animals went.

3. Why did people follow the animals?

ⓐ They needed to eat the animals for food.

ⓑ They felt bored.

4. What was a good thing about learning to farm?

ⓐ The people could save food.

ⓑ The people stopped eating animals.

5. Picture the people inside the caves. What gives them light?

ⓐ a flashlight

ⓑ a fire

Bruises

You bump your arm hard. You do not get cut. Your skin does not break. Still, you get a bruise. Your skin turns blue-black. What is a bruise? Why does your skin turn blue-black?

Blood flows in your body. It flows through tubes. Tubes that carry blood are called blood vessels. Some are big. Some tubes are tiny. The tiny tubes are called capillaries.

Living things are made of cells. Cells are like building blocks. They are the smallest building block of living things. Your body has lots of cells. It has many kinds of cells. You have bone cells. You have skin cells. You have lots of blood cells. Most of your blood cells are red blood cells. Red blood cells make your blood look red.

When you get bumped, you may not get cut. Still, you may hurt some capillaries. Some may break. Blood leaks from the capillaries. You bleed under your skin. When blood cells leak from the capillaries, they die. When the cells die, they turn blue-black. We see the blue-black color. We call the blue-black color a bruise.

Your body absorbs the dead blood cells. When something is absorbed, it is taken in. It is made part of itself. Fresh blood absorbs the dead blood cells. It takes many days. The bruise changes color. It changes color as the fresh blood absorbs the dead cells. It changes from blue-black to purple. It changes from purple to yellow. Finally, the bruise is gone. All the dead blood cells have been absorbed.

Bruises *(cont.)*

Directions: Fill in the bubble next to the right answer.

1. What are living things made of?

ⓐ blood
ⓑ cells
ⓒ vessels
ⓓ capillaries

2. This story is mainly about

ⓐ cells.
ⓑ blood.
ⓒ bruises.
ⓓ capillaries.

3. If your bruise is yellow, it means that

ⓐ your capillaries are leaking.
ⓑ you are bleeding under the skin.
ⓒ soon the bruise will change to blue-black.
ⓓ most of the dead blood cells have been absorbed.

4. Which statement is true?

ⓐ Vessels and capillaries are cells.
ⓑ You do not have many blood vessels.
ⓒ When you get a bruise, you cut your skin.
ⓓ Red blood cells make your blood look red.

5. Think about how the word *tiny* relates to *small*. Which words relate in the same way?

ⓐ many : lots
ⓑ blood : red
ⓒ bump : bruise
ⓓ yellow : color

Blind and Deaf

Helen Keller was born on June 27, 1880. She was a happy baby. Then, Helen got sick. Helen got a fever. It hurt her ears. Helen became deaf. She could not hear.

Think about how you learn to talk. You listen. You learn to say what other people say. Helen could not hear. She could not listen. She could not learn to talk. The high fever also hurt Helen's eyes. Helen became blind. She could not see.

Helen was not happy. She became wild. She hit. She screamed. She threw things. She hurt people.

Helen's parents found a teacher. The teacher was named Annie Sullivan. Annie did not let Helen hit. She did not let her break or throw things. Annie taught Helen how to talk. Helen was deaf. She was blind. How could Annie teach her how to talk?

Annie made signs with her fingers. She used the signs to spell words. She made the signs in Helen's hand. At first, Helen did not know what the signs meant. Annie did not give up. She took Helen to a water pump. Annie pumped. Water came out. Helen felt the water. At the same time, Annie signed. She signed w-a-t-e-r. Then, Helen knew!

Blind and Deaf *(cont.)*

Directions: Fill in the bubble next to the right answer.

1. In the story, how did Helen learn to talk?

ⓐ by looking at people make signs
ⓑ by listening to what people said
ⓒ by feeling words spelled into her hand

2. This story is mainly about

ⓐ how to talk with signs.
ⓑ a girl who was blind and deaf.
ⓒ what a high fever did to a girl.

3. Why did Helen become wild?

ⓐ She was unhappy because she could not talk.
ⓑ She was unhappy because her sister was born.
ⓒ She was unhappy because her teacher made finger signs.

4. What month was Helen born in?

ⓐ June
ⓑ July
ⓒ April
ⓓ August

5. Think about how the word *eye* relates to *see*. Which words relate in the same way?

ⓐ ear : deaf
ⓑ eye : ears
ⓒ ear : hear
ⓓ eye : blind

Better Than Gold

King Midas loved gold. He thought gold was the most important thing in the world. He had a lot of gold. He wanted more. One day, a man said to King Midas, "I will grant you one wish." When you grant something, you give what is asked for.

King Midas knew what he wanted. He wanted gold. He said, "I want to turn everything I touch into gold." The man granted the wish. King Midas was very happy. He touched grass. The grass turned to gold. He touched flowers. The flowers turned to gold. Everything King Midas touched turned to gold.

King Midas got hungry. He picked up his fork. The fork turned to gold. King Midas put food in his mouth. The food turned to gold! King Midas could not eat. King Midas had a child. She ran to her father. When she touched him, she turned to gold.

King Midas cried, "I am sad. My heart is broken. Gold cannot mend my broken heart. Gold cannot fill my hungry belly." After King Midas spoke, the man came back. He said he would grant one more wish. King Midas wished for everything to go back the way it was before. King Midas hugged his child. He said, "My heart is mended. You are worth more than gold. Now, let's eat!"

Better Than Gold *(cont.)*

Directions: Fill in the circle next to the correct answer.

1. What, according to the story, are the two most important things in the world?

ⓐ gold and wishes
ⓑ children and food
ⓒ grass and flowers

2. When you grant something, you

ⓐ mend a broken heart.
ⓑ turn things to gold.
ⓒ give what is asked for.

3. This story is mainly about

ⓐ a story with a lesson about wishing.
ⓑ a story with a lesson about the world.
ⓒ a story with a lesson about what is important.

4. In the story, what did King Midas turn to gold first?

ⓐ food
ⓑ grass
ⓒ a chair
ⓓ flowers

5. Think about how the word *broken* relates to *mended*. What words relate in the same way?

ⓐ sad : happy
ⓑ chair : table
ⓒ lesson : story
ⓓ golden : touch

The First Step

The day was July 20th. The year was 1969. Neil Armstrong stepped out onto the moon. It had taken him three days to get there. He had to wear a spacesuit. He had to wear a suit because there was no air on the moon. There was no water. No one had ever gone to the moon before. Neil was the first man on the moon.

Neil did something. He did it right away. He did it as soon as he stepped out. What did Neil do? He took some lunar soil. Lunar soil is ground. It is ground from the moon. Lunar soil is rocky. It is dusty. Neil put the lunar soil in a bag. He put the bag in a pocket. The pocket was special. It was in his spacesuit. It was made just for the lunar soil.

Why did Neil take lunar soil? No one had ever been to the moon before. Scientists did not know what would happen. What if Neil had to leave the moon quickly? What if he had to leave before he could find out things for the scientists? Neil picked up the soil first. He did it so that if he had to come back quickly, he would not be empty-handed. Scientists could look at the rocks. They could study them. They could learn about the moon.

The First Step *(cont.)*

Directions: Fill in the circle next to the correct answer.

1. This story is mainly about

ⓐ big and small craters.
ⓑ scientists and lunar soil.
ⓒ Neil Armstrong and the moon.

2. How long did it take Neil to get to the moon?

ⓐ one day ⓑ 20 years
ⓒ three days ⓓ 1969 years

3. Think about how the word *mountain* relates to *snowy*. Which words relate in the same way?

ⓐ step : out ⓑ rock : pocket
ⓒ spacesuit : air ⓓ moon: rocky

4. What is not true about the first step on the moon?

ⓐ The ground was wet.
ⓑ It happened on July 20th.
ⓒ It happened in 1969.
ⓓ Neil Armstrong took the first step.

5. Which answer is in the right order?

ⓐ Neil put on a spacesuit; he got soil; he stepped out.
ⓑ Neil stepped out; he got soil; he put soil in his pocket.
ⓒ Neil went to the moon; he stepped out; he put on a spacesuit.

Sharks

A shark has lots more teeth than you do. Some sharks have hundreds of teeth. Sharks lose more teeth than you, too. In fact, sharks lose their teeth all the time. Feel your teeth. They are set firmly into your jaw. When something is firmly set, it does not move. It is fixed. A shark's teeth are not firmly set.

Losing a tooth does not bother a shark. Why not? Sharks have many new teeth. The new teeth are in the jaws. The new teeth come out fast. How fast? It takes only 24 hours for some teeth to grow in. A shark can have new teeth in just one day!

Most sharks are born alive. They are born ready to hunt. Nurse sharks have about 20 to 30 babies at a time. Nurse-shark babies are about one foot (30 centimeters) long when they are born. Great White shark babies are bigger. Some are four-and-a-half feet (137 centimeters) long!

Other sharks are hatched out of eggs. The eggs are not hard. The eggs are thick. They are rubbery. The thick, rubbery eggs protect the babies inside. Most of the eggs have strings on them. The strings catch on seaweed. The strings catch on coral. They keep the eggs from floating away.

Sharks *(cont.)*

Directions: Fill in the circle next to the correct answer.

1. This story is mainly about

ⓐ eggs.
ⓑ pups.
ⓒ teeth.
ⓓ sharks.

2. Why are shark eggs thick and rubbery?

ⓐ to catch on seaweed
ⓑ to firmly fix strings
ⓒ to protect the babies inside

3. Think about how the word *tooth* relates to *teeth*. Which words relate in the same way?

ⓐ babies : baby
ⓑ shark : sharks
ⓒ eggs : strings
ⓓ seaweed : coral

4. From the story you can tell that

ⓐ all sharks are born alive.
ⓑ one baby shark is born at a time.
ⓒ there is more than one kind of shark.

5. When something is firm, it

ⓐ does not move.
ⓑ is thick and rubbery.
ⓒ grows back in 24 hours.

Steel

Steel is strong. Steel is light. We make many things out of steel. Bridges need to be strong and light. We make many bridges out of steel. We use steel in tall buildings. The strong, light steel helps hold up the building. We use steel in cars. We make tools out of steel. We make pots and pans. We make spoons and knives. We use steel every day.

Where do we get steel? Is it a plant? Is it a rock? Steel is not a plant. We cannot grow steel. It is not alive. Steel is not a rock. We cannot just find it. We have to make it.

Steel is a special metal. We make it from iron. Iron is found in a rock called iron ore. We mine iron ore. When we mine something, we dig it out.

The iron ore is sent to a steel plant. The steel plant has big ovens. Some ovens are used to heat the iron ore. The ovens get so hot that the iron ore melts. It turns from a solid into a liquid. The liquid iron is poured into more ovens. These ovens blow oxygen through the melted iron. The oxygen burns out everything but the iron.

The iron is changed to steel. We mix things into the melted iron. When we add different things, we make different kinds of steel. What do we do with the hot steel? We pour some steel into molds. We form it into blocks. We pass some steel between rollers. The rollers shape the steel into flat pieces. We can make things from the blocks. We can make things from the flat pieces.

Steel *(cont.)*

Directions: Fill in the circle next to the correct answer.

1. Which statement is true?

ⓐ We can mine steel.
ⓑ We can grow steel.
ⓒ Steel is made from iron.

2. This story is mainly about

ⓐ metal.
ⓑ steel.
ⓒ bridges.
ⓓ iron ore.

3. Which answer is in the correct order?

ⓐ mine iron ore, melt it, pour steel into molds
ⓑ mine iron ore, melt it, send it to a steel plant
ⓒ send iron ore to a steel plant, melt it, mine it

4. What do some ovens blow through the melted iron?

ⓐ metal
ⓑ oxygen
ⓒ rollers
ⓓ iron ore

5. Think about how the word *iron* relates to *metal*. Which words relate in the same way?

ⓐ steel : solid
ⓑ steel : liquid
ⓒ iron ore : mine
ⓓ iron ore : rock

Abraham Lincoln

Directions: Read the passage below. Answer the questions at the bottom of the page.

Abraham Lincoln was born on February 12, 1809. As a child, he loved to read books. He borrowed books from other people. Abraham Lincoln became the 16th president in 1860. The Civil War began while he was president. It lasted for four years. During the war, Lincoln worked to keep our country together. Abraham Lincoln was killed five days after the war ended. The people of the United States were very sad. They had lost their president. Lincoln will always be remembered. Many people believe that he was one of our greatest presidents. The Lincoln Memorial honors him today.

1. When was Abraham Lincoln born? ____________________

2. When did Abraham Lincoln become president of the United States? ____________________

3. What did Lincoln do during the war? ____________________

____

Answer Key

Page 188
1. cake
2. oven
3. person

Page 189
1. grass
2. plants

Page 190
1. dog
2. pet

Page 191
1. Jack and Jill
2. He fell and broke his crown.

Page 192
1. tub
2. bug

Page 193
1. reads a story
2. about his/her day
3. with sweet dreams

Page 194
1. b
2. a
3. c
4. a

Page 195
1. b
2. a
3. c

Page 197
1. a
2. b
3. a
4. b
5. a

Page 199
1. a
2. b
3. b
4. a
5. a

Page 201
1. a
2. b
3. a
4. a
5. b

Page 203
1. b
2. a
3. a
4. a
5. b

Page 205
1. b
2. b
3. a
4. b
5. a

Page 207
1. b
2. a
3. b
4. b
5. b

Page 209
1. a
2. a
3. b
4. b
5. b

Page 211
1. b
2. b
3. a
4. b
5. a

Page 213
1. b
2. b
3. b
4. a
5. b

Page 215
1. b
2. b
3. a
4. a
5. a

Answer Key *(cont.)*

Page 217
1. a
2. b
3. b
4. a
5. a

Page 219
1. a
2. b
3. b
4. b
5. a

Page 221
1. a
2. b
3. a
4. b
5. a

Page 223
1. a
2. b
3. a
4. b
5. a

Page 225
1. b
2. a
3. b
4. b
5. a

Page 227
1. b
2. b
3. a
4. b
5. a

Page 229
1. b
2. b
3. a
4. a
5. b

Page 231
1. a
2. b
3. a
4. a
5. b

Page 233
1. b
2. c
3. d
4. d
5. a

Page 235
1. c
2. b
3. a
4. a
5. c

Page 237
1. b
2. c
3. c
4. b
5. a

Page 239
1. c
2. c
3. d
4. a
5. b

Page 241
1. d
2. c
3. b
4. c
5. a

Page 243
1. c
2. b
3. a
4. b
5. d

Page 244
1. February 12, 1809
2. 1860
3. He worked to keep our country together.

Practice and Learn

WORKBOOK

Addition & Subtraction

Adding Zero

Directions: Look at each picture. Add 0 animals. Write how many there are in all. What do you notice happens when you add 0?

1.

5 + 0 = ☐

2.

2 + 0 = ☐

3.

3 + 0 = ☐

4.

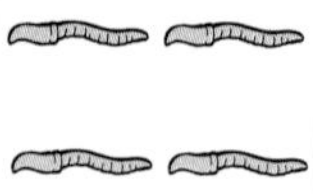

4 + 0 = ☐

5.

1 + 0 = ☐

6.

3 + 0 = ☐

7.

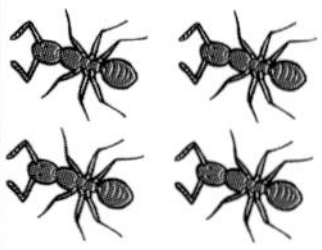

4 + 0 = ☐

8.

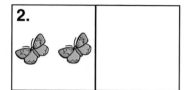

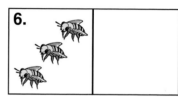

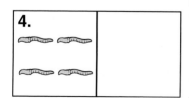

2 + 0 = ☐

Adding to 10

Directions: When adding, two sets of numbers are put together to make one larger set.

For example: 2 + 6 = 8

2 + 6 = 8

1. 5 + 2 = ____
2. 6 + 3 = ____
3. 8 + 1 = ____
4. 7 + 2 = ____
5. 10 + 0 = ____
6. 5 + 4 = ____
7. 3 + 5 = ____
8. 2 + 6 = ____
9. 3 + 4 = ____
10. 5 + 3 = ____
11. 1 + 9 = ____
12. 3 + 7 = ____

Auto Addition

Directions: Add the cars and write the total on the line.

1.

4 plus 2 is ____________

2.

1 plus 3 is ____________

3.

3 plus 3 is ____________

4.

1 plus 5 is ____________

Truck Addition

Directions: Add the trucks and write the total on the line.

1.

3 plus 4 is ______________

2.

1 plus 5 is ______________

3.

5 plus 2 is ______________

4.

6 plus 1 is ______________

Insect Addition

Directions: Add the bugs and write the total on the line.

1.

6 plus 2 is ______

2.

2 plus 4 is ______

3.

4 plus 4 is ______

4.

1 plus 7 is ______

Adding Animals

Directions: Look at the pictures. Add the animals together to tell how many there are in all.

1.

2 + 1 = ☐

2.
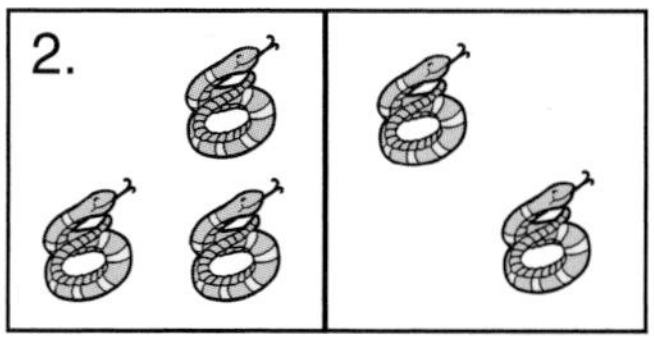

3 + 2 = ☐

3.
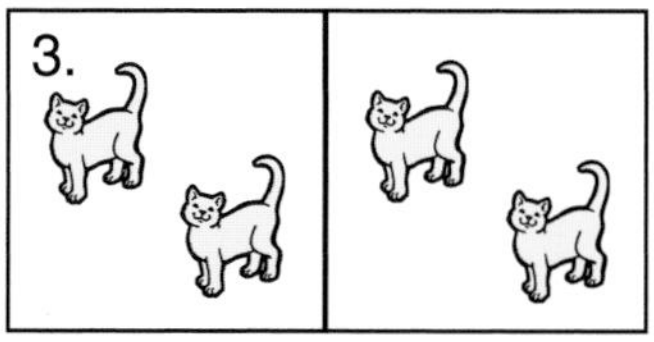

2 + 2 = ☐

4.

1 + 2 = ☐

5.

4 + 1 = ☐

6.

1 + 3 = ☐

7.
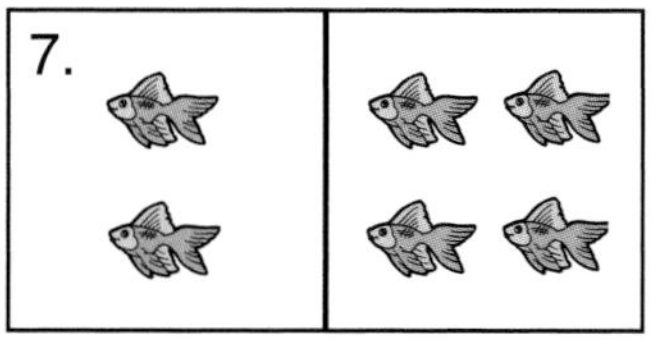

2 + 4 = ☐

8.
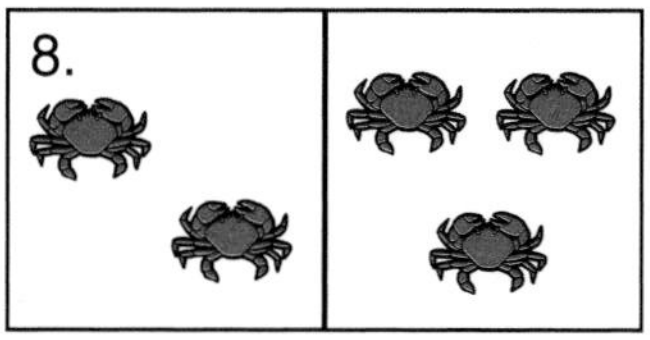

2 + 3 = ☐

Under the Sea

Directions: Look at each picture. Write an addition problem to match the picture.

1.

___ + ___ = ___

2.

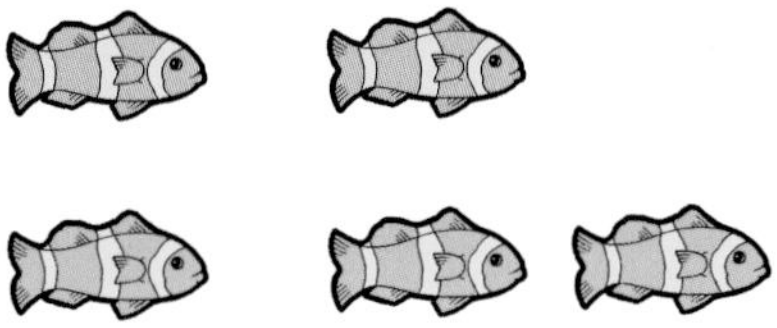

___ + ___ = ___

3.

___ + ___ = ___

4.

___ + ___ = ___

5.

___ + ___ = ___

6.

___ + ___ = ___

More and Less

Directions: Count the number of items in each group. Write the number of items on the line. In each box, circle the group that has more items.

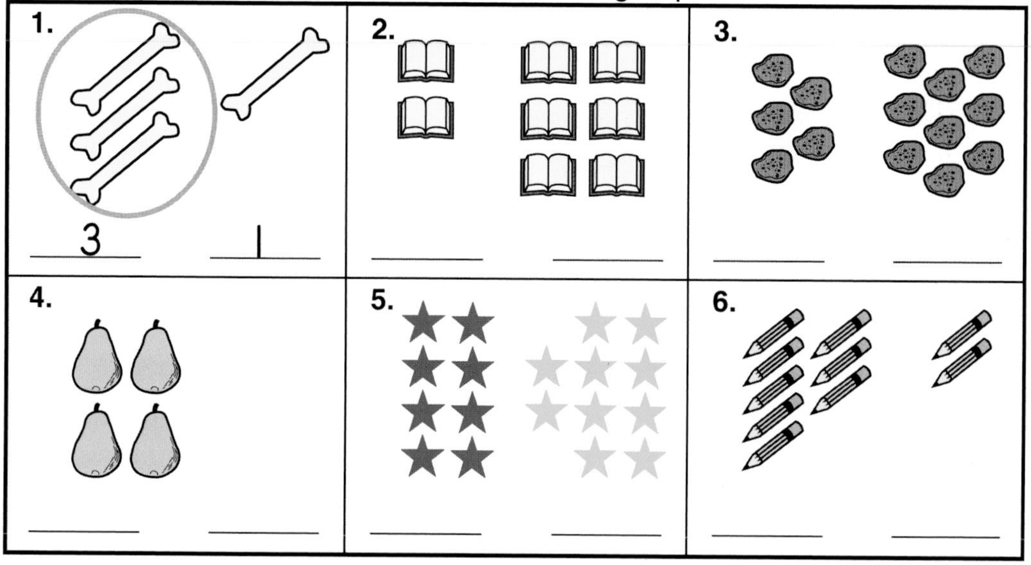

Directions: Count the number of items in each group. Write the number of items on the line. In each box, circle the group that has fewer items.

Show Addition

Directions: Write a number sentence to go with each picture.

1.

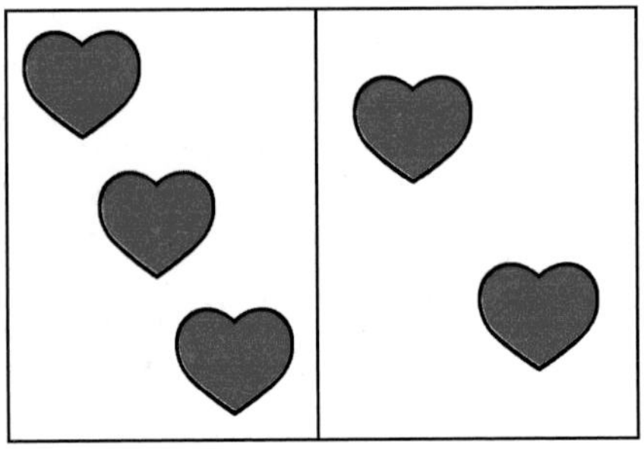

____ + ____ = ____

2.

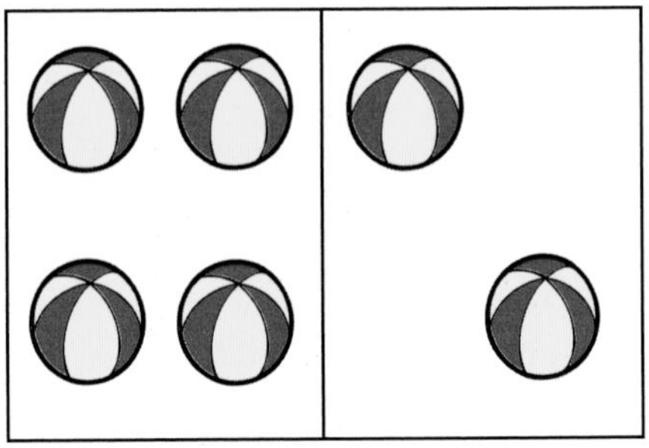

____ + ____ = ____

3..

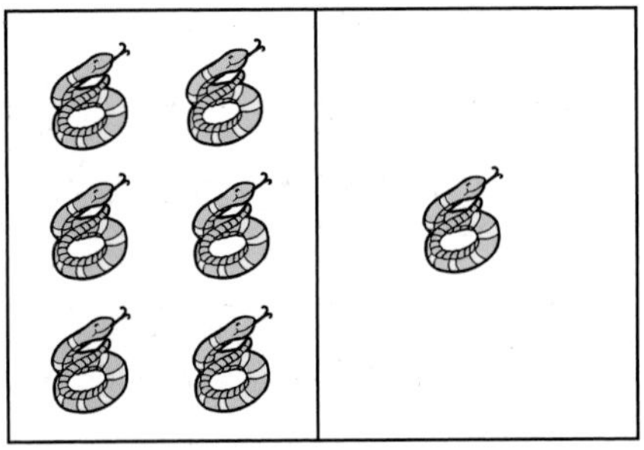

____ + ____ = ____

4.

____ + ____ = ____

5.

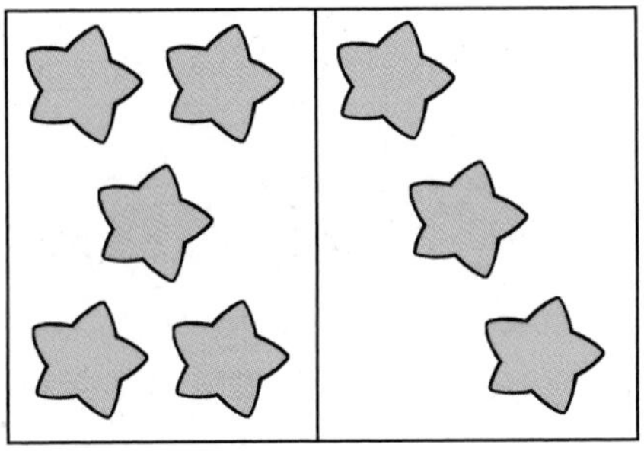

____ + ____ = ____

6.

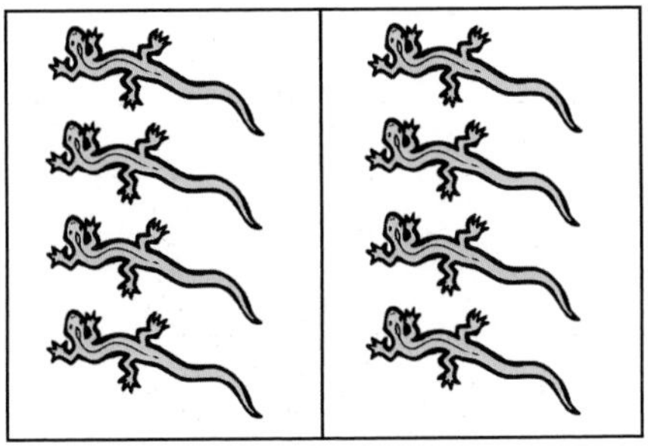

____ + ____ = ____

Ways to Make Six

Directions: Color the stars to match the number sentence. Use different colors for each group of stars in the sentence. The first one has been done for you.

1.

3 + 3 = 6

2.

2 + 4 = 6

3.

0 + 6 = 6

4.

1 + 5 = 6

5.

3 + 3 = 6

6.

4 + 2 = 6

7.

6 + 0 = 6

8.

5 + 1 = 6

Jump to Add

Directions: Count forward to add. Put your finger where the frog is. Jump forward 1 jump. Write the number you land on.

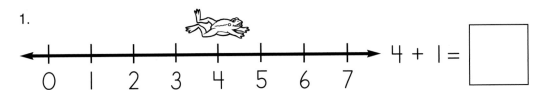

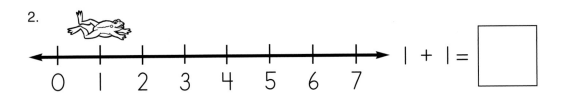

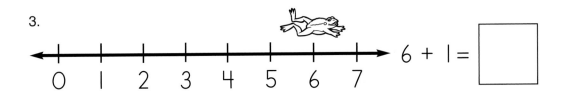

1.

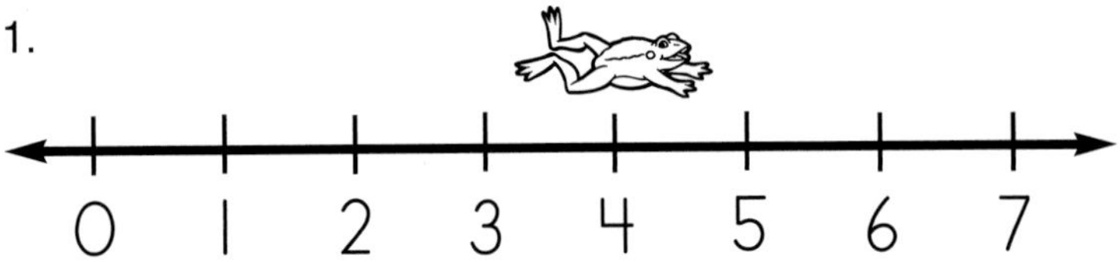

4 + 1 = ☐

2.

1 + 1 = ☐

3.

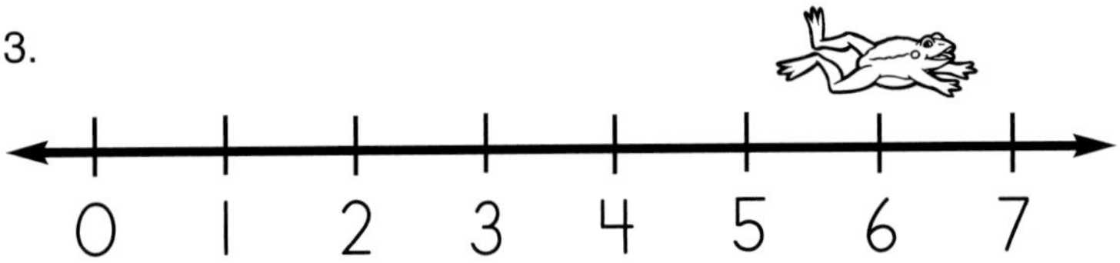

6 + 1 = ☐

4.

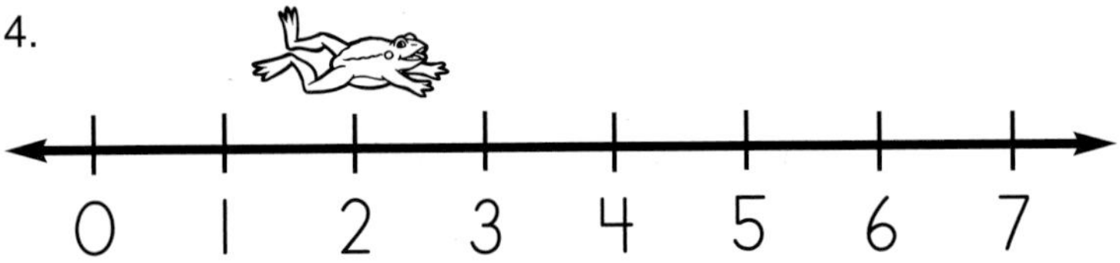

2 + 1 = ☐

5.

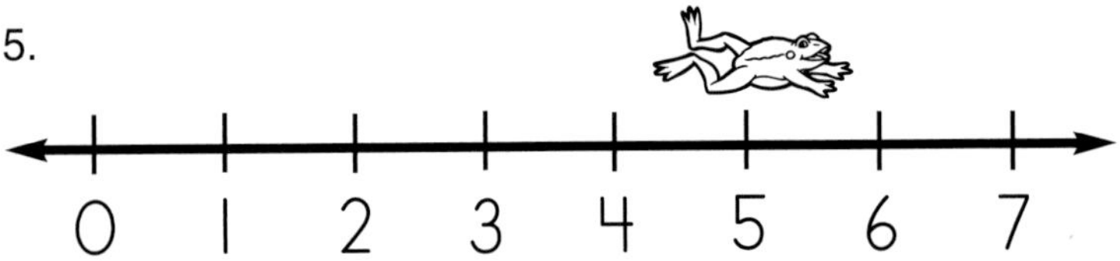

5 + 1 = ☐

Busy Bees

Directions: Add to solve the problems below. Count forward on the number line to help.

1. 4 + 2 = ☐

6. 2 + 7 = ☐

2. 7 + 1 = ☐

7. 9 + 1 = ☐

3. 5 + 3 = ☐

8. 4 + 5 = ☐

4. 8 + 2 = ☐

9. 2 + 6 = ☐

5. 3 + 6 = ☐

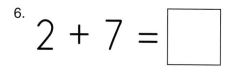

10. 8 + 1 = ☐

Using a Number Line

Directions: Use the number line to help you solve the word problems.

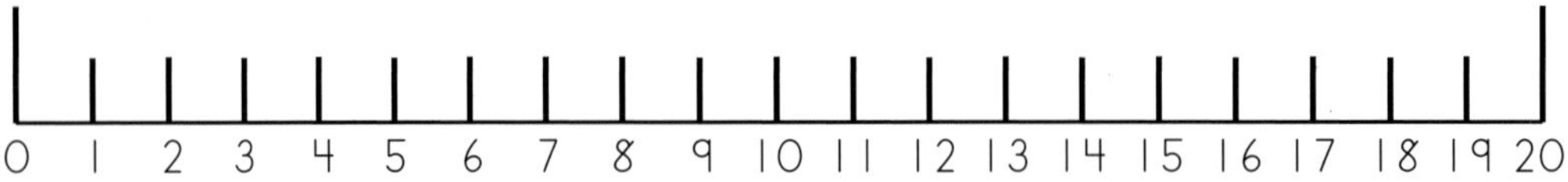

1. Start on 5. Count forward 7.
   What number are you on?

   ____

2. Start on 4. Count forward 10.
   What number are you on?

   ____

3. Start on 8. Count forward 10.
   What number are you on?

   ____

4. Start on 6. Count forward 9.
   What number are you on?

   ____

5. Start on 9. Count forward 9.
   What number are you on?

   ____

6. Start on 7. Count forward 0.
   What number are you on?

   ____

Practice and Learn

Number Line Addition

Directions: Use the number line to help you solve the addition problems.

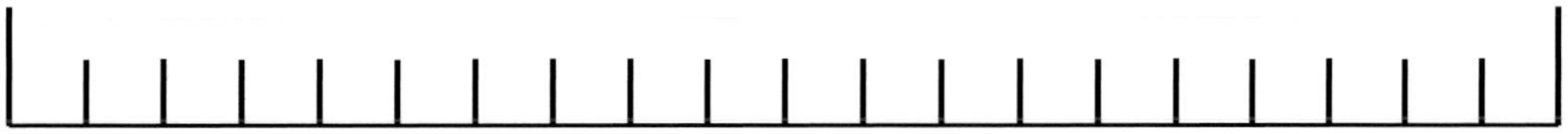

1. $3 + 9 =$ ____

2. $5 + 8 =$ ____

3. $13 + 3 =$ ____

4. $0 + 11 =$ ____

5. $7 + 7 =$ ____

6. $6 + 10 =$ ____

7. $2 + 12 =$ ____

8. $4 + 13 =$ ____

9. $10 + 1 =$ ____

10. $17 + 1 =$ ____

11. $18 + 0 =$ ____

12. $9 + 7 =$ ____

Home Sweet Home

Directions: Solve each addition problem. Color the puzzle.

4 = brown 5 = orange 6 = green

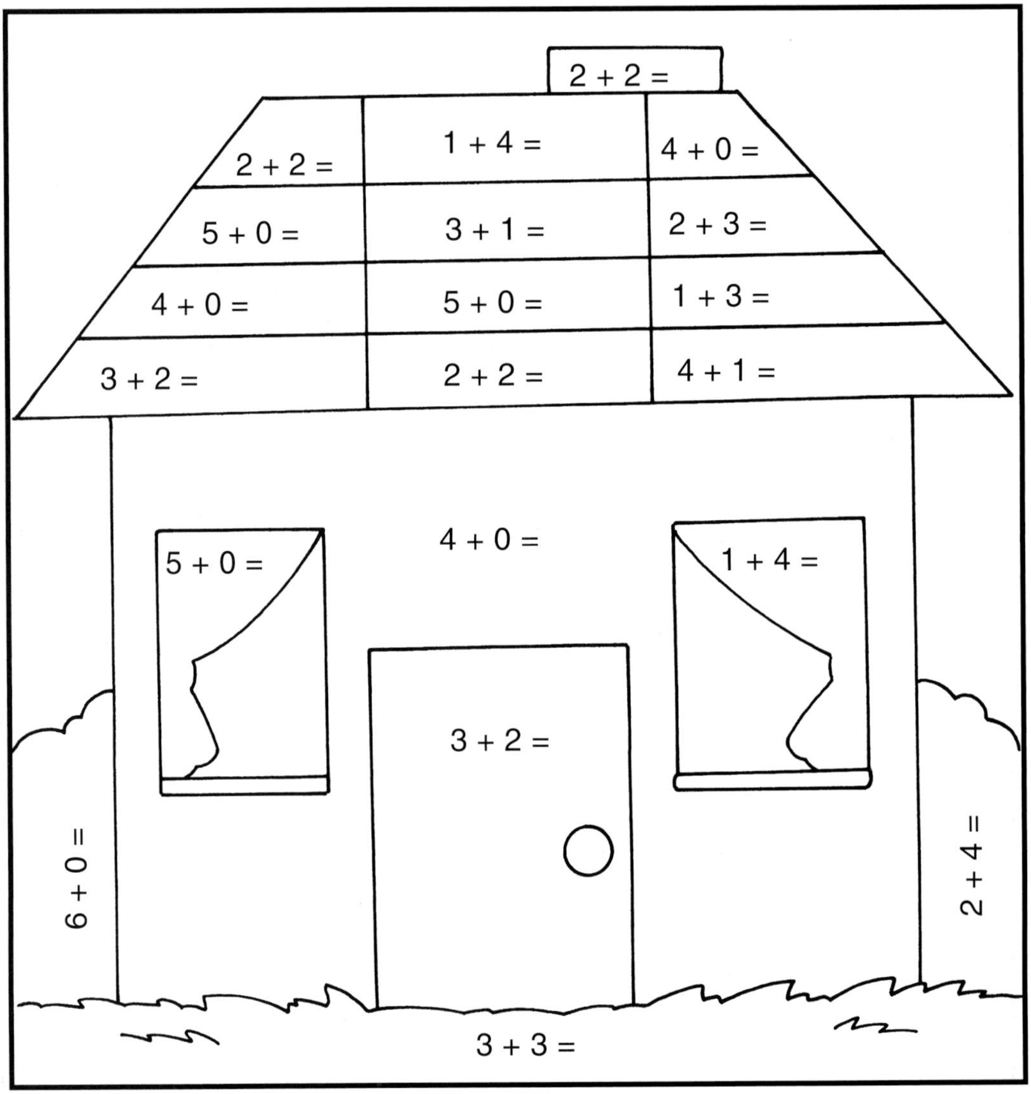

Fluttering By

Directions: Solve each addition problem. Color the puzzle.

7 = orange   8 = yellow   9 = green   10 = blue

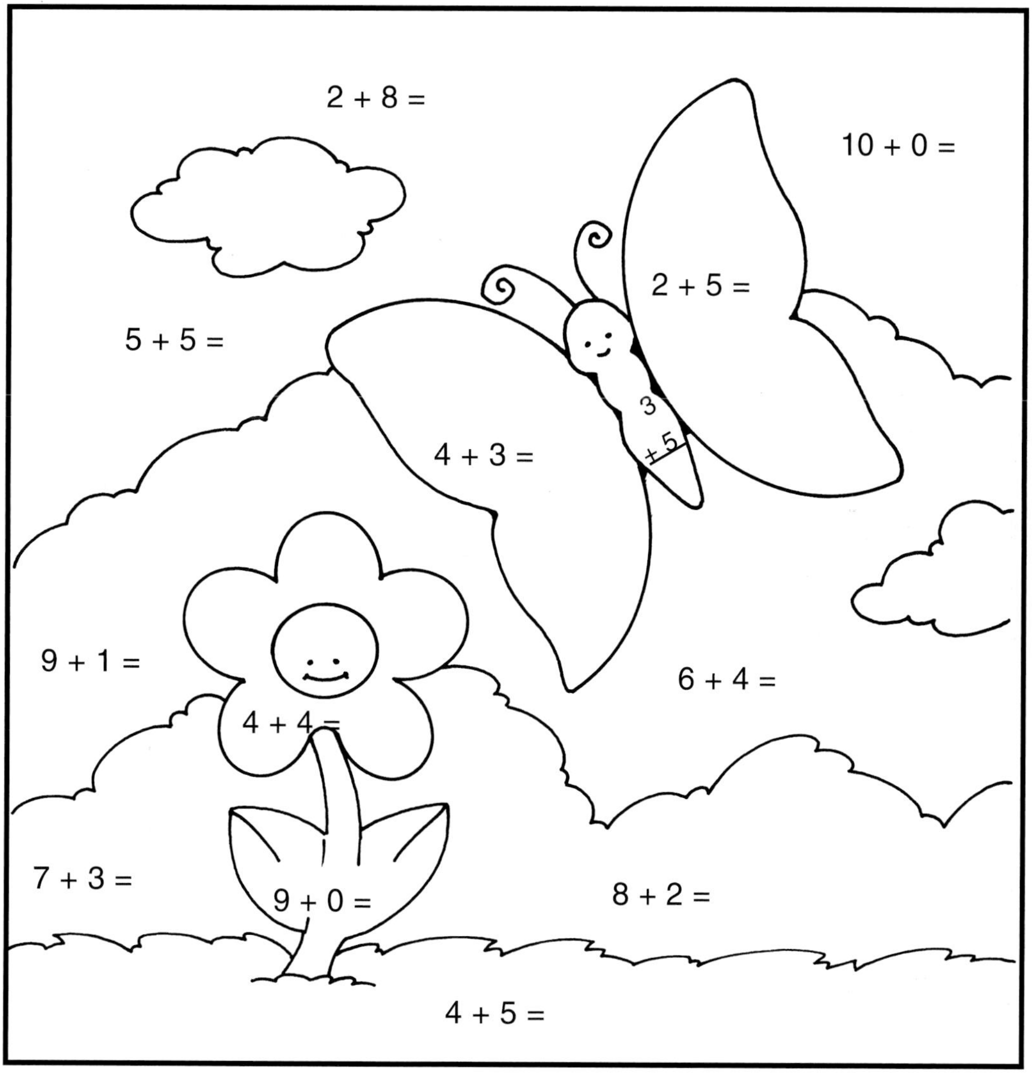

Buzzing Through the Numbers

Directions: Solve each addition problem. Color the puzzle.

11 = yellow	12 = brown	13 = purple	14 = blue

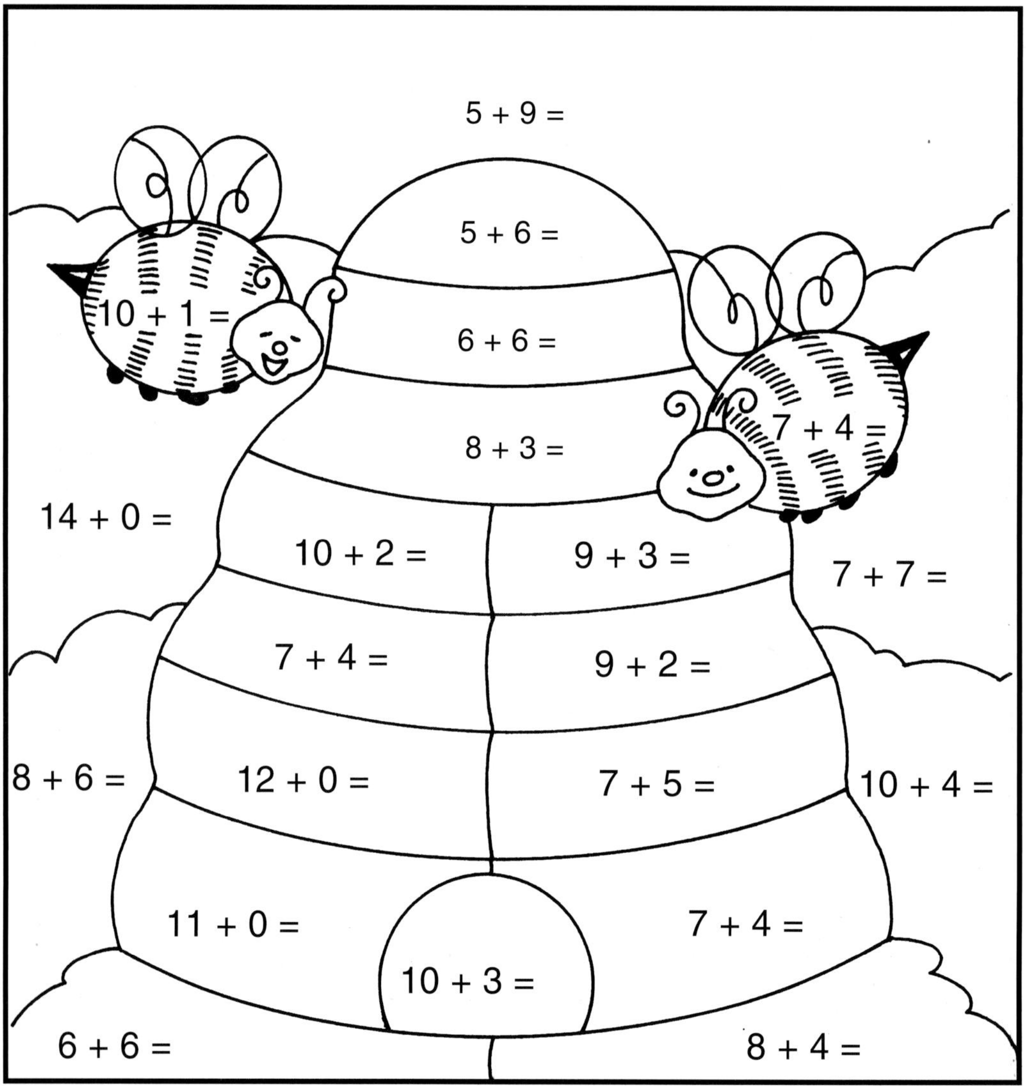

Addition Mystery Picture

Directions: Solve each addition problem. Then, color using this code:

1–4 = Red 5–6 = Orange 7–8 = Yellow 9–10 = Blue

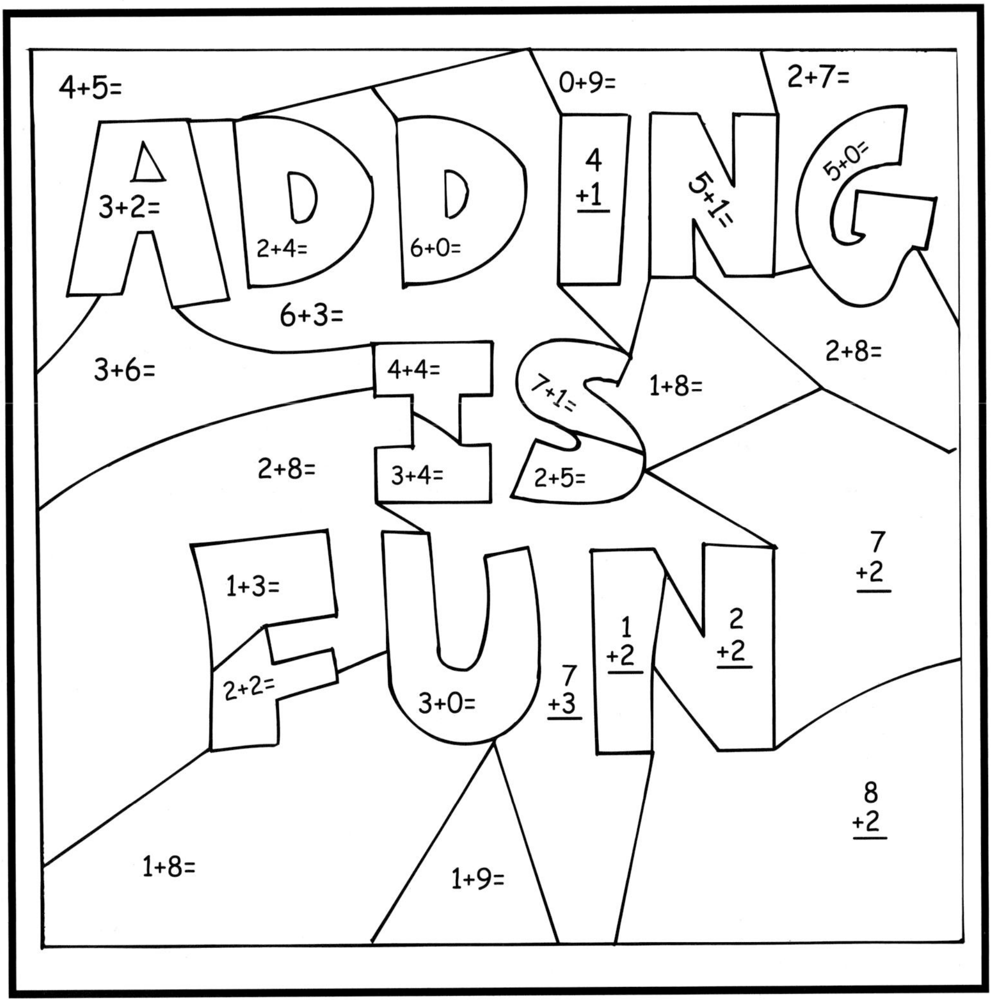

Ways to Equal a Sum

Directions: Circle each addend that equals the sum in the cloud. There may be more than one way to equal the sum.

1.	8	2 + 2	5 + 4	3 + 5	7 + 1	6 + 2	4 + 3
2.	4	2 + 2	3 + 2	4 + 0	5 + 1	3 + 1	0 + 4
3.	6	6 + 0	2 + 5	4 + 2	3 + 3	5 + 1	6 + 2
4.	2	2 + 0	3 + 1	4 + 1	1 + 1	0 + 2	1 + 2
5.	9	4 + 6	3 + 6	1 + 8	1 + 9	8 + 2	9 + 0
6.	3	3 + 1	2 + 0	3 + 0	2 + 1	0 + 3	1 + 2
7.	7	6 + 1	2 + 5	3 + 5	6 + 3	4 + 3	7 + 0
8.	5	2 + 2	5 + 0	3 + 2	1 + 4	4 + 2	3 + 2

Missing Addends

Directions: Find the missing addends. Use the letters to answer the question: Why did the chicken cross the playground?

1. 3 + ☐ = 4
   E

2. 3 + ☐ = 8
   H

3. ☐ + 5 = 9
   R

4. 4 + ☐ = 7
   O

5. ☐ + 5 = 7
   T

6. ☐ + 0 = 10
   D

7. ☐ + 2 = 9
   I

8. 8 + ☐ = 8
   S

9. 1 + ☐ = 9
   L

10. 3 + ☐ = 9
    G

___ ___   ___ ___ ___   ___ ___   ___ ___ ___
2 3   6 1 2   2 3   2 5 1

___ ___ ___ ___ ___   ___ ___ ___ ___ ___
3 2 5 1 4   0 8 7 10 1

Adding with Pictures

Directions: Write the answer to each addition problem.

1.  +  = ________ rabbits

2.  +  = ________ cows

3.  + = ________ butterflies

Directions: Write the addition problem for each set of pictures.

4.  +  = ________ snails

________ ________

5.  +  = ________ books

________ ________

6.  +  = ________ birds

________ ________

Addition Word Problems

Directions: Read each word problem and write the numbers to make an addition problem. Write the answer below the addition word problem.

1. Kevin has 7 marbles. His dad gives him 5 more. How many marbles does Kevin have now?	________ + ________ = ________ marbles
2. Julia found 9 pennies. Then she found 8 more. How many pennies does Julia have now?	________ + ________ = ________ pennies
3. Rachel made 10 placemats. Her dad gave her 4 more. How many placemats does Rachel have now?	________ + ________ = ________ placemats
4. Jacob has 6 toy dinosaurs. He bought 6 more. How many toy dinosaurs does Jacob have now?	________ + ________ = ________ toy dinosaurs

More Word Problems

Directions: Solve the word problems below. Show your work with a number sentence or a picture to the right.

1. Tom has 3 toy cars. He gets 2 more for his birthday. How many toy cars does Tom have now?	Show Your Work
2. Sarah and Michelle are playing together. Kim and her sister come to play with them. How many girls are now playing?	Show Your Work
3. Micah has 8 trading cards. He buys 5 more. How many trading cards does Micah have in all?	Show Your Work

Equal on Both Sides

Directions: Write the missing addend in order to make the equation equal on both sides of the equal sign. Cross off the numbers you use on the boat at the bottom of the page.

1. $2 + 3 = 3 + \square$
2. $4 + 1 = 1 + \square$
3. $3 + \square = 5 + 3$
4. $4 + 0 = \square + 4$
5. $6 + 2 = 2 + \square$
6. $\square + 3 = 3 + 7$
7. $3 + 5 = 5 + \square$
8. $\square + 5 = 5 + 1$
9. $2 + \square = 8 + 2$
10. $\square + 1 = 1 + 9$

Addition Crossword

Directions: Solve the problems below. Write the number names in the crossword puzzle.

Across

3. $8 + 6 =$

6. $10 + 7 =$

9. $7 + 5 =$

Down

1. $6 + 7 =$

2. $9 + 6 =$

4. $8 + 2 =$

5. $5 + 6 =$

7. $12 + 7 =$

Word Bank

ten
eleven
twelve
thirteen
fourteen
fifteen
sixteen
seventeen
eighteen
nineteen
twenty

Make Them Equal

Directions: Write the missing addend in order to make the equation equal on both sides of the equal sign.

1. $4 + 1 = 2 + \square$	**6.** $5 + \square = 8 + 1$
2. $2 + 8 = 7 + \square$	**7.** $6 + 2 = 4 + \square$
3. $4 + \square = 6 + 1$	**8.** $8 + 0 = \square + 7$
4. $\square + 0 = 2 + 2$	**9.** $\square + 2 = 3 + 4$
5. $3 + \square = 4 + 2$	**10.** $9 + \square = 4 + 5$

Challenge: $18 + 2 = 14 + \square$

Addition Wheels

Directions: Add the number in the center circle to each number in the middle circle. Write each sum in the outer circle.

1.

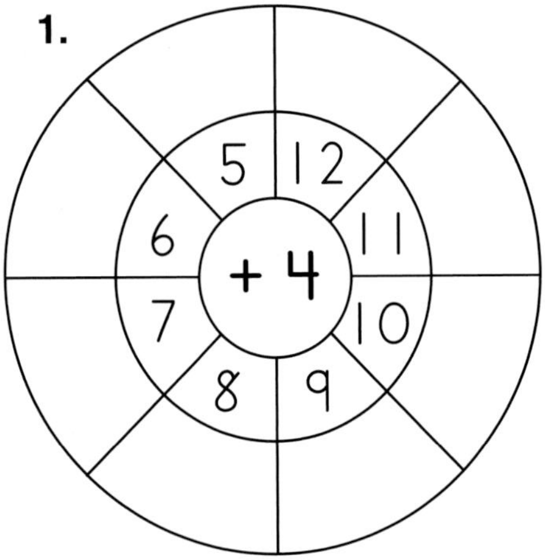

2.

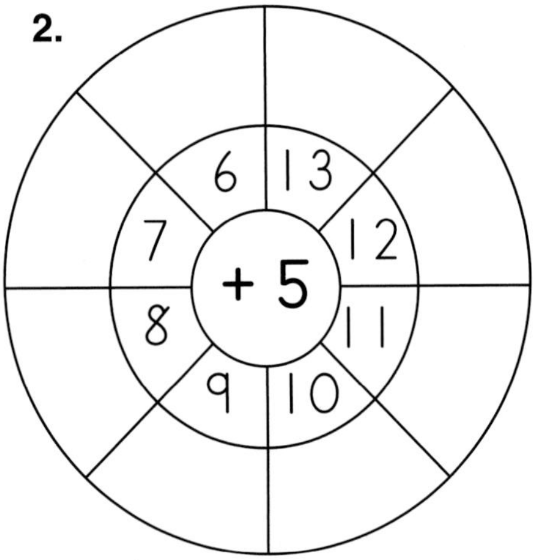

3.

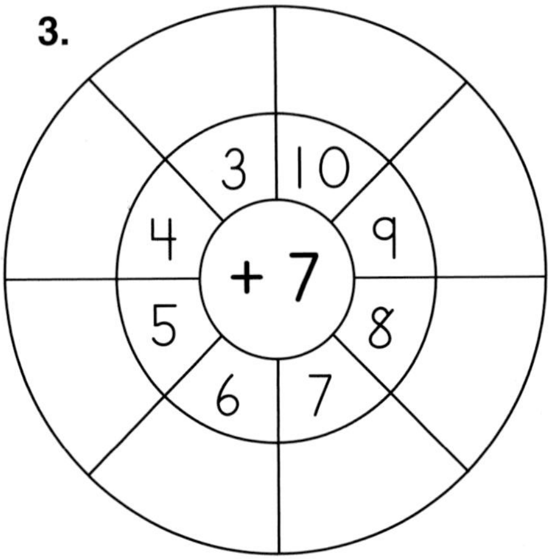

4.

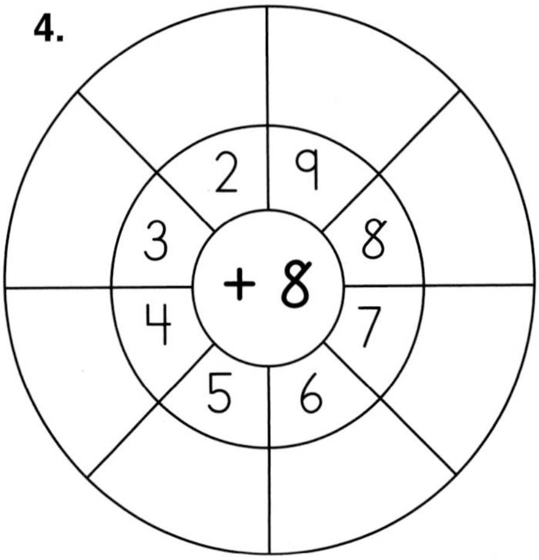

Writing Number Sentences

Directions: Place a paperclip on the X. Then, place the tip of a pencil inside the paperclip. Use the paperclip as a spinner. Spin the paperclip around the pencil. The paperclip will act as the pointer.

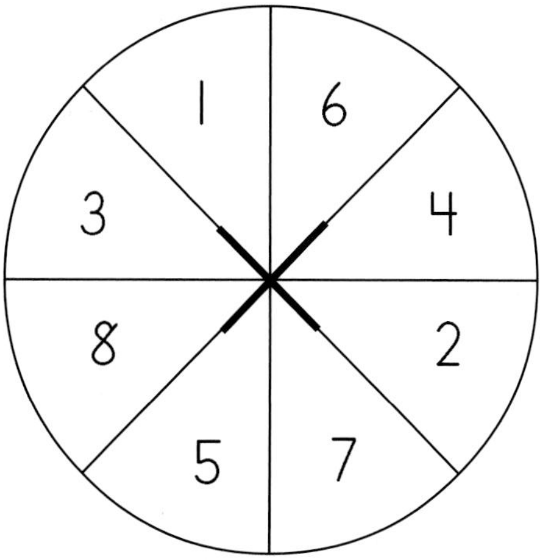

Spin the paperclip two times for each problem. Use the numbers that are spun as the addends. Solve the problems.

1. _____ + _____ = _____ **5.** _____ + _____ = _____

2. _____ + _____ = _____ **6.** _____ + _____ = _____

3. _____ + _____ = _____ **7.** _____ + _____ = _____

4. _____ + _____ = _____ **8.** _____ + _____ = _____

Adding 3 Numbers

Directions: Solve each problem. Use the sums to figure out what to color the fish in the tank below.

1. 3 2 + 5  Green	**2.** 4 1 + 3  Blue	**3.** 5 5 + 2  Red
4. 6 1 + 0  Orange	**5.** 3 4 + 4  Yellow	**6.** 5 7 + 1  Purple
7. 4 3 + 2  Pink	**8.** 3 2 + 1  Brown	**9.** 6 5 + 3  Black

Writing the Answer

Directions: Solve each problem. Write the answer on the line.

1. 6 − 6 = ____	7. 2 − 1 = ____
2. 6 − 4 = ____	8. 4 − 0 = ____
3. 5 − 1 = ____	9. 5 − 5 = ____
4. 4 − 2 = ____	10. 6 − 2 = ____
5. 2 − 0 = ____	11. 3 − 0 = ____
6. 4 − 4 = ____	12. 3 − 3 = ____

Dog Subtraction

Directions: Solve the problems.

1.

9 minus 6 is ________

2.

6 minus 4 is ________

3.

4 minus 1 is ________

4.

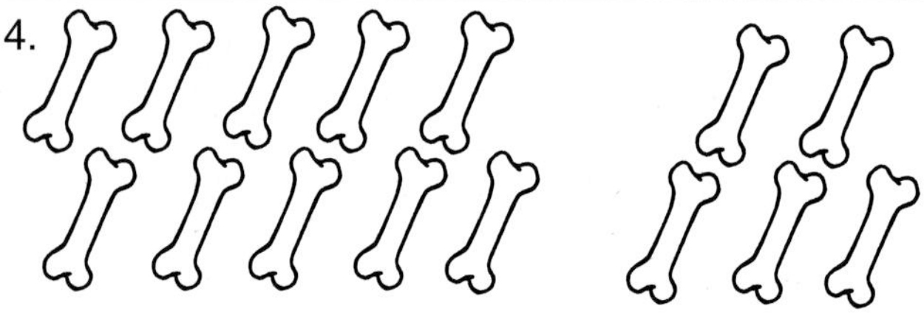

10 minus 5 is ________

Kite Subtraction

Directions: Count the kites. Cross out the number to be subtracted. Write the remainder below the line.

1.

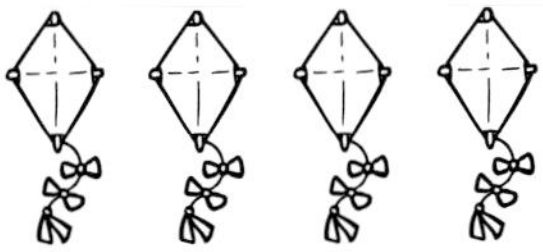

$$\begin{array}{r} 4 \\ -\ 2 \\ \hline \end{array}$$

2.

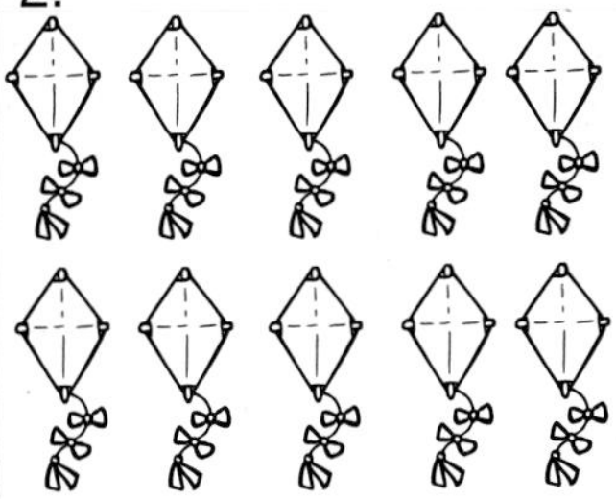

$$\begin{array}{r} 10 \\ -\ 7 \\ \hline \end{array}$$

3.

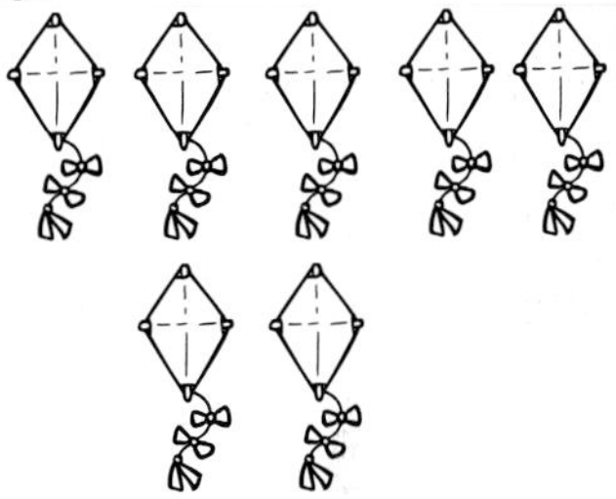

$$\begin{array}{r} 7 \\ -\ 2 \\ \hline \end{array}$$

4.

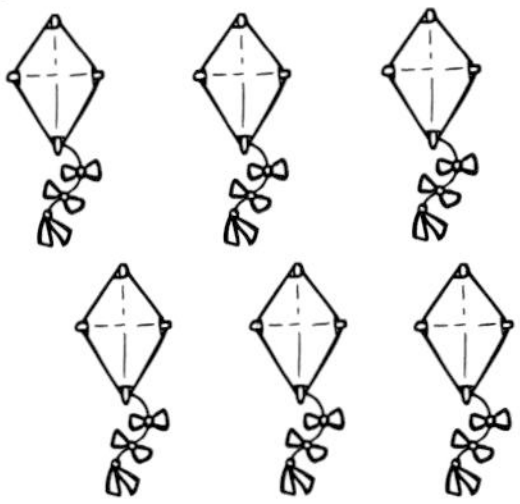

$$\begin{array}{r} 6 \\ -\ 1 \\ \hline \end{array}$$

5.

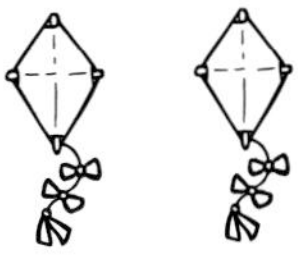

$$\begin{array}{r} 2 \\ -\ 1 \\ \hline \end{array}$$

6.

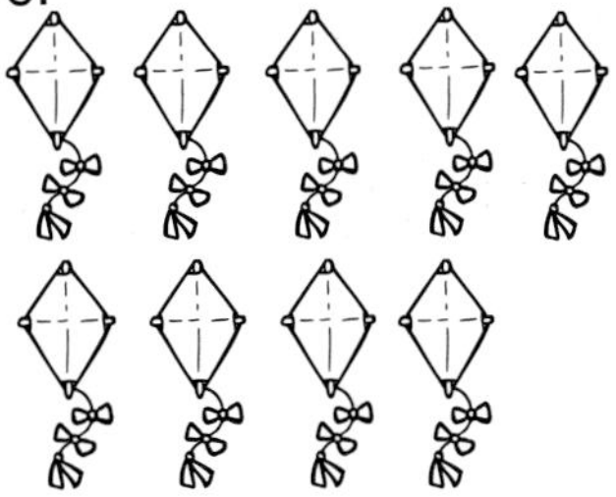

$$\begin{array}{r} 9 \\ -\ 3 \\ \hline \end{array}$$

Showing Subtraction

Directions: Write a number sentence to go with each picture.

1.

______ – ______ = ______

2.

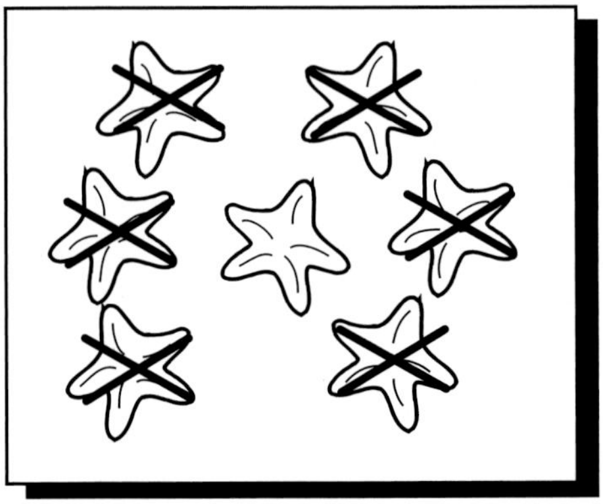

______ – ______ = ______

3.

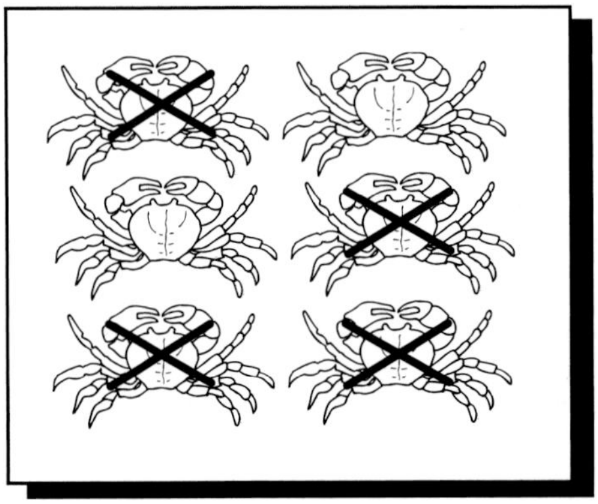

______ – ______ = ______

4.

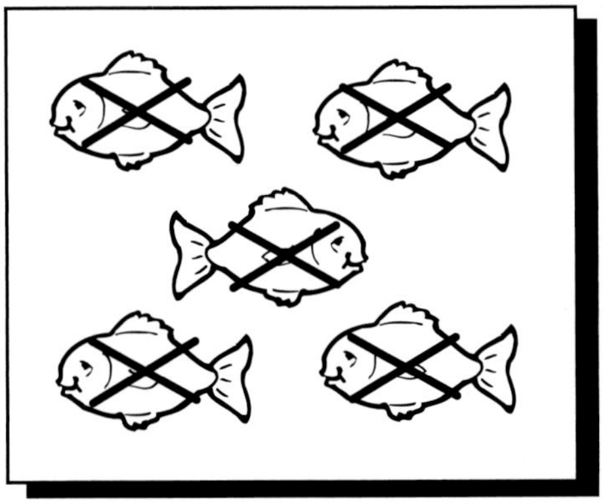

______ – ______ = ______

Drawing Subtraction

Directions: Draw a picture to illustrate each number sentence.

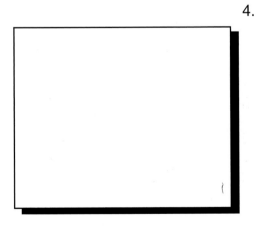

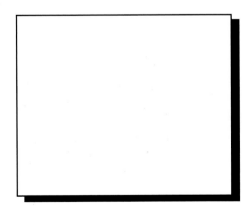

1.

$3 - 2 = 1$

2.

$5 - 4 = 1$

3.

$4 - 2 = 2$

4.

$7 - 5 = 2$

Jump Back to Subtract

Directions: Count backward to subtract. Put your finger where the kangaroo is. Jump backward 1 jump. Write the number you land on.

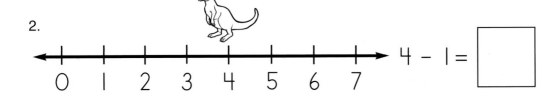

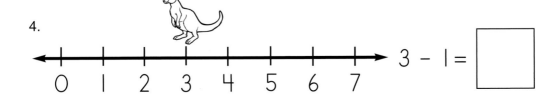

1.

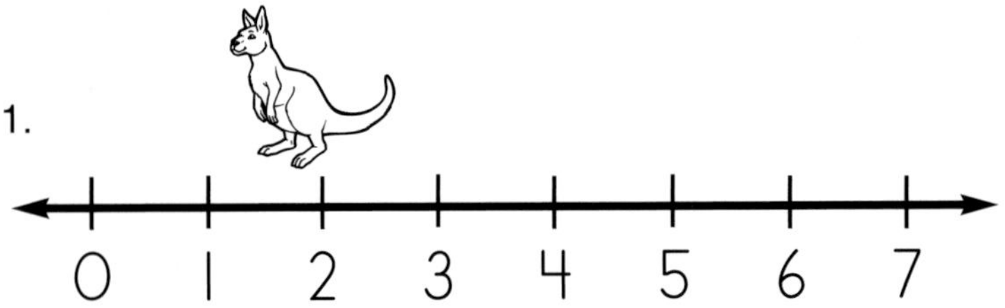

2 − 1 = ☐

2.

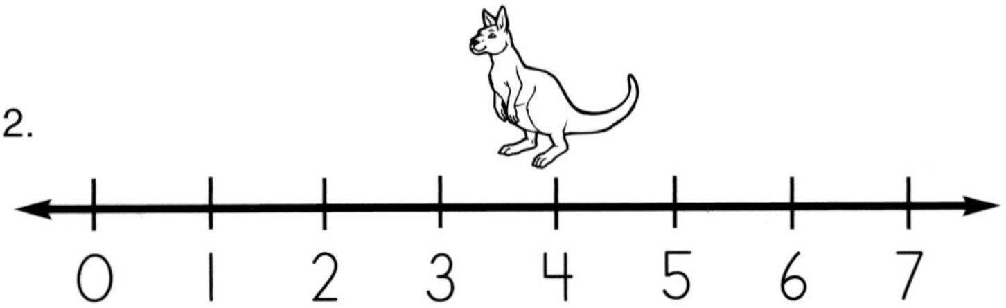

4 − 1 = ☐

3.

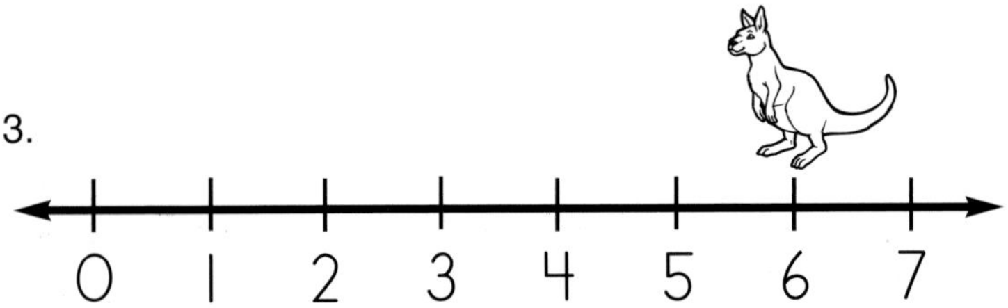

6 − 1 = ☐

4.

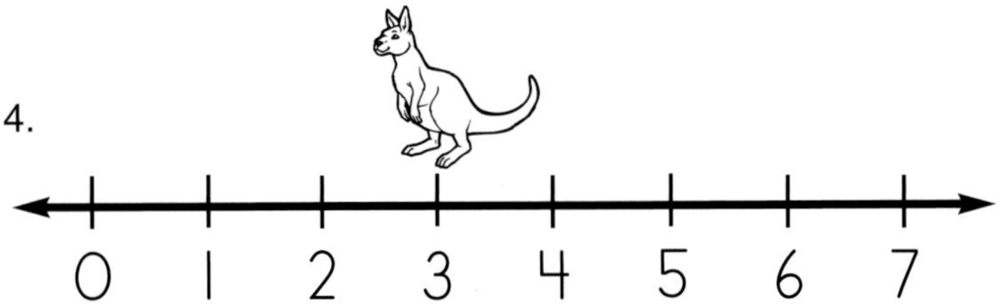

3 − 1 = ☐

5.

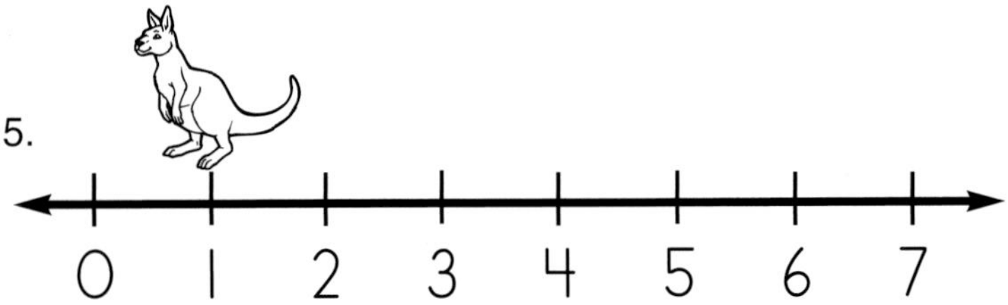

1 − 1 = ☐

Number Line Subtraction

Directions: Use the number line to help you solve the word problems.

1. Start on 15. Count backward 9. What number are you on?

   ____

2. Start on 12. Count backward 3. What number are you on?

   ____

3. Start on 18. Count backward 0. What number are you on?

   ____

4. Start on 16. Count backward 7. What number are you on?

   ____

5. Start on 14. Count backward 5. What number are you on?

   ____

6. Start on 17. Count backward 16. What number are you on?

   ____

Use the number line to help you solve these subtraction problems.

7. $16 - 9 =$ ____

8. $15 - 5 =$ ____

9. $18 - 14 =$ ____

10. $13 - 9 =$ ____

Dots

Directions: Finish the subtraction sentences. Write the answer. Draw the number of dots.

1. 6 dots take away 4 dots = ______________ dots

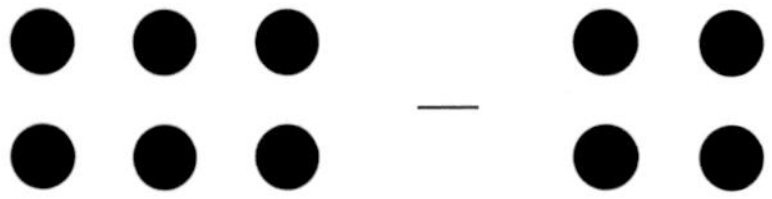

2. 6 dots take away 2 dots = ______________ dots

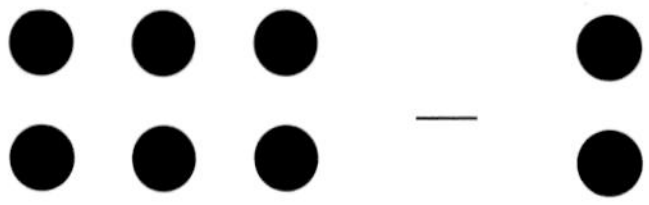

3. 6 dots take away 1 dot = ______________ dots

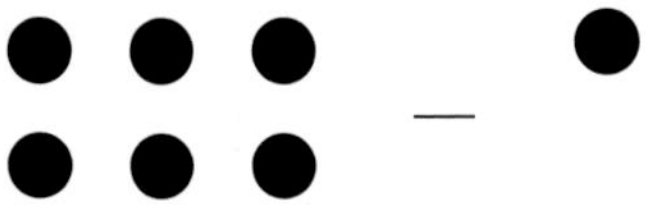

4. 6 dots take away 3 dots = ______________ dots

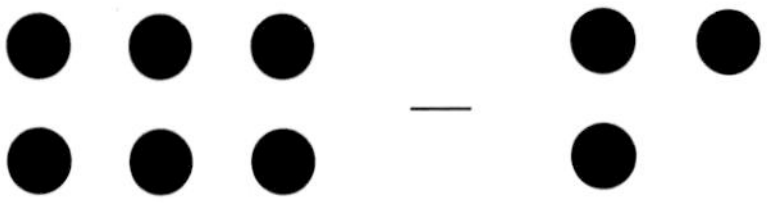

5. 6 dots take away 5 dots = ______________ dots

6. 6 dots take away 6 dots = ______________ dots

Odd or Even?

Directions: Solve the subtraction problems below. Then, color the box using the key below.

Odd = Blue Even = Red

1. 9 − 4	**2.** 6 − 5	**3.** 7 − 2	**4.** 8 − 3
5. 5 − 2	**6.** 8 − 6	**7.** 9 − 5	**8.** 6 − 3
9. 1 − 0	**10.** 5 − 3	**11.** 6 − 4	**12.** 4 − 1

What's Missing?

Directions: Write the missing numbers to complete the number sentences. Color the numbers in the balloons as you use them.

1. 7 - ☐ = 5
2. 4 - ☐ = 1
3. ☐ - 4 = 4
4. 8 - ☐ = 5
5. 9 - ☐ = 6
6. 6 - ☐ = 4
7. ☐ - 2 = 3
8. ☐ - 1 = 2
9. 7 - ☐ = 3
10. 8 - ☐ = 6

Subtraction Machines

Directions: Apply the rule at the top of each box to the numbers on the left. Write the differences in the boxes on the right.

1.

− 5	
7	
9	
5	
6	

2.

− 3	
4	
6	
5	
9	

3.

− 7	
8	
7	
9	
10	

4.

− 6	
6	
9	
8	
7	

5.

− 1	
9	
4	
2	
6	

6.

− 4	
5	
8	
4	
7	

7.

− 8	
8	
10	
9	
11	

8.

− 2	
3	
5	
7	
2	

9.

− 3	
4	
9	
5	
8	

Blooming Buds

Directions: Solve each subtraction problem. Color the puzzle.

4 = green	5 = orange	6 = purple	7 = yellow

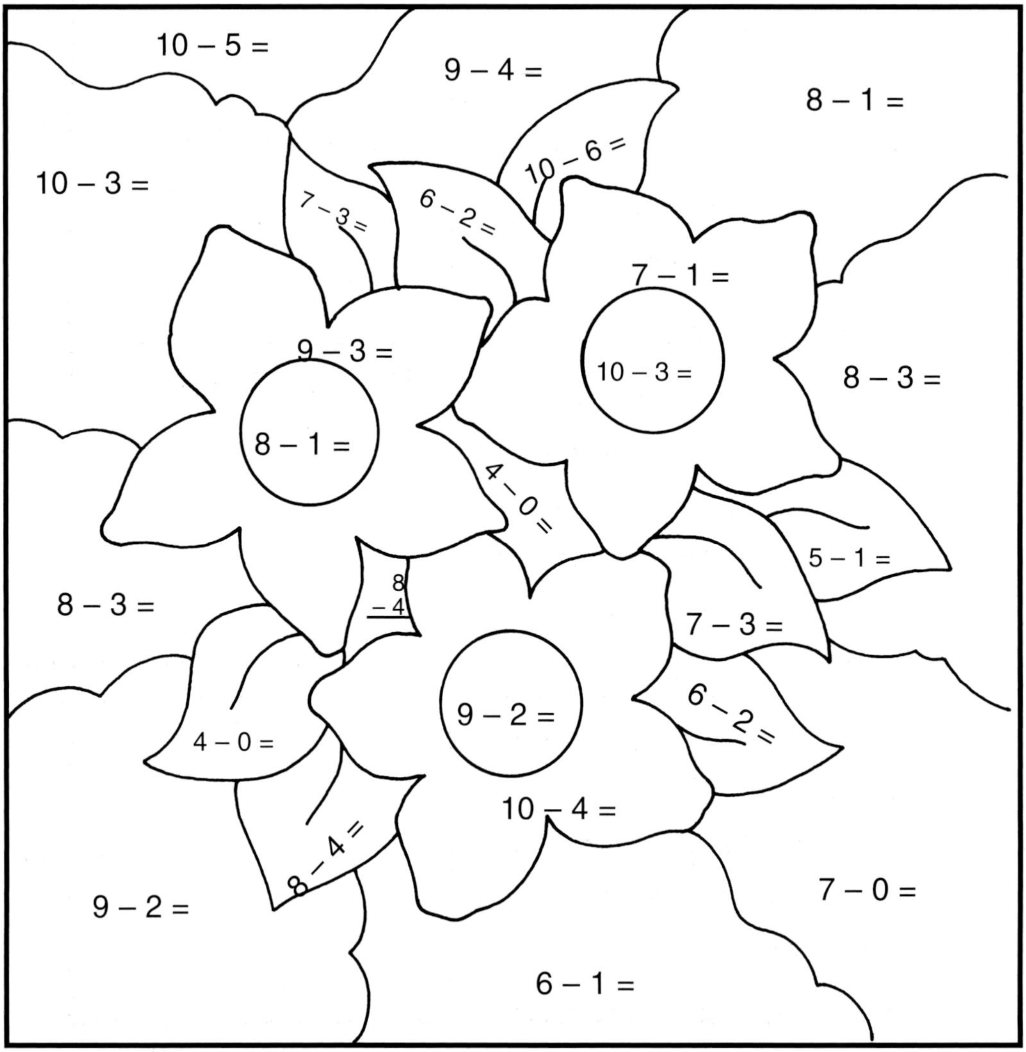

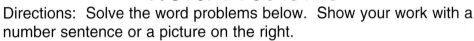

Subtraction Word Problems

Directions: Solve the word problems below. Show your work with a number sentence or a picture on the right.

1. Tyler shoots 7 baskets. He misses 3 times How many baskets did he make? ____________	Show Your Work
2. Six children are playing hockey. Two children have to go home. How many children are left? ____________	Show Your Work
3. There are five cookies on a plate. Mandi comes home from school and eats some. Now there are only two cookies on the plate. How many cookies did Mandi eat? ____________	Show Your Work
4. Bernice's homework packet has 8 pages in it. She has completed 6 pages. How many more pages of homework does Bernice have to do? ____________	Show Your Work

Solving Word Problems

Directions: Read each word problem and write the numbers to make a subtraction problem. Write the answer below each problem.

1. Janet had 17 books. She gave 9 of the books to her sister. How many books does Janet have left?

   ____

   − ________

   ________ books

2. Eric had 18 comic books. Nine of the comic books got wet. How many comic books are not wet?

   ____

   − ________

   ________ comic books

3. David had 12 toy cars. He gave 4 of the cars to his friend. How many cars does David have left?

   ____

   − ________

   ________ cars

4. Jackie had 16 basketballs. Nine of them are flat. How many basketballs still bounce?

   ____

   − ________

   ________ basketballs

Subtraction Riddle

Directions: Solve each problem. Then, match each solution to the numbers at the bottom of the page. Write the corresponding letter in each blank to solve the riddle.

Why are seagulls called seagulls?

1. $19 - 6$ (e)	**2.** $14 - 5$ (g)	**3.** $19 - 7$ (y)	**4.** $12 - 5$ (t)
5. $14 - 3$ (a)	**6.** $16 - 6$ (s)	**7.** $13 - 7$ (l)	**8.** $15 - 7$ (b)

They live by the ______ ______ ______.
10 13 11

If they lived by the ______ ______ ______, they would be
8 11 12

called ______ ______ ______ ______ ______ ______.
8 11 9 13 6 10

Subtraction Wheels

Directions: Write a number in the middle circle so that when it is subtracted from the number in the outer circle, the difference is the number in the center.

1.

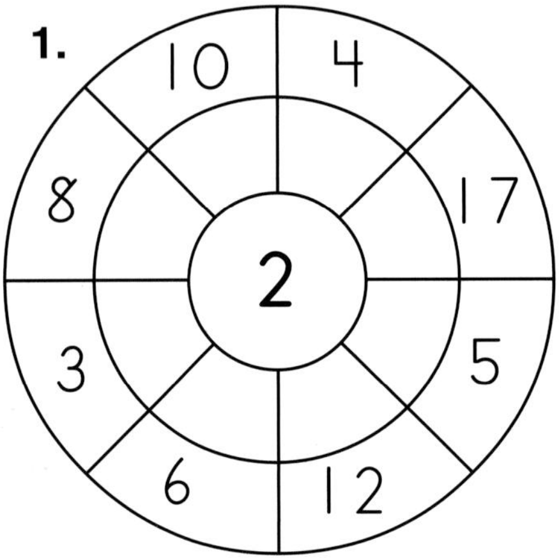

3.

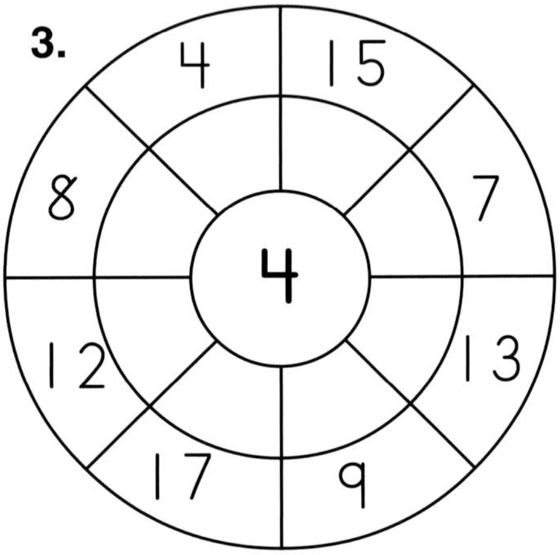

2.

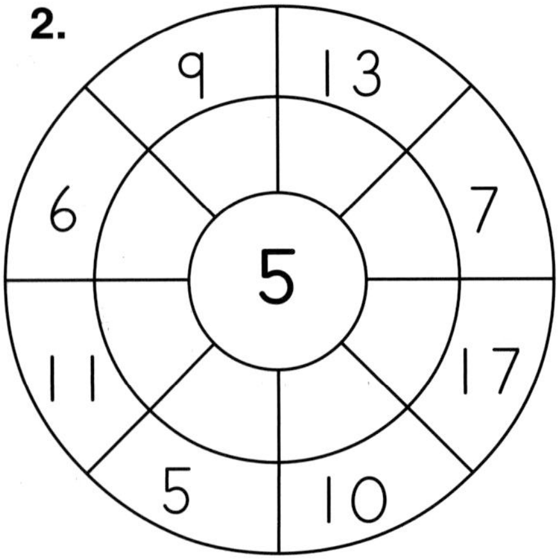

4.

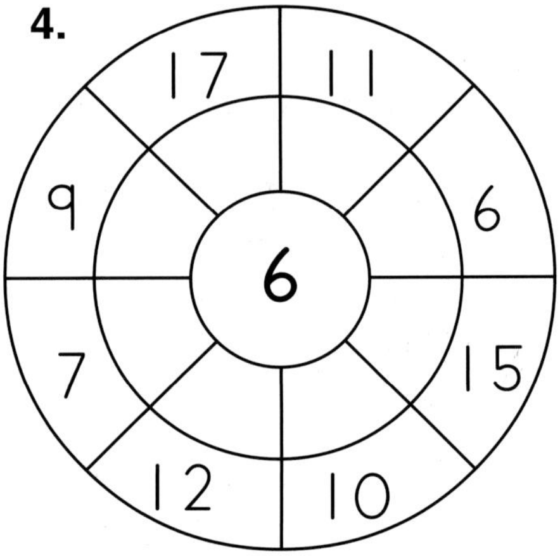

Adding and Subtracting

Directions: Add or subtract to solve each problem. Pay careful attention to the addition signs (+) and subtraction signs (–).

1. $\begin{array}{r} 10 \\ -\ 9 \\ \hline \end{array}$

2. $\begin{array}{r} 6 \\ +\ 3 \\ \hline \end{array}$

3. $\begin{array}{r} 8 \\ +\ 2 \\ \hline \end{array}$

4. $\begin{array}{r} 6 \\ -\ 4 \\ \hline \end{array}$

5. $\begin{array}{r} 7 \\ +\ 0 \\ \hline \end{array}$

6. $\begin{array}{r} 4 \\ +\ 4 \\ \hline \end{array}$

7. $\begin{array}{r} 0 \\ -\ 0 \\ \hline \end{array}$

8. $\begin{array}{r} 9 \\ +\ 8 \\ \hline \end{array}$

Directions: Read each word problem. Circle the math operation (add or subtract) that needs to be done to solve the word problem.

9. Melinda had $9. She spent $6 at the pet store. How much money does Melinda have left? add subtract

10. Jeremy had 8 fish in his tank. Now there are only 3 fish in the tank. How many fish are no longer in the tank? add subtract

Package Math

Directions: Complete each problem. The answer will be a clue to the present inside. Write the present on the line under each package.

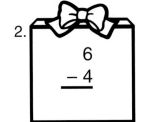

1. $\begin{array}{r} 3 \\ +\ 2 \\ \hline \end{array}$

____

2. $\begin{array}{r} 6 \\ -\ 4 \\ \hline \end{array}$

____

3. $\begin{array}{r} 1 \\ +\ 3 \\ \hline \end{array}$

____

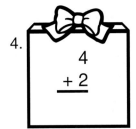

4. $\begin{array}{r} 4 \\ +\ 2 \\ \hline \end{array}$

____

5. $\begin{array}{r} 7 \\ -\ 4 \\ \hline \end{array}$

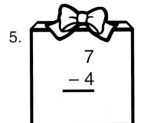

____

Cars

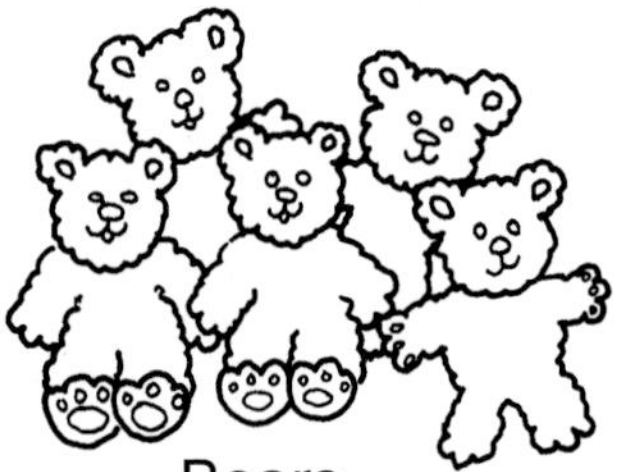
Bears

Dominoes

Dolls

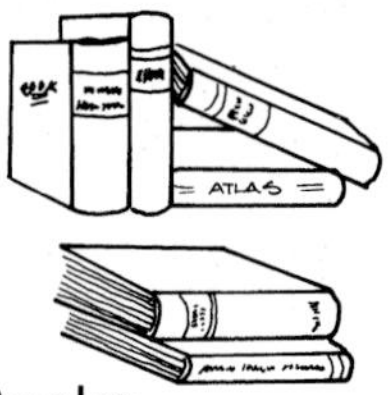

Books

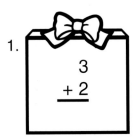

More Package Math

Directions: Complete each problem. The answer will be a clue to the present inside. Write the present on the line under each package.

1. $6 + 5 =$ __________

2. $4 + 8 =$ __________

3. $16 - 3 =$ __________

4. $15 - 5 =$ __________

5. $7 + 7 =$ __________

Marbles

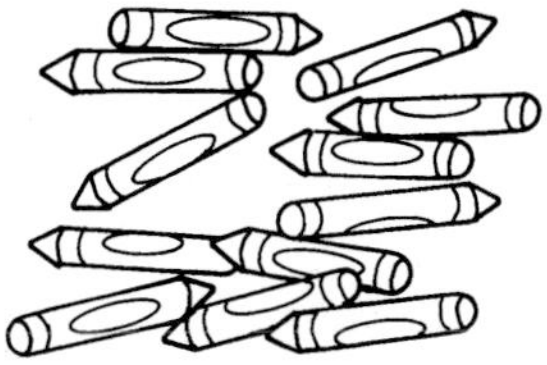
Crayons

Jacks

Tops

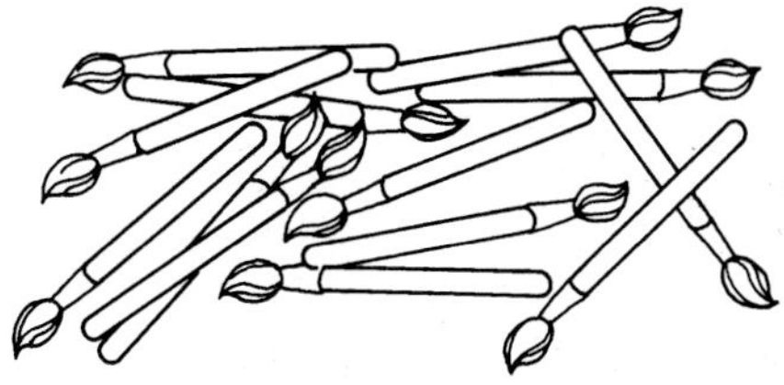
Paintbrushes

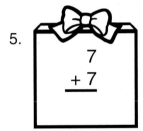

Follow the Arrow

Directions: Solve each problem. Color the puzzle.

0 = brown 1 = red 2 = green 3 = blue 4 = yellow

Blast Off!

Directions: Solve each problem. Color the puzzle.

5 = blue	6 = red	7 = gray	8 = purple

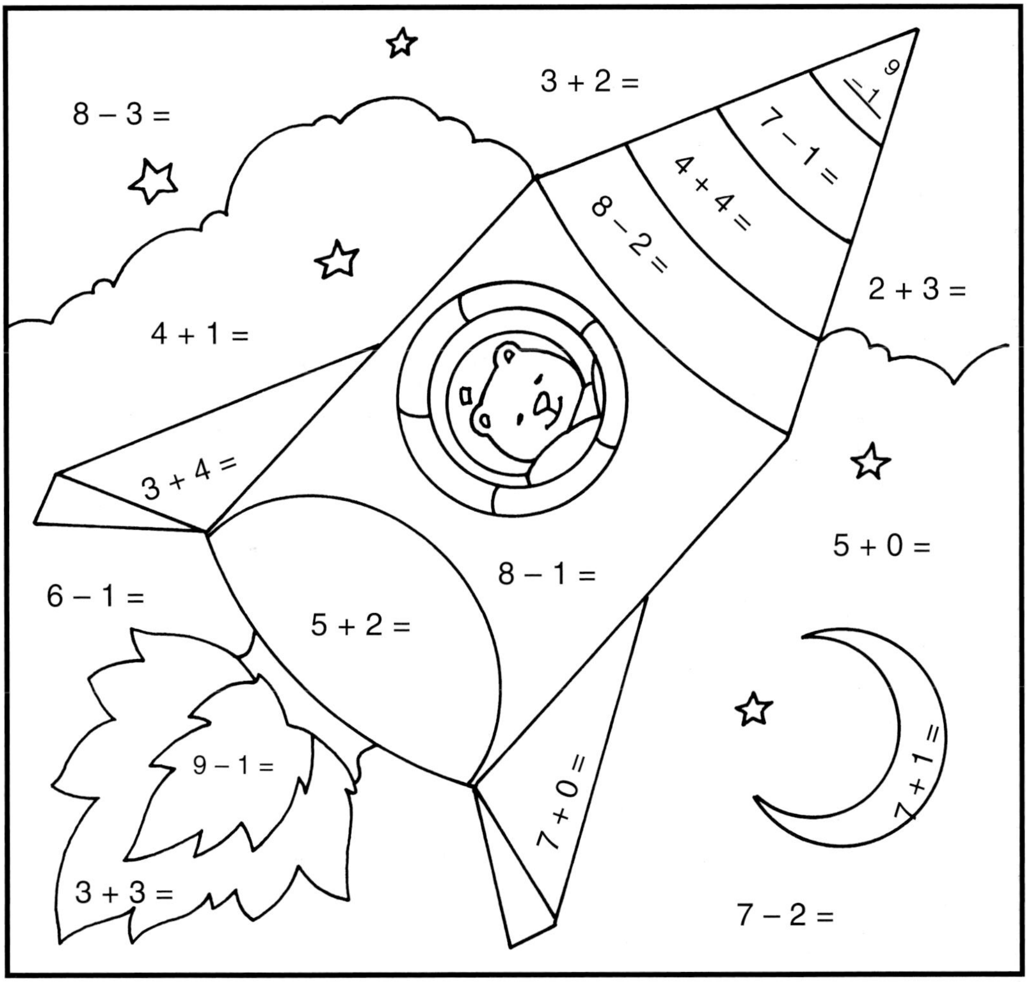

At The Barn

Directions: Solve each problem. Color the puzzle.

9 = brown	10 = yellow	11 = red	12 = pink

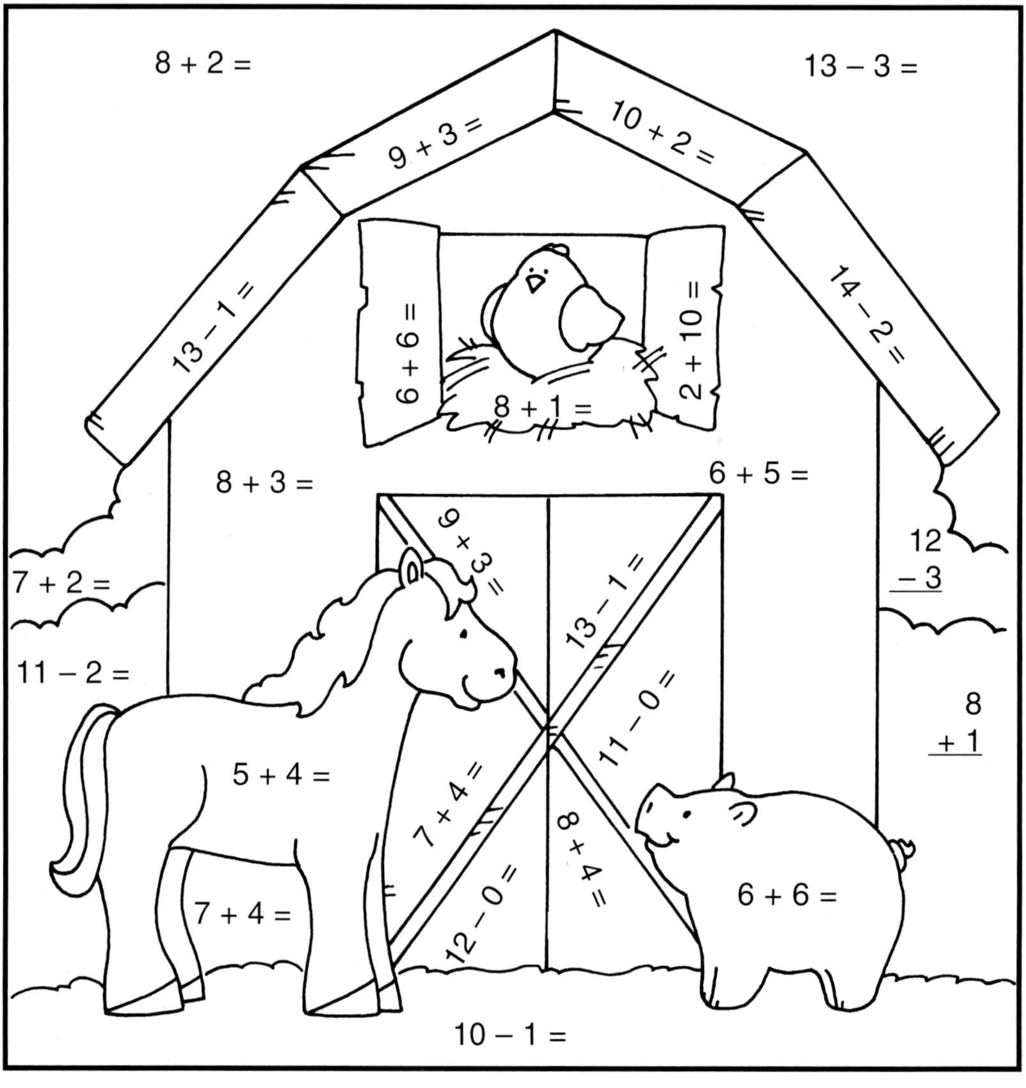

On the Road

Directions: Solve each problem. Color the puzzle.

13 = green	14 = orange	15 = black	16 = blue

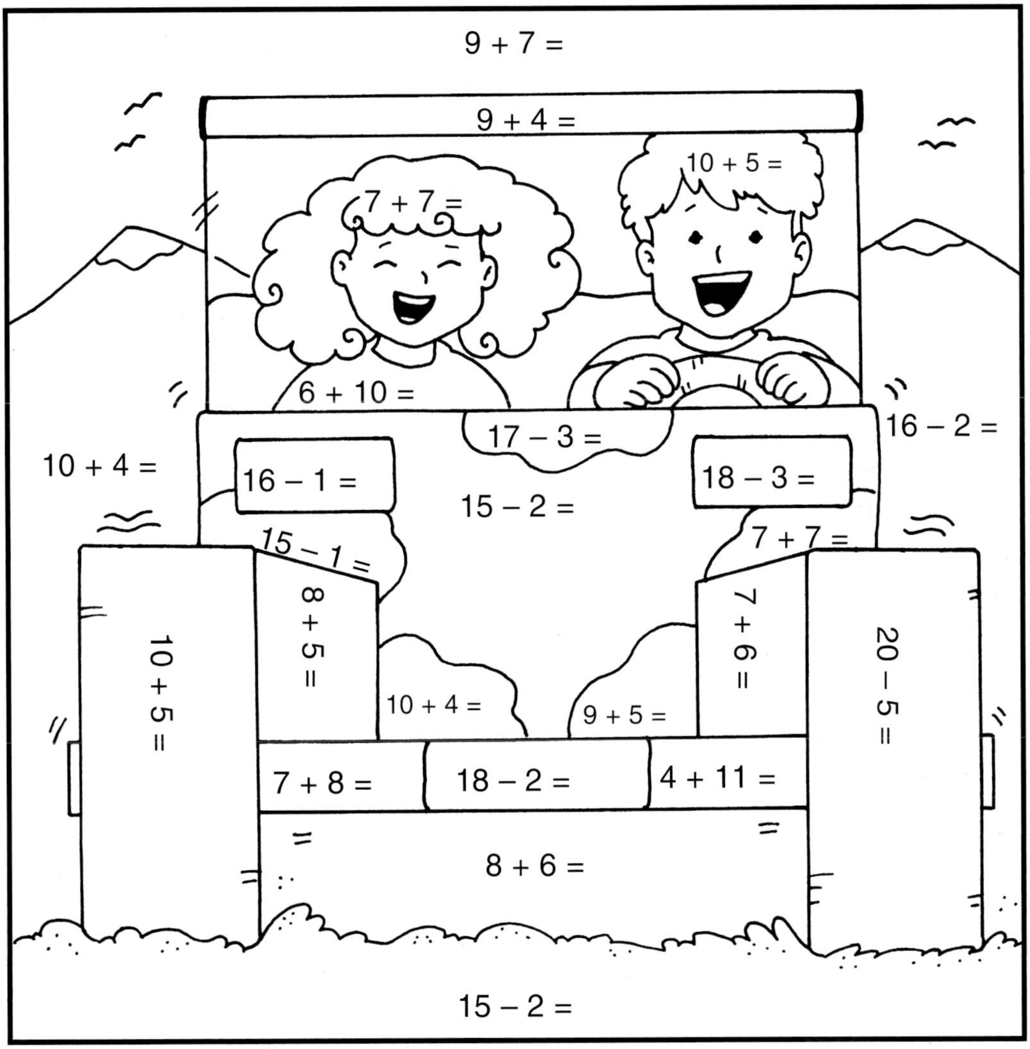

Bubble Colors

Directions: One of the most amazing things about bubbles is their colors. When light bounces off of a bubble, we see a rainbow of colors. Solve the problems in the bubbles. Find the answer in the code box below and color the bubbles.

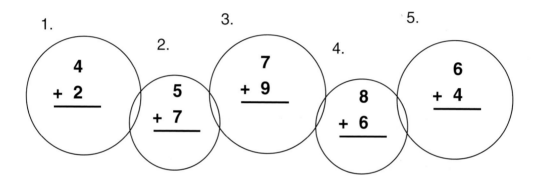

1. $4 + 2 =$ ____
2. $5 + 7 =$ ____
3. $7 + 9 =$ ____
4. $8 + 6 =$ ____
5. $6 + 4 =$ ____
6. $15 - 5 =$ ____
7. $13 - 5 =$ ____
8. $10 - 3 =$ ____
9. $17 - 2 =$ ____
10. $14 - 8 =$ ____

Color Code

6 = blue	8 = pink	12 = purple	15 = orange
7 = blue/green	10 = yellow	14 = red	16 = green

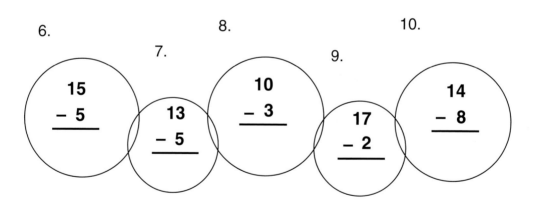

Break the Code!

Directions: Solve each problem. Use your answers to break the code!

____ H 7 + 5 =	S 8 + 7 =
____ T 4 + 9 =	G 5 + 3 =
____ O 7 + 7 =	A 9 + 2 =
____ E 8 + 9 =	K 6 + 3 =
____ R 3 + 7 =	I 7 + 9 =

___ ___ ___   ___ ___ ___   ___ ___ ___ ___ ___
15 17 17   13 12 17   9 16 13 17 15

___ ___ ___ ___   ___ ___ ___ ___!
15 14 11 10   12 16 8 12

____ U 9 – 2 =	K 5 – 5 =
____ S 10 – 2 =	A 7 – 3 =
____ R 6 – 4 =	F 4 – 1 =
____ T 8 – 3 =	E 10 – 1 =
____ I 9 – 3 =	N 3 – 2 =

___ ___ ___ ___ ___   ___ ___ ___   ___ ___ ___!
0 6 5 9 8   4 2 9   3 7 1

Forward and Backward

Directions: Use the number line to help you solve the word problems.

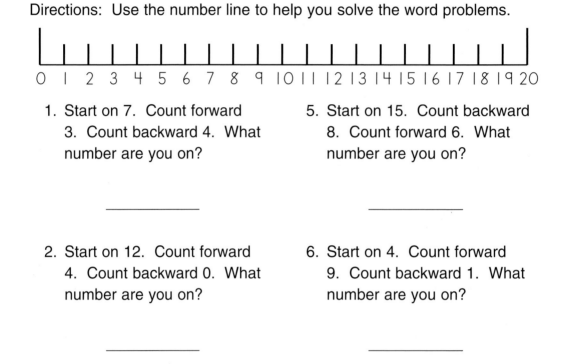

1. Start on 7. Count forward 3. Count backward 4. What number are you on?

   ____

5. Start on 15. Count backward 8. Count forward 6. What number are you on?

   ____

2. Start on 12. Count forward 4. Count backward 0. What number are you on?

   ____

6. Start on 4. Count forward 9. Count backward 1. What number are you on?

   ____

3. Start on 10. Count backward 9. Count forward 5. What number are you on?

   ____

7. Start on 5. Count backward 1. Count forward 7. What number are you on?

   ____

4. Start on 11. Count backward 4. Count forward 7. What number are you on?

   ____

8. Start on 2. Count forward 14. Count backward 10. What number are you on?

   ____

How Many?

Directions: Solve each problem. Write a number sentence to show your work.

1. 

There are 7 cookies in all. How many are in the bag?

2. 

There are 6 kittens in all. How many are in the box?

3. 

There are 2 pencils in all. How many are in the box?

4. 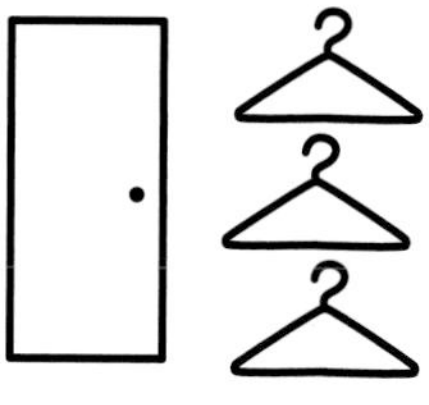

There are 20 hangers in all. How many are in the closet?

5. 

There are 5 people in the family. How many are in the house?

Answer Key

Page 248
1. 5
2. 2
3. 3
4. 4
5. 1
6. 3
7. 4
8. 2

Page 249
1. 7
2. 9
3. 9
4. 9
5. 10
6. 9
7. 8
8. 8
9. 7
10. 8
11. 10
12. 10

Page 250
1. 6
2. 4
3. 6
4. 6

Page 251
1. 7
2. 6
3. 7
4. 7

Page 252
1. 8
2. 6
3. 8
4. 8

Page 253
1. 3
2. 5
3. 4
4. 3
5. 5
6. 4
7. 6
8. 5

Page 254
1. 3 + 2 = 5
2. 2 + 3 = 5
3. 2 + 2 = 4
4. 1 + 2 = 3
5. 3 + 3 = 6
6. 1 + 3 = 4

Page 255
1. 3, 1
2. 2, 6
3. 5, 9
4. 4, 0
5. 8, 10
6. 8, 2
7. 5, 9
8. 3, 1
9. 10, 4
10. 8, 6
11. 0, 3
12. 6, 5

Page 256
1. 3 + 2 = 5
2. 6 + 1 = 7
3. 5 + 3 = 8
4. 4 + 2 = 6
5. 3 + 0 = 3
6. 4 + 4 = 8

Page 257
Answers will vary.

Page 258
1. 5
2. 2
3. 7
4. 3
5. 6

Page 259
1. 6
2. 8
3. 8
4. 10
5. 9
6. 9
7. 10
8. 9
9. 8
10. 9

Page 260
1. 12
2. 14
3. 18
4. 15
5. 18
6. 7

Page 261
1. 12
2. 13
3. 16
4. 11
5. 14
6. 16
7. 14
8. 17
9. 11
10. 18
11. 18
12. 16

Page 262

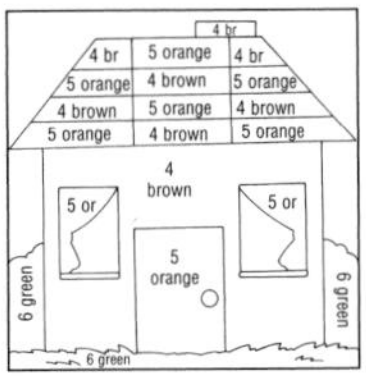

Page 263

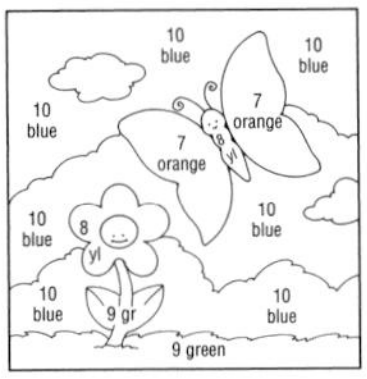

Page 264

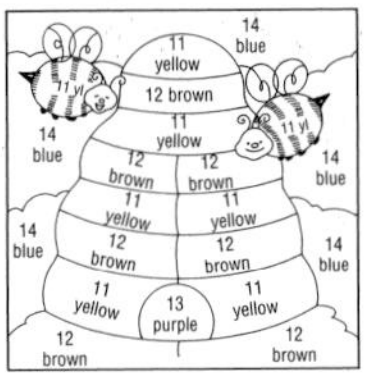

Page 265

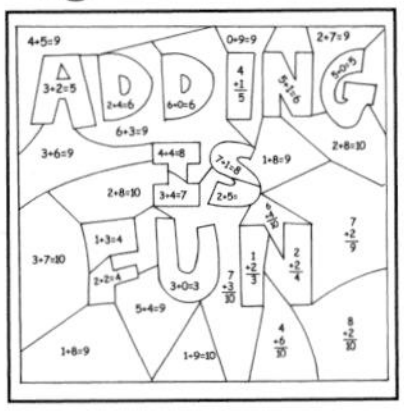

Page 266
1. 3 + 5; 7 + 1;
   6 + 2
2. 2 + 2; 4 + 0;
   3 + 1; 0 + 4
3. 6 + 0; 4 + 2;
   3 + 3; 5 + 1
4. 2 + 0; 1 + 1;
   0 + 2
5. 3 + 6; 1 + 8;
   9 + 0
6. 3 + 0; 2 + 1;
   0 + 3; 1 + 2
7. 6 + 1; 2 + 5;
   4 + 3; 7 + 0
8. 5 + 0; 3 + 2;
   1 + 4; 3 + 2

Page 267
1. 1
2. 5
3. 4
4. 3
5. 2
6. 10
7. 7
8. 0
9. 8
10. 6

Riddle: To get to the other slide.

Page 268
1. 5
2. 7
3. 6
4. 4
5. 5
6. 6

Answer Key *(cont.)*

Page 269
1. 7 + 5 = 12
2. 9 + 8 = 17
3. 10 + 4 = 14
4. 6 + 6 = 12

Page 270
1. 5; 3 + 2 = 5
2. 4; 2 + 2 = 4
3. 13; 8 + 5 = 13

Page 271
1. 2
2. 4
3. 5
4. 0
5. 6
6. 7
7. 3
8. 1
9. 8
10. 9

Page 272

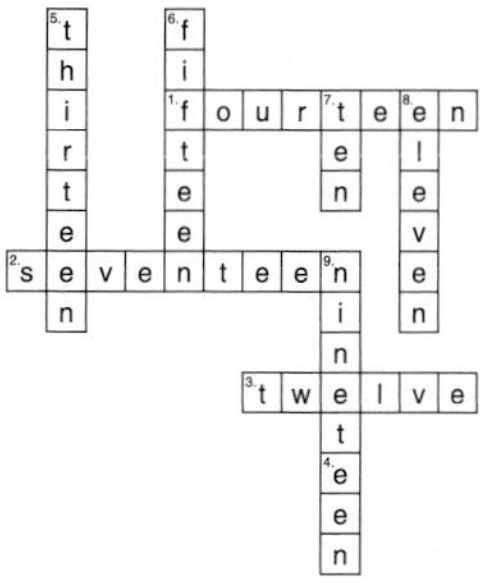

Page 273
1. 3
2. 3
3. 3
4. 4
5. 3
6. 4
7. 4
8. 1
9. 5
10. 0

Challenge: 6

Page 274
from top, going clockwise:
1. 16, 15, 14, 13, 12, 11, 10, 9
2. 18, 17, 16, 15, 14, 13, 12, 11
3. 17, 16, 15, 14, 13, 12, 11, 10
4. 17, 16, 15, 14, 13, 12, 11, 10

Page 275
Answers will vary.

Page 276
1. 10
2. 8
3. 12
4. 7
5. 11
6. 13
7. 9
8. 6
9. 14

Page 277
1. 0
2. 2
3. 4
4. 2
5. 2
6. 0
7. 1
8. 4
9. 0
10. 4
11. 3
12. 0

Page 278
1. 3
2. 2
3. 3
4. 5

Page 279
1. 2
2. 3
3. 5
4. 5
5. 1
6. 6

Page 280
1. 5 – 2 = 3
2. 7 – 6 = 1
3. 6 – 4 = 2
4. 5 – 5 = 0

Page 281
Answers will vary.

Page 282
1. 1
2. 3
3. 5
4. 2
5. 0

Page 283
1. 6
2. 9
3. 18
4. 9
5. 9
6. 1
7. 7
8. 10
9. 4
10. 4

Page 284
1. 2
2. 4
3. 5
4. 3
5. 1
6. 0

Page 285
1. 5
2. 1
3. 5
4. 5
5. 3
6. 2
7. 4
8. 3
9. 1
10. 2
11. 2
12. 3

Page 286
1. 2
2. 3
3. 8
4. 3
5. 3
6. 2
7. 5
8. 3
9. 4
10. 2

Page 287
1. 2, 4, 0, 1
2. 1, 3, 2, 6
3. 1, 0, 2, 3
4. 0, 3, 2, 1
5. 8, 3, 1, 5
6. 1, 4, 0, 3
7. 0, 2, 1, 3
8. 1, 3, 5, 0
9. 1, 6, 2, 5

Page 288

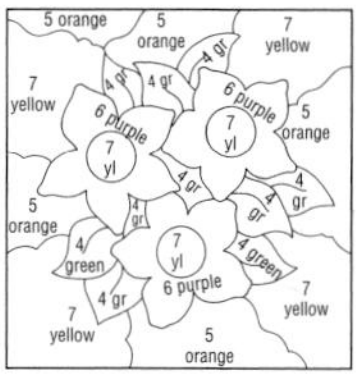

Page 289
1. 4; 7 – 3 = 4
2. 4; 6 – 2 = 4
3. 3; 5 – 2 = 3
4. 2; 8 – 6 = 2

Page 290
1. 17 – 9 = 8
2. 18 – 9 = 9
3. 12 – 4 = 8
4. 16 – 9 = 7

Answer Key *(cont.)*

Page 291

1. 13
2. 9
3. 12
4. 7
5. 11
6. 10
7. 6
8. 8

Riddle: They live by the sea. If they lived by the bay, they would be called bagels.

Page 292

from top, going clockwise:

1. 2, 15, 3, 10, 4, 1, 6, 8
2. 8, 2, 12, 5, 0, 6, 1, 4
3. 11, 3, 9, 5, 13, 8, 4, 0
4. 5, 0, 9, 4, 6, 1, 3, 11

Page 293

1. 1
2. 9
3. 10
4. 2
5. 7
6. 8
7. 0
8. 17
9. subtract
10. subtract

Page 294

1. 5, Bears
2. 2, Cars
3. 4, Dominoes
4. 6, Books
5. 3, Dolls

Page 295

1. 11, Tops
2. 12, Crayons
3. 13, Paintbrushes
4. 10, Jacks
5. 14, Marbles

Page 296

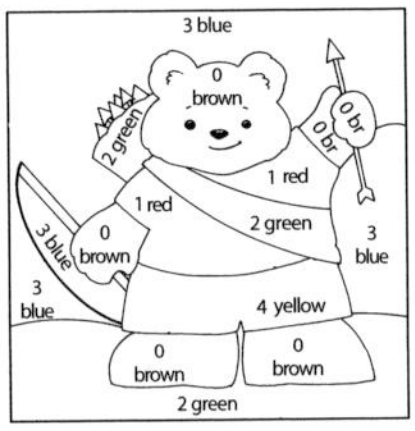

Page 297

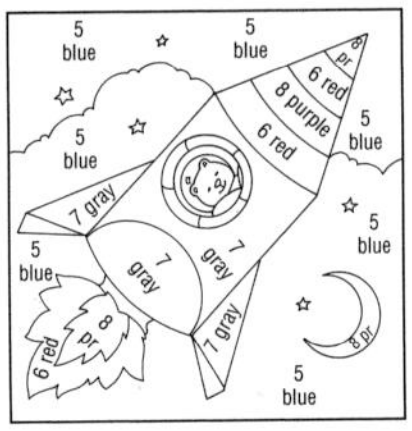

Page 298

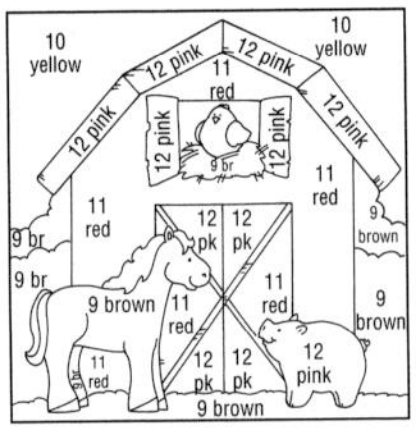

Page 299

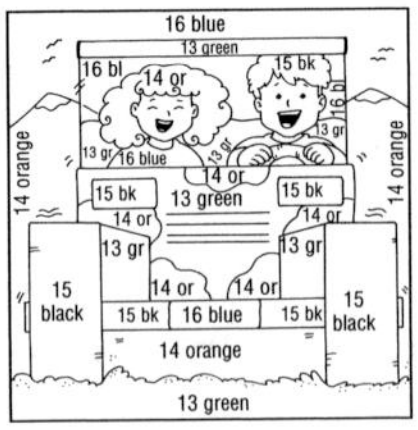

Page 300

1. 6
2. 12
3. 16
4. 14
5. 10
6. 10
7. 8
8. 7
9. 15
10. 6

Page 301

Addition Code: See the kites soar high!
Subtraction Code: Kites are Fun!

Page 302

1. 6
2. 16
3. 6
4. 14
5. 13
6. 12
7. 11
8. 6

Page 303

1. 3; $7 - 4 = 3$
2. 5; $6 - 1 = 5$
3. 0; $2 - 2 = 0$
4. 17; $20 - 3 = 17$
5. 3; $5 - 2 = 3$

Practice and Learn

WORKBOOK

Word Games

Word Puzzle #1

Directions: Look at each picture. Read the word that goes with each picture. Write the missing letter in the circle. After all of the circles have been filled in, find the mystery word.

1.  c a ◯

2.  n ◯ t

3.  m a ◯

4.  ◯ a t

5.  ◯ c e

6.  ◯ e a f

What is the mystery word?

___ ___ ___ ___ ___ ___

Word Puzzle #2

Directions: Look at each picture. Read the word that goes with each picture. Write the missing letter in the circle. After all of the circles have been filled in, find the mystery word.

1. 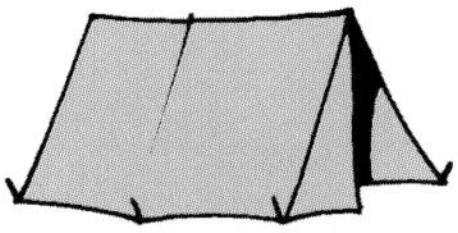 ○ e n t

2. 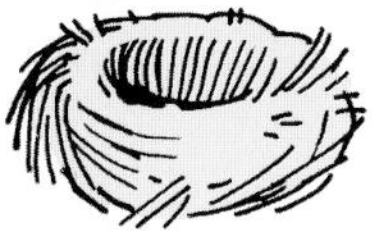 n ○ s t

3.  p ○ d d l e

4.  ○ a n o e

5.  ○ a m b u r g e r

6. 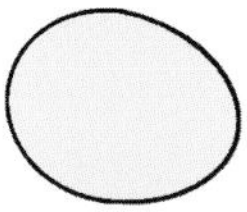 ○ g g

7.  c ○ a b

What is the mystery word?

____ ____ ____ ____ ____ ____ ____

Word Puzzle #3

Directions: Look at each picture. Read the word that goes with each picture. Write the missing letter in the circle. After all of the circles have been filled in, find the mystery word.

1.  s h ◯ l l

2.  s c a ◯ e c r o w

3.  f l ◯ g

4. 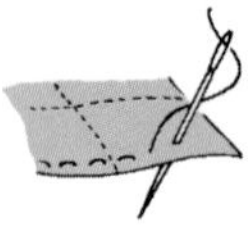 ◯ e w

5. 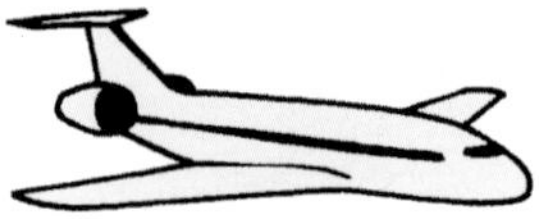 j ◯ t

6.  b e a ◯

What is the mystery word?

___ ___ ___ ___ ___ ___

Word Puzzle #4

Directions: Look at each picture. Read the word that goes with each picture. Write the missing letter in the circle. After all of the circles have been filled in, find the mystery word.

1.  ◯ e e r

2.  b ◯ d

3.  b a ◯ k e t

4. 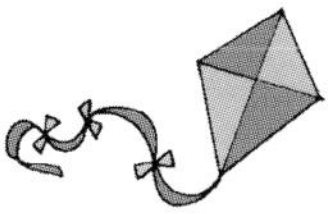 ◯ i t e

What is the mystery word?

___ ___ ___ ___

Use the mystery word in a sentence.

Word Puzzle #5

Directions: Look at each picture. Read the word that goes with each picture. Write the missing letter in the circle. After all of the circles have been filled in, find the mystery word.

1.  ◯ l o w n

2.  ◯ a t

3.  b ◯ n d

4.  b ◯ k e

5.  s t a ◯

What is the mystery word?

___ ___ ___ ___ ___

Use the mystery word in a sentence.

Scramble Cats

Directions: Unscramble the words. Write them correctly on the lines.

1. 

2. 

3. 

4. 

5. 

6. 

7. 

8. 

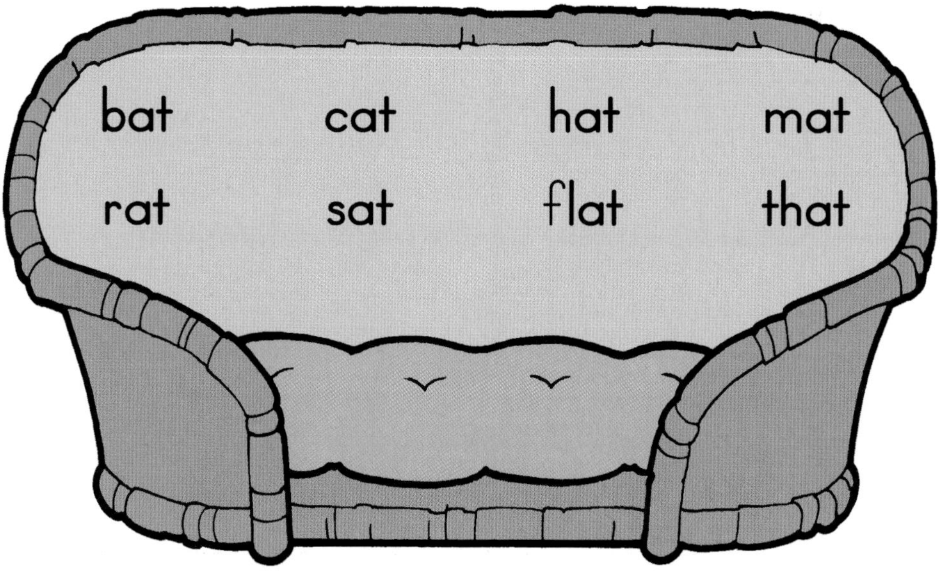

Order the Names

Directions: Read the list of names on the left side of the page. Write the names from the box on the right to complete the alphabetical class list.

Ann
Billy
Fran
Hank
Kate
Matt
Olivia

Will

Jill

Pablo

Dan

Lola

Order the Words

Directions: Write the numbers **1**, **2**, or **3** to put each group of words in alphabetical order. The first one is done for you.

1. dog 2 cat 1 rat 3	**2.** mug ___ cup ___ pan ___	**3.** hat ___ glove ___ coat ___
4. net ___ ball ___ club ___	**5.** zebra ___ yak ___ bear ___	**6.** bug ___ rock ___ tree ___
7. wet ___ sun ___ boat ___	**8.** shark ___ whale ___ fish ___	**9.** log ___ frog ___ pond ___

Animal ABC Order

Directions: Put these words in alphabetical order.

1.

cat dog
lizard bird

____

____

____

____

2.

lion giraffe
tiger elephant

____

____

____

____

3.

pig cow
horse sheep

____

____

____

____

4.

fish crab
octopus shark

____

____

____

____

Which Comes First?

Directions: For each pair of words, circle the word that comes first and underline the word that comes second in alphabetical order. The first one is done for you.

1. give gave	**2.** cat cot	**3.** wag wig
4. big bug	**5.** hop hat	**6.** not net
7. sit sat	**8.** pig peg	**9.** top tap
10. lap lip	**11.** zig zag	**12.** fin fun

Alphabetical Order

Directions: Put the words in alphabetical order.

mirror	baby
football	monkey
bath	dress
igloo	wombat
wooly	ice
dash	foot

1. ____________________
2. ____________________
3. ____________________
4. ____________________
5. ____________________
6. ____________________
7. ____________________
8. ____________________
9. ____________________
10. ____________________
11. ____________________
12. ____________________

More Alphabetical Order

Directions: Put the words in alphabetical order.

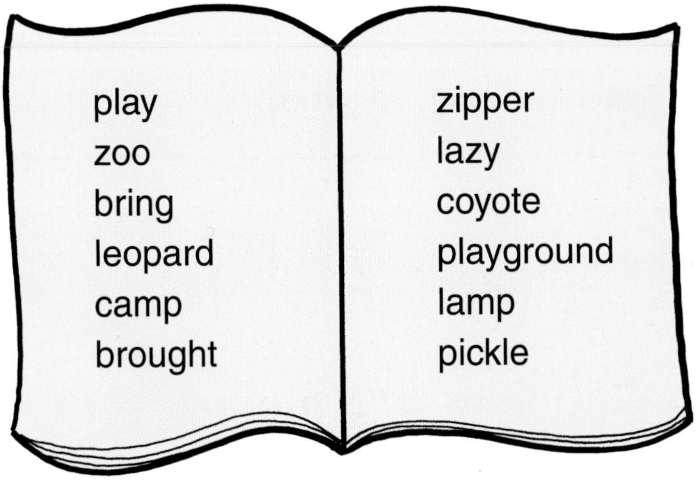

1. ____________________
2. ____________________
3. ____________________
4. ____________________
5. ____________________
6. ____________________
7. ____________________
8. ____________________
9. ____________________
10. ____________________
11. ____________________
12. ____________________

Names of Things

Directions: Write the name for each picture on the line below it.

bat	**dog**	**log**	**mop**	**tub**	**web**

1. 

2. 

3. 

4. 

5. 

6. 

More Names of Things

Directions: Write the name for each picture on the line below it.

bell	**cat**	**pig**	**ring**	**sock**	**star**

1.

2.

3.

4.

5.

6.

Circle the Name

Directions: Say the name of each picture. Circle its name.

1.  thin thirty three	2.  wheat white why	3. 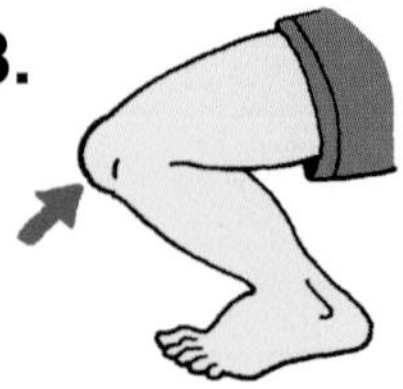 knot knob knee
4.  chin chips chain	5.  sheep ship sheet	6.  thick thank think
7.  knit knife knock	8. 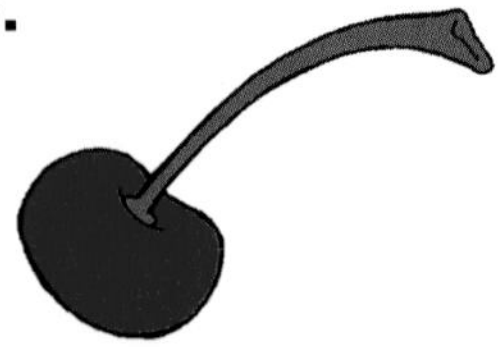 chip chair cherry	9.  whip white while
10. 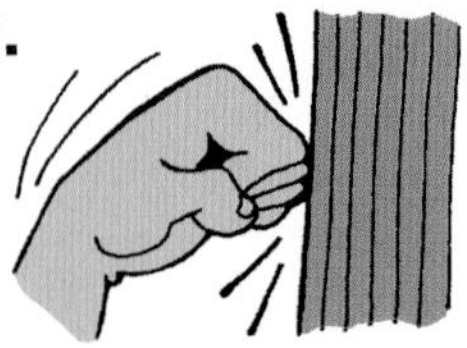 knot knob knock	11.  chum church chill	12.  throne thorn tie

Add a Letter

Directions: Add the letter in the circle to the word shown in the picture to form a new word.

1. (s) +  wing = ______________

2. (t) +  wig = ______________

3. (c) +  lock = ______________

4. (s) +  lip = ______________

5. (b) +  ring = ______________

6. (s) +  pot = ______________

7. (b) +  rain = ______________

What's the Rule?

Directions: Look at the words on the list below. What do they all have in common? Choose words from the Word Bank that meet the rule. Write the words from the Word Bank on the lines.

Word Bank

Ben	**October**	**March**
May	**Paula**	**Marla**
Carla	**April**	**Donald**
June	**Zachary**	**July**

1. February
2. December
3. September
4. August
5. November
6. January
7. ______________________
8. ______________________
9. ______________________
10. ______________________
11. ______________________
12. ______________________

What is the rule?

____

____

Name the Rule

Directions: Look at the words on the list below. What do they all have in common? Choose words from the Word Bank that meet the rule. Write the words from the Word Bank on the lines.

Word Bank

orange	house	green
desk	purple	phone
brown	yellow	red
flower	table	tape

1. pink **7.** ______________________

2. gray **8.** ______________________

3. blue **9.** ______________________

4. black **10.** ______________________

5. white **11.** ______________________

6. gold **12.** ______________________

What is the rule?

____

____

Secret Message

Directions: Decode the secret message.

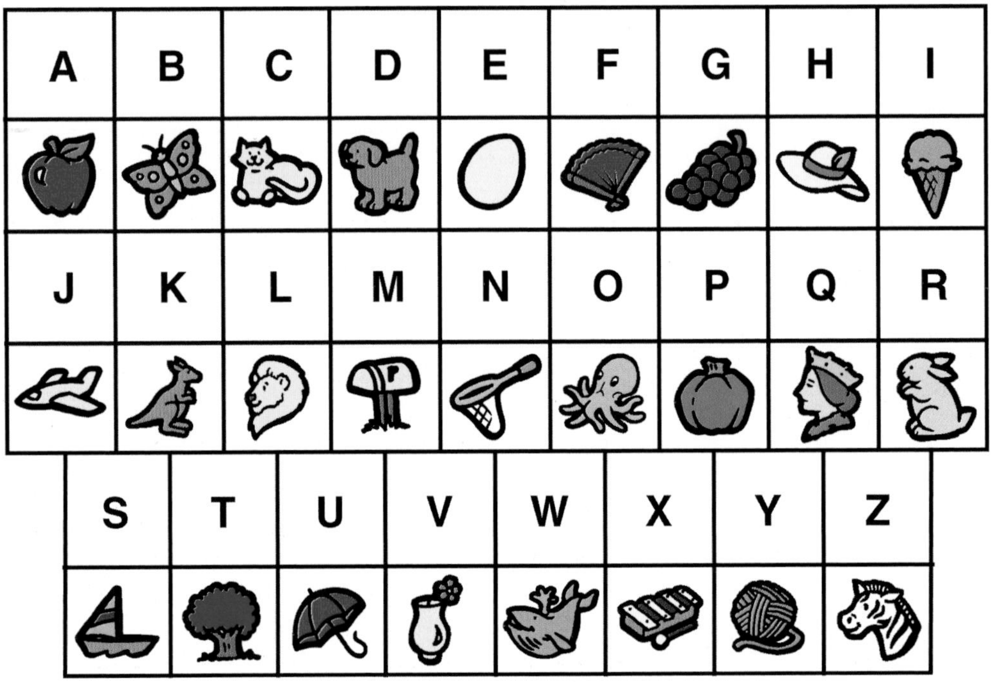

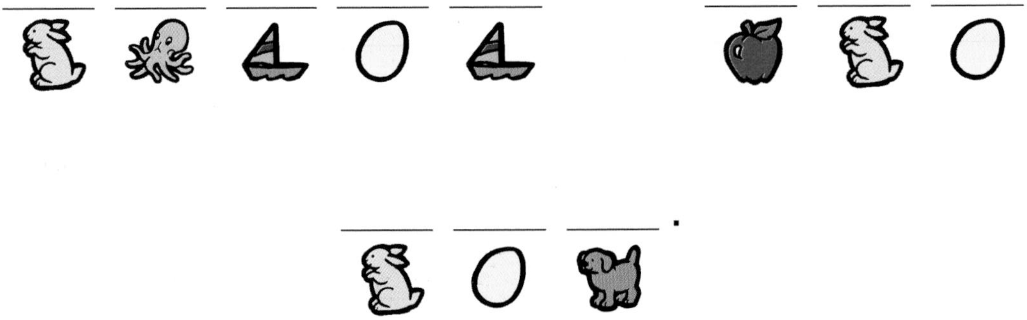

Another Secret Message

Directions: Decode the secret message.

A	B	C	D	E	F	G	H	I

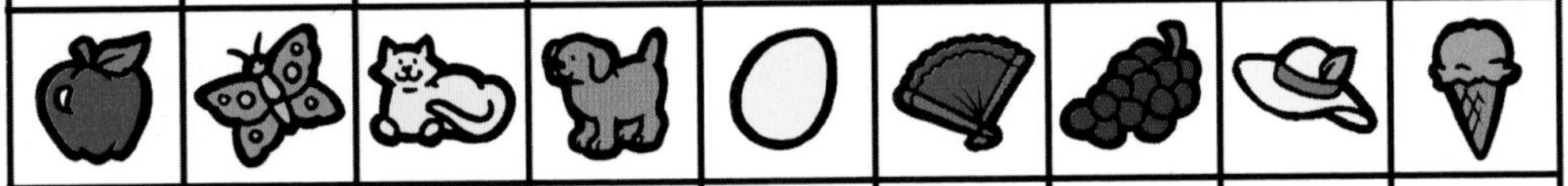

J	K	L	M	N	O	P	Q	R

S	T	U	V	W	X	Y	Z

_____ _____ _____ _____ _____ _____ _____

_____ _____ _____   _____ _____ _____ _____

Mama Tree

Directions: Use the code below to help you solve the riddle. Write each letter below the circle to solve it.

What did the mama pine tree say to the baby pine trees?

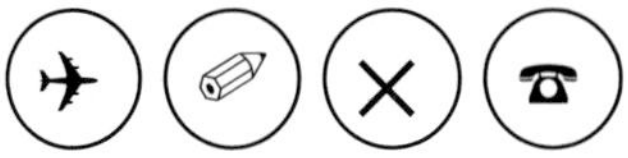

____ ____ ____ ____

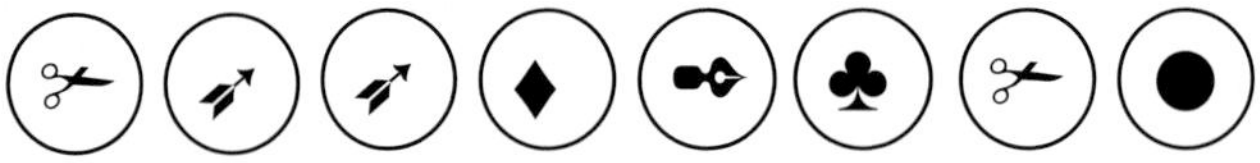

____ ____ ____ ____ ____ ____ ____ ____

____ ____ ____ ____   ____ ____ ____ ____ ____!

Answer Code

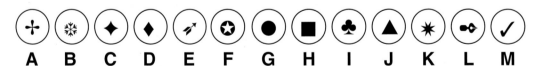

A B C D E F G H I J K L M

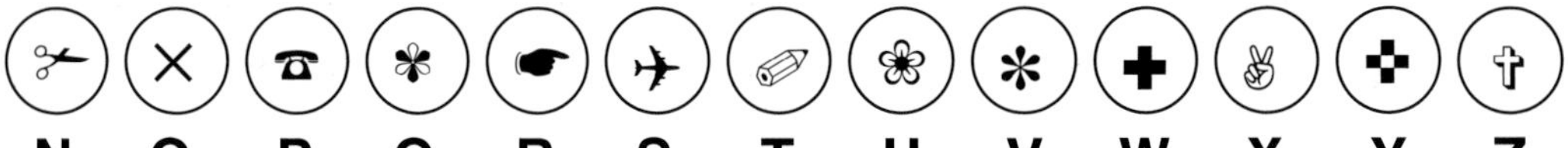

N O P Q R S T U V W X Y Z

Alphabet Soup

Directions: Search for words in the bowl of soup below. Color each word as you find it. One word is not in the soup. Which word is missing? ________________

MADE	**THEIR**	**KNOW**	**WITH**	**YOU**
YOUR	**FROM**	**DOWN**	**THAT**	**THEY**

"Ate" in All

Directions: Read the clues below. Each of the words being described ends with "ate." Choose the word from the Word Box that is being described and write it on the line. Good luck!

Word Box

gate	plate	skate
date	hate	late

1. Not on time: ______________________________

2. On a fence: ______________________________

3. Used to eat on: ______________________________

4. Done on ice: ______________________________

5. Do not like: ______________________________

6. A day on the calendar: ______________________________

Which Month Am I?

Directions: Fill in the crossword puzzle. Use words from the word box.

Across

2. The month before July.

4. A cold winter month.

5. ___________ showers bring May flowers.

Down

1. A month for Valentines!

3. A warm summer month.

January	**February**	**July**	**April**	**June**

What Makes "Scents"

Directions: Choose a final consonant from the flower to complete each word on the skunk.

"Ake" in All

Directions: Read the clues below. Each of the words being described ends with "ake." Choose the word from the Word Box that is being described and write it on the line. Good luck!

Word Box		
cake	rake	bake
fake	quake	lake

1. Can do in an oven: ____________________

2. For birthdays: ____________________

3. A place to swim: ____________________

4. For picking up leaves: ____________________

5. Shakes the earth: ____________________

6. Not real: ____________________

Snowman's Good Grades

Use the code below to help you solve the riddle. Write each letter below the shape to solve it.

Why did the snowman get straight A's?

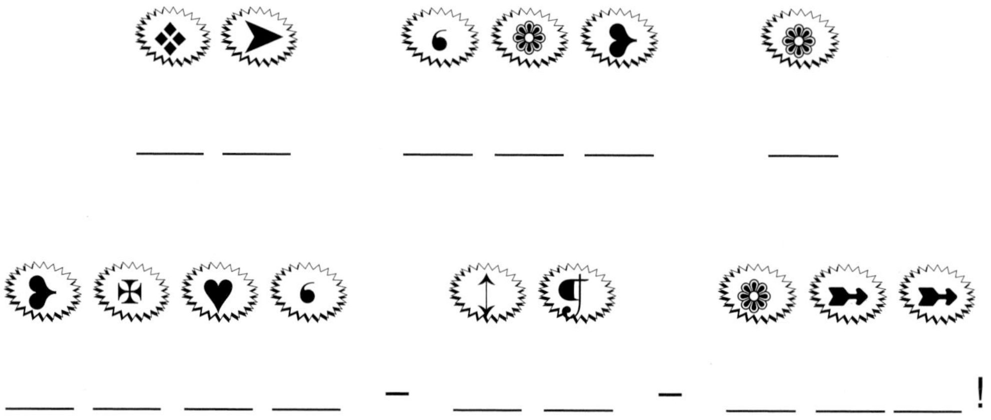

Answer Code

A B C D E F G H I J K L M

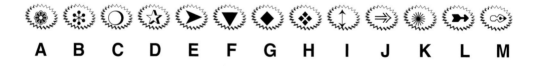

N O P Q R S T U V W X Y Z

Hummingbirds

Directions: Use the code below to help you solve the riddle. Write each letter below the shape to solve it.

Why do hummingbirds hum?

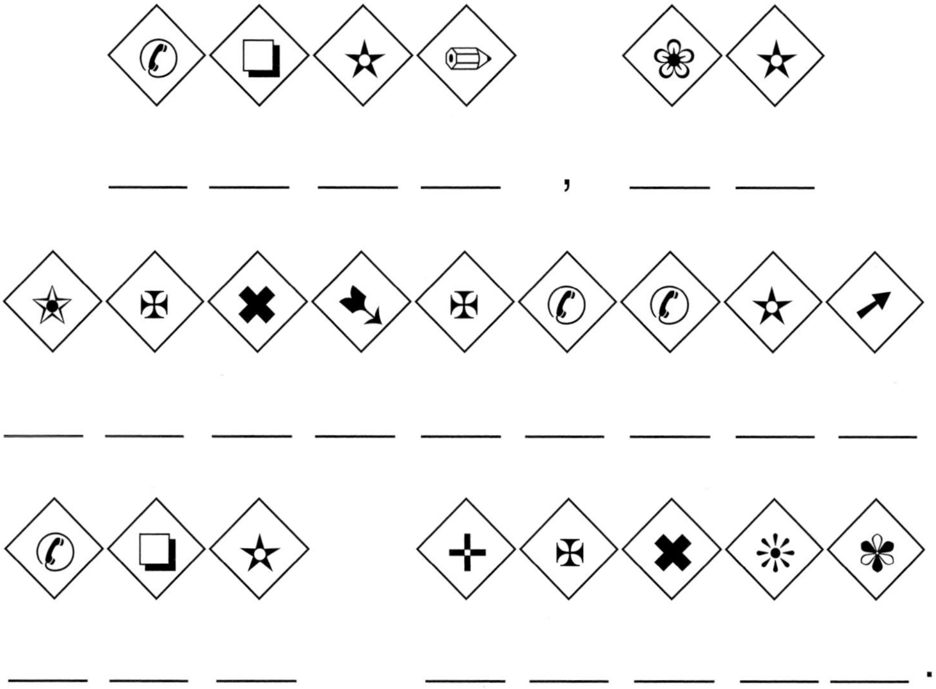

Answer Code

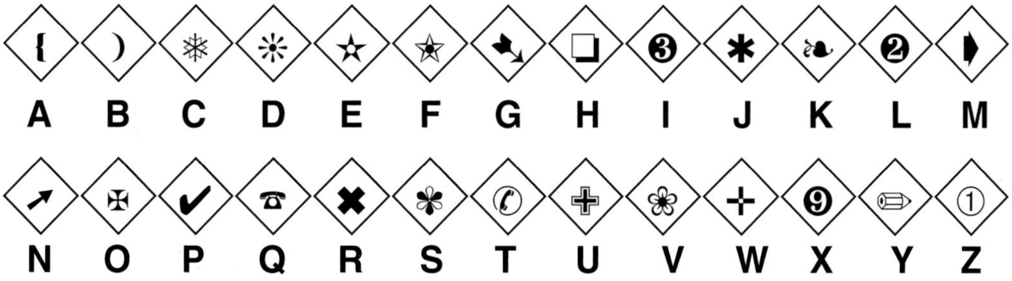

Frog Drink

Directions: Use the code below to help you solve the riddle. Write each letter below the square to solve it.

What do frogs drink in the winter?

➤	✗	❛
___	___	___

✧	☞	✗	❄	➢	✗
___	___	___	___	___	___

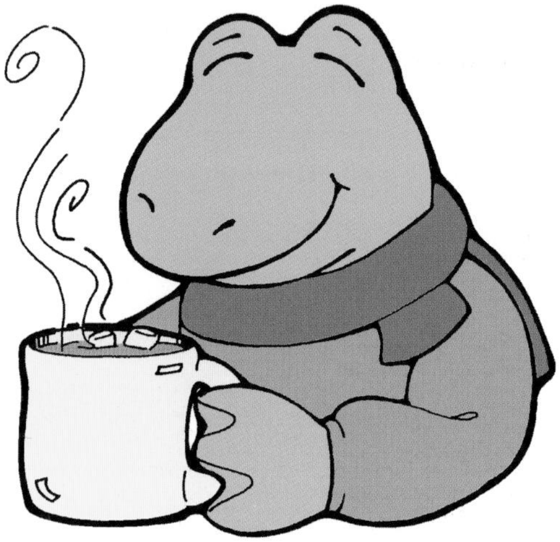

Answer Code

❄	✢	✧	⑦	●	✪	♣	➤	▲	⇨	➢	✸	✑
A	**B**	**C**	**D**	**E**	**F**	**G**	**H**	**I**	**J**	**K**	**L**	**M**

❤	✗	➠	✿	☞	⑥	❛	✛	⊃	➒	➸	✌	✎
N	**O**	**P**	**Q**	**R**	**S**	**T**	**U**	**V**	**W**	**X**	**Y**	**Z**

Decoding

Directions: Match each number to the letter in the code to find the color names.

A	B	C	D	E	F	G	H	I	J	K	L	M
1	2	3	4	5	6	7	8	9	10	11	12	13
N	O	P	Q	R	S	T	U	V	W	X	Y	Z
14	15	16	17	18	19	20	21	22	23	24	25	26

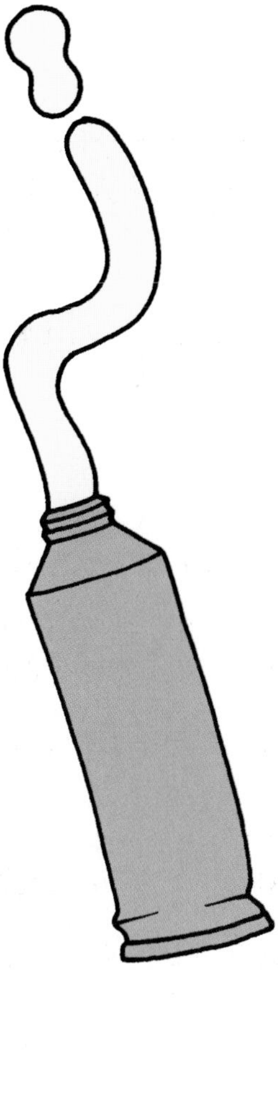

1. 2 12 21 5 ________________

2. 18 5 4 ________________

3. 16 21 18 16 12 5 ________________

4. 7 18 5 5 14 ________________

5. 2 12 1 3 11 ________________

6. 25 5 12 12 15 23 ________________

7. 23 8 9 20 5 ________________

8. 19 9 12 22 5 18 ________________

9. 15 18 1 14 7 5 ________________

10. 16 9 14 11 ________________

11. 7 15 12 4 ________________

12. 2 18 15 23 14 ________________

Missing Letters

Directions: Fill in a missing letter to complete each word.

1. co___d

2. hap___y

3. fun___y

4. c___w

5. cro___

6. mo___her

7. rabbi___

8. jac___et

9. m___uth

10. ___ise

11. s___reet

12. monke___

More Missing Letters

Directions: Fill in a missing letter to complete each word.

1. s___ring
2. bac___
3. ___ix
4. hai___
5. poli___e
6. e___bow
7. s___eet
8. stomac___
9. flo___r
10. co___
11. ___lanket
12. fin___er

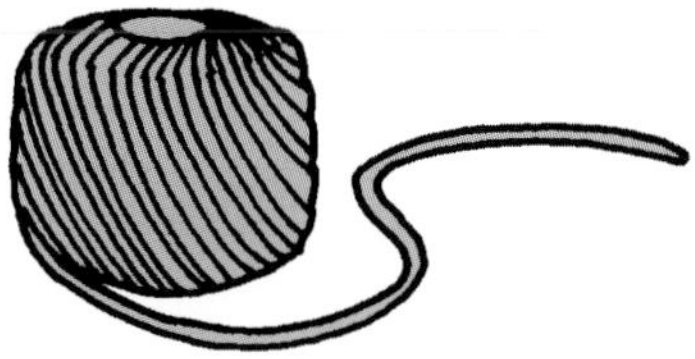

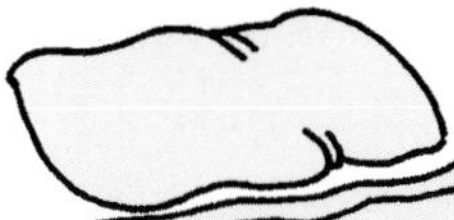
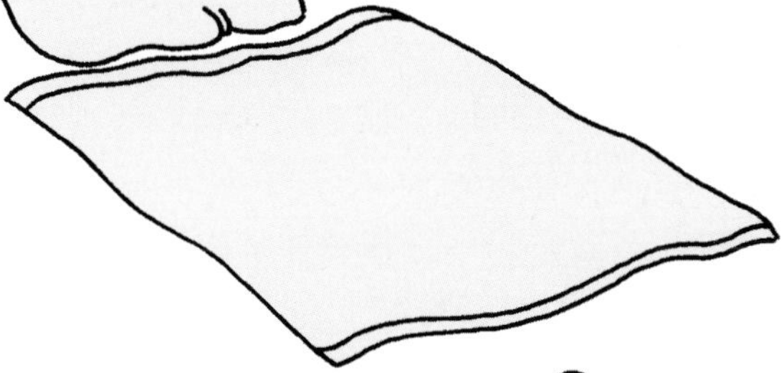
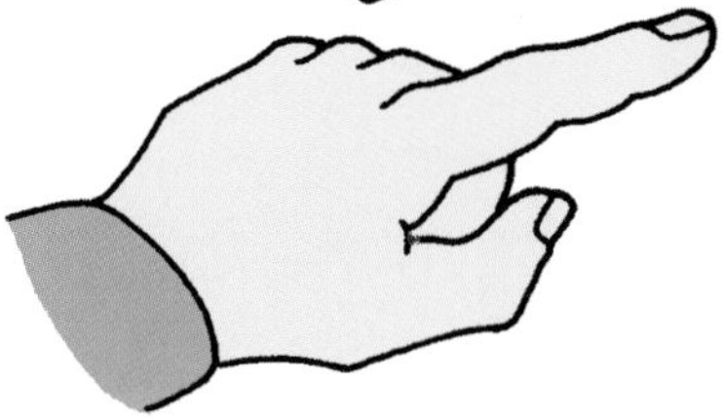

Missing Words

Directions: What word is missing from each set of words?

1. ________________ Bo Peep

________________ Boy Blue

________________ Red Riding Hood

2. The ________________ Little Pigs

The ________________ Bears

The ________________ Billy Goats Gruff

3. Rockabye ________________

Bye Bye ________________ Bunting

Hush, Little ________________

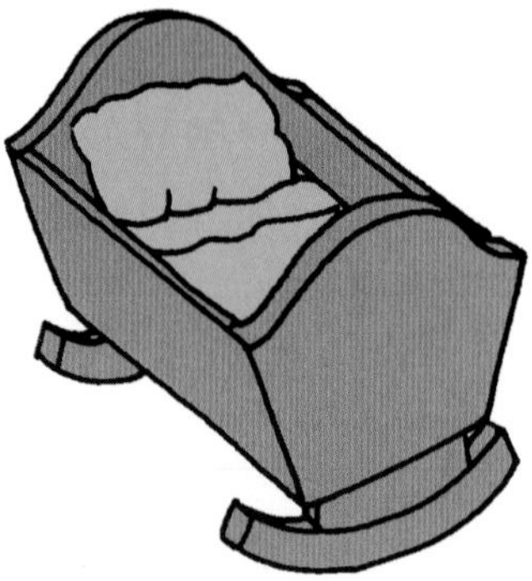

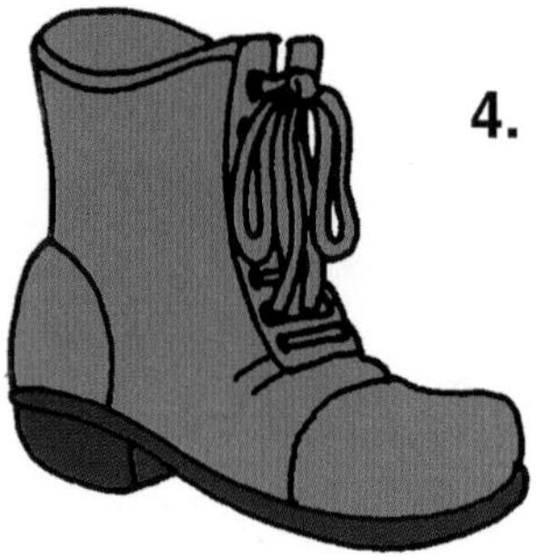

4. ________________ Mother Hubbard

This ________________ Man

The ________________ Woman in the Shoe

Fairy Tales

Directions: Fill in the missing words from the fairy tale titles.

1. The Three Little _______________

2. Goldilocks and the Three _______________

3. The Three _______________ Goats Gruff

4. _______________ White and the _______________ Dwarfs

5. The _______________ Mermaid

6. Beauty and the _______________

7. Aladdin and the Magic _______________

8. _______________ and the Beanstalk

9. The _______________That Laid the Golden _______________

10. _______________ Beauty

Change the Ending

Directions: Make a new word. Change the letter that makes the ending sound. Write the new word on the line.

1. Change **bet** to 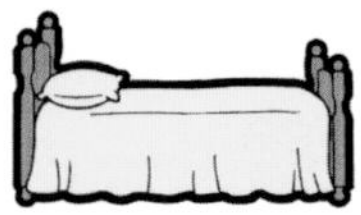 ______

2. Change **dot** to  ______

3. Change **hug** to  ______

4. Change **fit** to  ______

5. Change **pet** to  ______

6. Change **rub** to 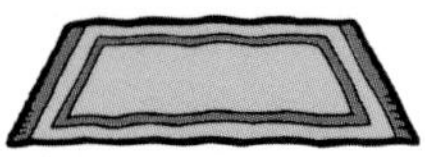 ______

7. Change **wet** to  ______

Word Families

Directions: Look at the pictures. Write two more words in the same word family. Draw a picture to match each word.

–ig

pig

–in

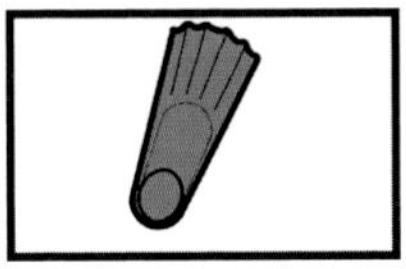

fin

–ip

tip

–it

hit

Scrambled Up Zoo

Directions: Amanda visited the zoo on Saturday. She made a list of the animals she saw. When she went home, her little brother tore up the list. Help her unscramble the letters so she can remember the names of the animals she saw. Hint: The circled letter is the first letter of each animal name.

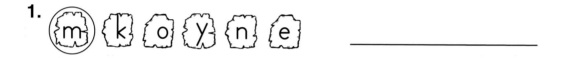

1. (m) k o y n e ____________________

2. o (l) n i ____________________

3. g (t) e r i ____________________

4. p i p (h) o ____________________

5. i e f (g) f a r ____________________

6. r o (g) l a i l ____________________

Sounds the Same

Directions: Study the word in each box. Then, print a word from the Word Bank that sounds the same as the boxed word but is spelled differently and has a different meaning.

Word Bank				
flour	aunt	sale	son	tale
right	ate	pear	not	

1.  eight ________	2. 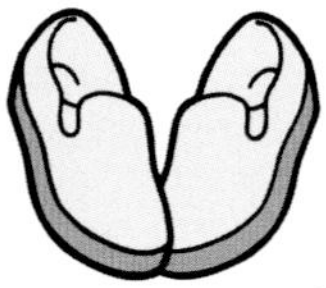 pair ________	3.  sun ________
4. 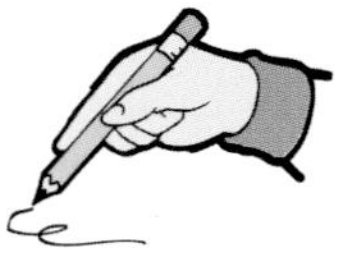 write ________	5.  sail ________	6.  knot ________
7.  flower ________	8.  ant ________	9.  tail ________

Opposites

Directions: List the opposites.

1. hot ____________________

2. dark ____________________

3. off ____________________

4. over ____________________

5. high ____________________

6. in ____________________

7. up ____________________

8. empty ____________________

9. happy ____________________

10. wet ____________________

11. tall ____________________

12. clean ____________________

Opposite Sentences

Directions: Complete each pair of sentences with words that mean the opposite of each other. Use the words in the box to help you.

hot	up	asleep	big	small
awake	open	cold	close	down

1. The cat is ____________________.

The cat is ____________________.

2. ____________________ the door.

____________________ the door.

3. The soup was ____________________.

The soup was ____________________.

4. Look at the ____________________ pumpkin.

Look at the ____________________ pumpkin.

5. The elevator is going ____________________.

The elevator is going ____________________.

Antonym Crossword

Directions: Choose the antonym from the box that has the opposite meaning as the puzzle clue below. Print the word in the puzzle.

shallow	girl	white	old
mean	go	child	light

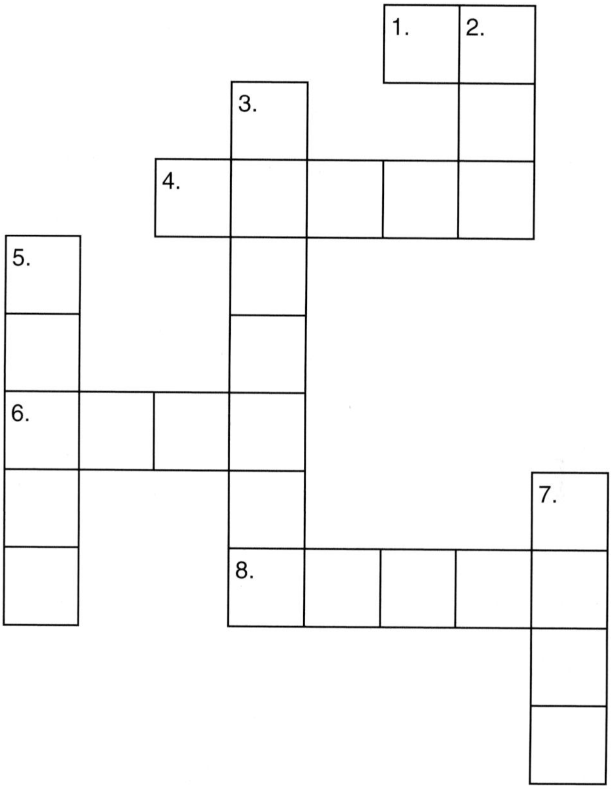

Across

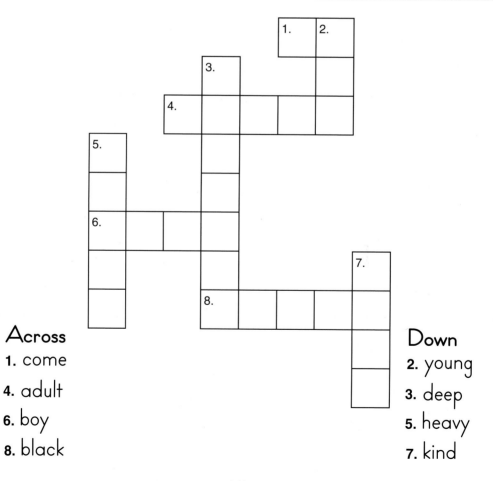

1. come
4. adult
6. boy
8. black

Down

2. young
3. deep
5. heavy
7. kind

Picture Clues

Directions: Underline the sentence that tells about the picture.

1.

We're taking a walk.
We're eating candy.
It's raining today.

2.

The bunny hopped away.
The bunny skated on the pond.
He jumped on the ramp.

3.

I can't find my kitty.
He's jumping on the beach.
The clothes are drying.

4.

We're making popcorn.
She's baking a cake.
They're riding bikes.

5.

He's riding a trike.
He's jogging on the track.
He's riding a horse.

How Old Are They?

Directions: There are three children, Susie, Jimmy, and Katie. They are each different ages. One child is 6, another is 7, and the third is 8-years-old. Can you use the clues below to figure out the age of each child? Draw a line to each child's correct age.

1. Susie is two years older than Jimmy.
2. Katie is in the middle.
3. Jimmy is the youngest.

Susie **6**

Jimmy **7**

Katie **8**

Favorite Sports

Directions: Three friends, Tran, Henry, and Maya, each enjoy a different sport. When they play together, they take turns choosing the game they will play. Use the clues below to figure out each child's favorite sport. Draw a line to connect each child to his or her favorite sport.

1. Tran's favorite sport uses a bat.
2. Henry's favorite sport uses a hoop.
3. Maya's favorite sport does not use a bat or a hoop.

Tran

soccer

Henry

baseball

Maya

basketball

Word Jumbles

Directions: Unscramble the letters to find things used in a house.

1. dbe ________________
2. mlpa ________________
3. voen ________________
4. lvsnteeiio ________________
5. batle ________________

6. nkis ________________
7. salgs ________________
8. hraic ________________

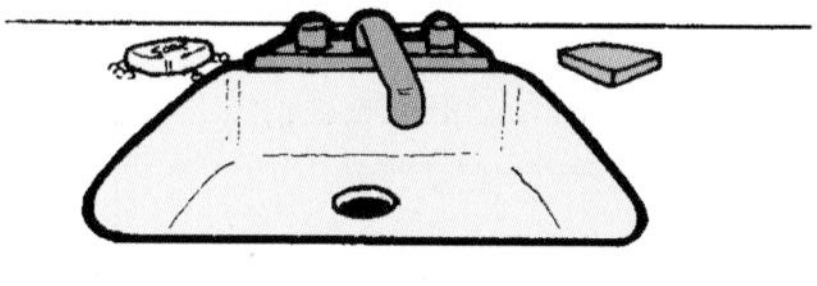

9. lewto ________________
10. lptea ________________

Rhymes

Directions: Write four words that rhyme with each word below.

ten

bee

do

top

bat

peep

Make a Compound Word

Directions: Look at each picture. Say the words that name the pictures. Then, write the words together to make a compound word. Use the words in the box to help you.

house	dog	tea	foot	rain
ball	pot	shell	bow	sea

1.  +  = ____________________

2. 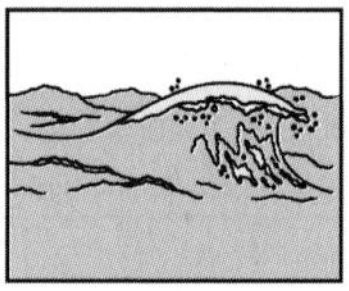 + 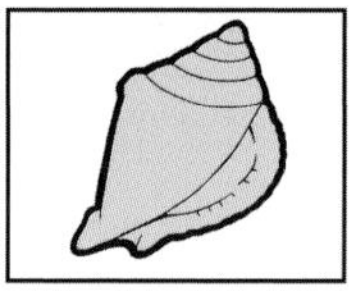 = ____________________

3.  +  = ____________________

4.  +  = ____________________

5. 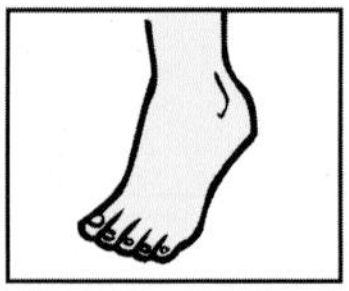 + 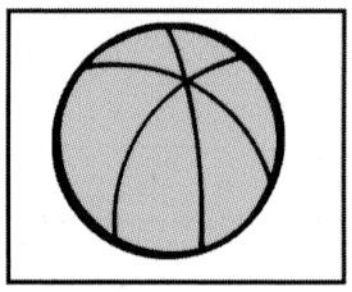 = ____________________

Word Roundup

Directions: This cowboy is roping base words and endings. Help him with his word roundup. Put base words and endings together to make new words. Write the new words in the word corral.

Word Corral

Base Words

Endings

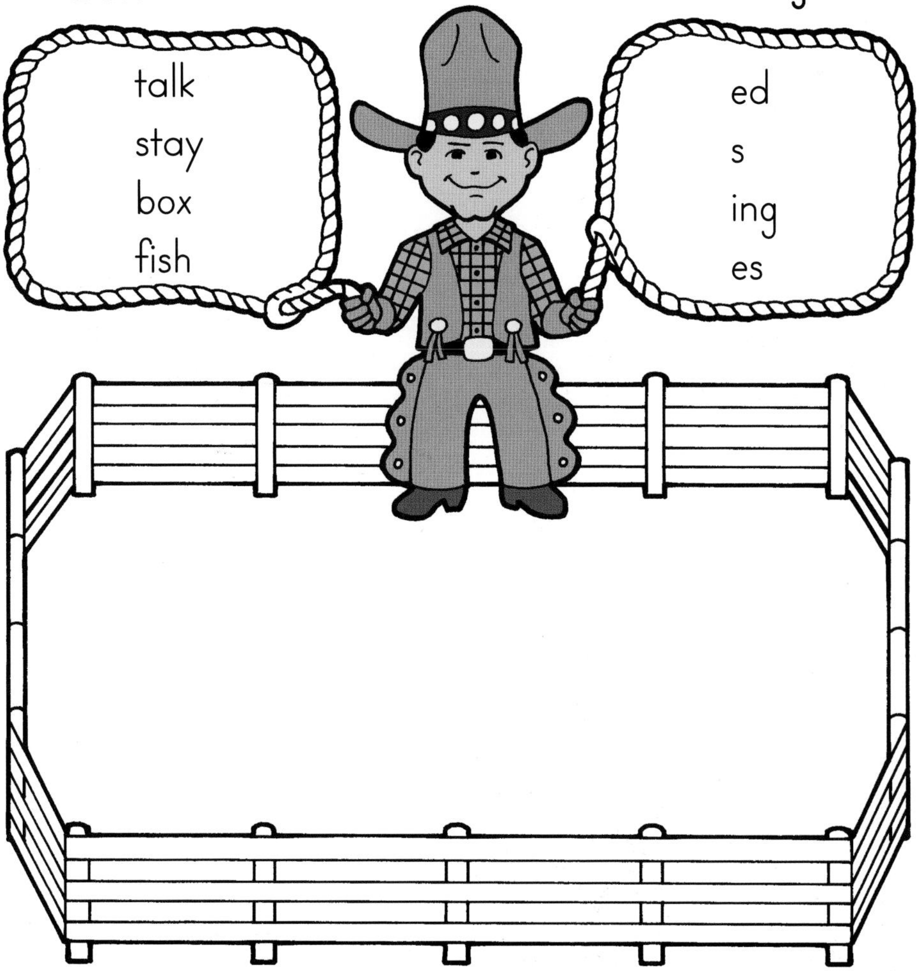

Words in Words!

Directions: A carpenter is a person who builds things with wood. How many words can you find hidden inside the word *carpenter*? Write one word on each wooden board below. Look for words that have three or more letters only! An example has been done for you.

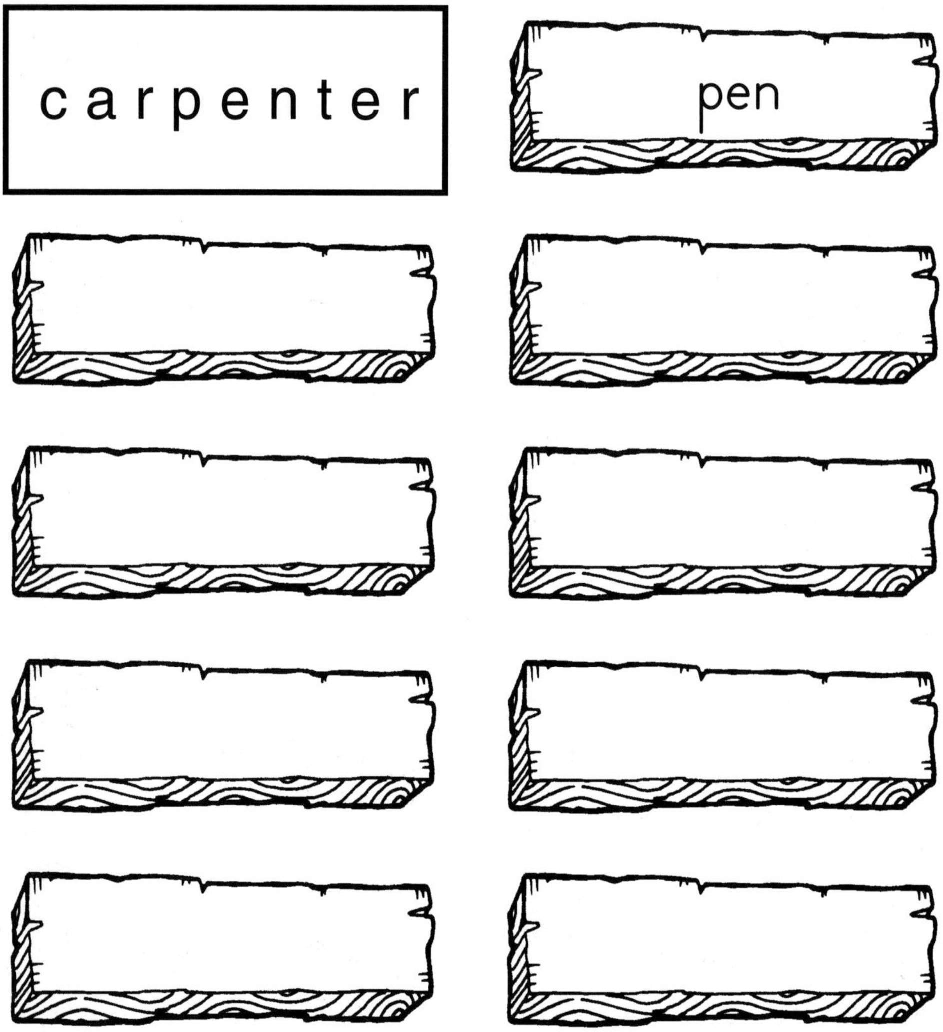

Earthworms

Directions: Search for words inside the word *earthworms*. Write each word that you discover on a worm below. Each word must have three or more letters. Remember, only use each word one time! An example has been done for you.

e a r t h w o r m s

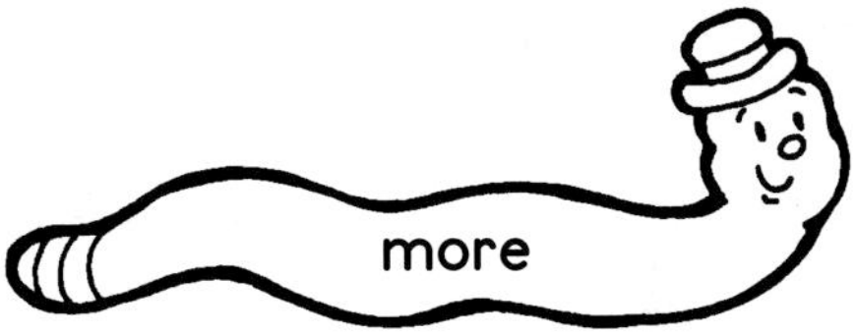

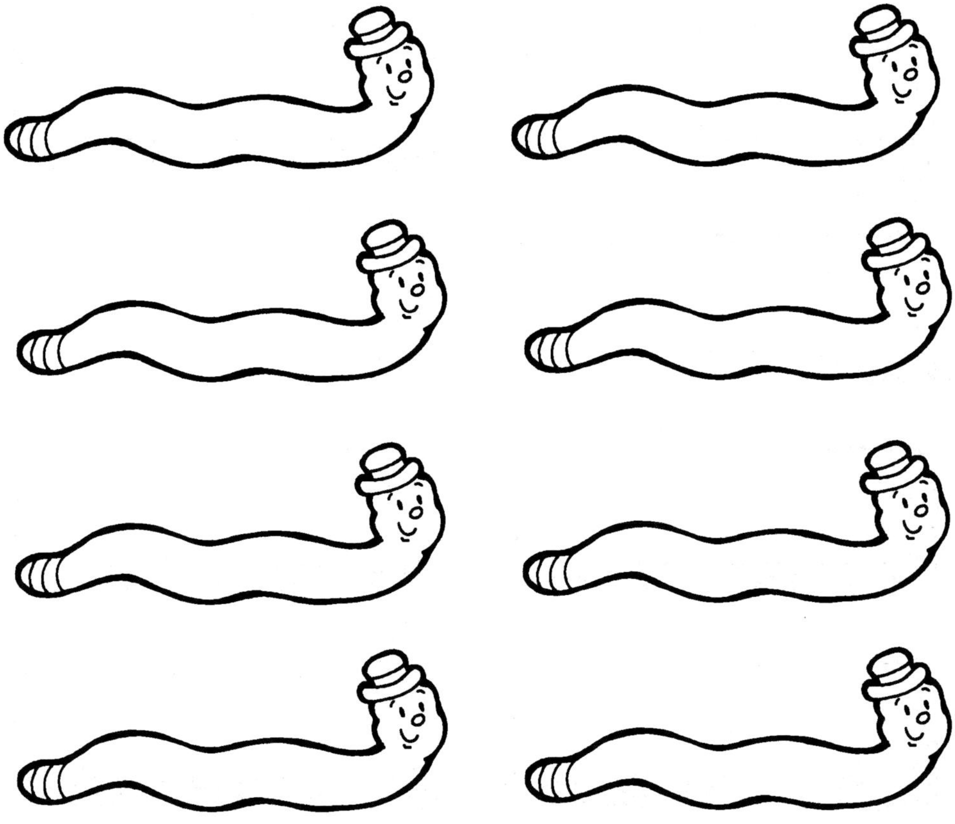

Sneaky, the "Sn" Snake

Directions: Find the words on Sneaky the snake's spots that begin with the "sn" sound and that finish the sentences. Write them on the blank lines.

1. I eat a ______________________ after school.
2. The feathers made me ______________________ .
3. A ______________________ moves very slowly.
4. It began to ______________________ last night.
5. Do you ______________________ when you sleep?

A Whopper of a Whale

Directions: Read the words that begin with the "wh" sound on the whale's spout. Write the words on the lines to finish the sentences.

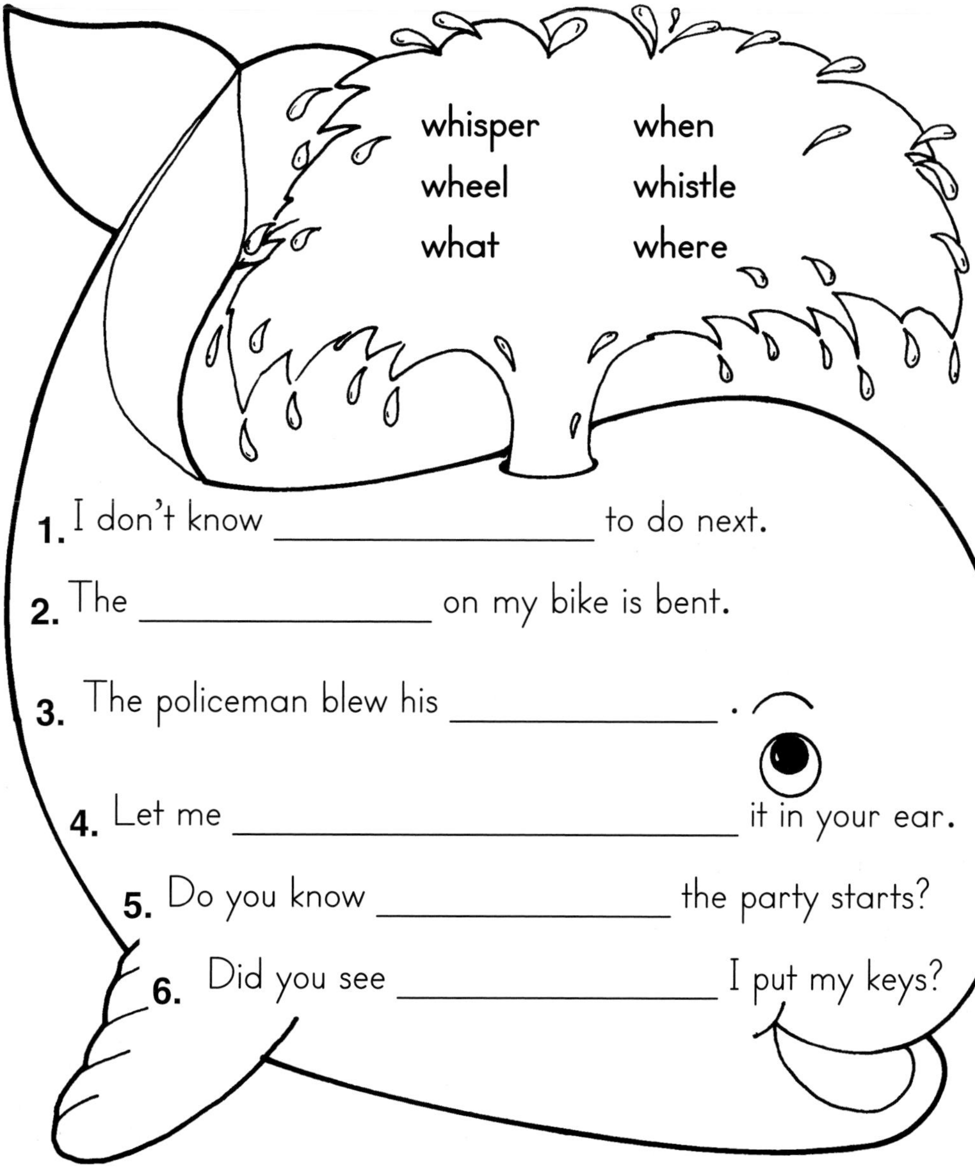

whisper	when
wheel	whistle
what	where

1. I don't know ______________ to do next.
2. The ______________ on my bike is bent.
3. The policeman blew his ______________ .
4. Let me ______________________ it in your ear.
5. Do you know ______________ the party starts?
6. Did you see ______________ I put my keys?

In the Barn

Directions: The words on this page are stuck in the boards of the barn. Can you help the farmer by unscrambling his farm words? Write the ten words on the haystacks below the barn.

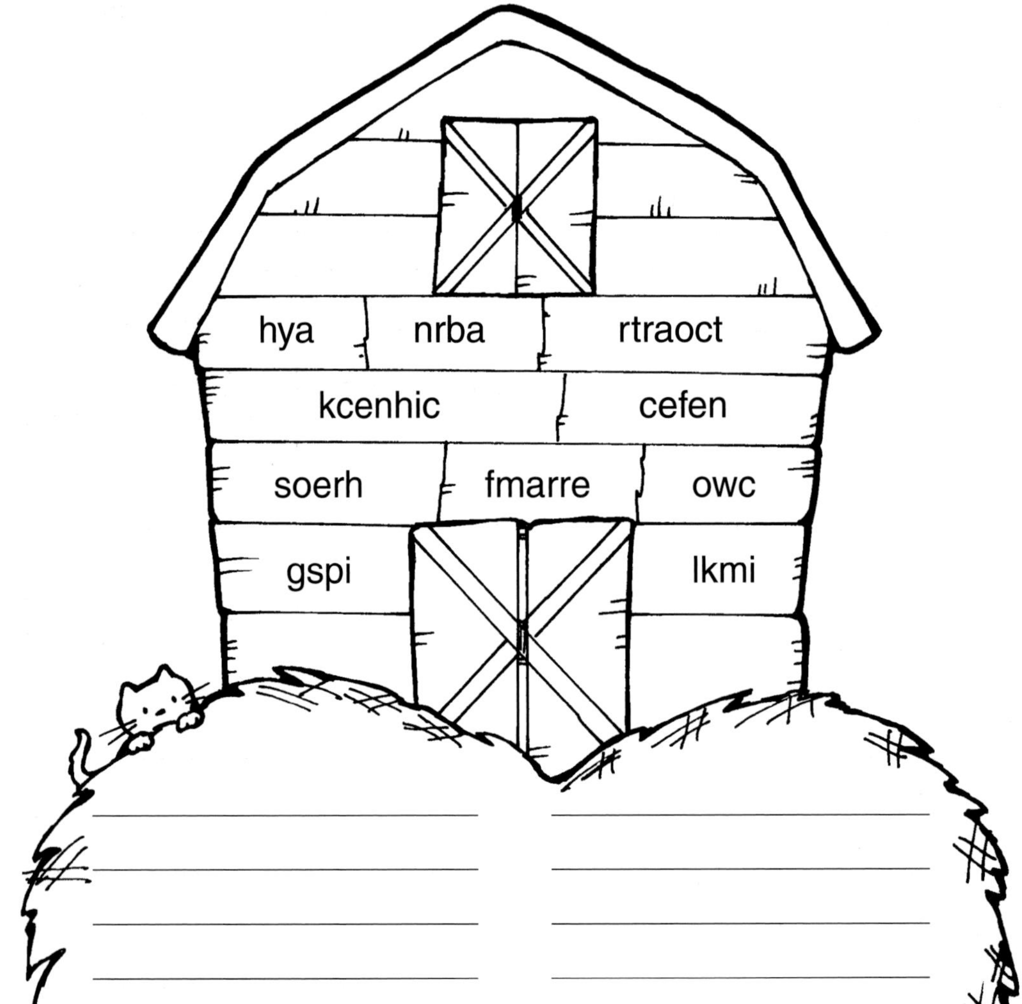

Where in the Word?

Directions: Use every word in the box to complete the chart below. Find the words that have the beginning, middle, and final consonant of that specific letter. Write the words in the correct column.

gift	ring	bus	vest	fall
play	milk	rain	duck	camel
gum	nut	lid	cup	
apple	ladder	leaf	sack	

	Beginning Consonant	Middle Consonant	Final Consonant
d			
f			
m			
n			
p			
s			

Tell the Truth

Directions: Read each sentence below. Only one of the sentences is true. Which one is it? Circle the one that is true. Next, cross out the word or number that makes each sentence untrue and add the word or number that will make it correct.

1. Cats have three legs.

2. George Washington was the first United States President.

3. The U.S. flag is red, white, and black.

4. A five-dollar bill is in the shape of a circle.

5. Pine trees are blue.

6. The opposite of *up* is *run*.

7. Chocolate ice cream is usually green.

8. The alphabet has 28 letters.

Sports Stuff

Directions: Look at the groups of words below the box. Each is a clue describing a different sport. Read each clue and decide which sport it is describing.

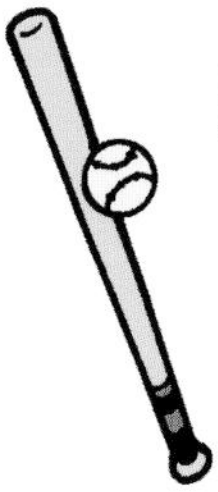

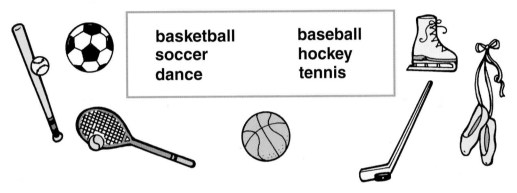

basketball	**baseball**
soccer	**hockey**
dance	**tennis**

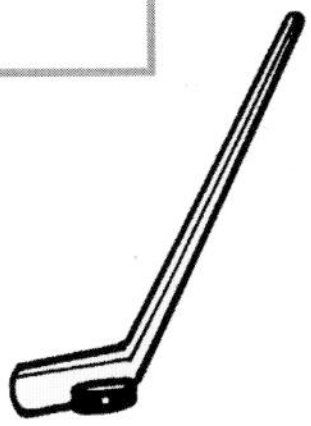

1. a racket and a small bouncy ball

____

2. soft slippers and tap shoes

____

3. a ball and bases

____

4. a long stick with a bend and a small black circle

____

5. large orange ball and a net

____

6. black and white ball and a net

____

In My Neighborhood

Directions: Look at the words in the box. Read the story below and write the correct words in the blanks. Cross out each word as you use it.

door	**cars**	**mailman**	**sunny**
gas station	**grocery store**		**school**

One ______________ (1) day, I wanted to take a walk in my neighborhood. I opened the ______________ (2) and started to walk down the street. Soon, I saw the ______________ (3) delivering the mail and Mrs. Jones taking out the trash. The birds were singing in the trees, and ______________ (4) were turning to go to the freeway. At the corner, I saw that there were many people getting gas at the ______________ (5) Others were going in and out of the ______________ (6) with sacks of food. Suddenly, I looked at my watch. I needed to to get home and get my backpack. It was time for ______________ (7)!

Answer Key

Page 308

1. p 3. n 5. i
2. e 4. c 6. l

The mystery word is pencil.

Page 309

1. t 5. h
2. e 6. e
3. a 7. r
4. c

The mystery word is teacher.

Page 310

1. e 3. a 5. e
2. r 4. s 6. r

The mystery word is eraser.

Page 311

1. d 3. s
2. e 4. k

The mystery word is desk.

Page 312

1. c 4. i
2. h 5. r
3. a

The mystery word is chair.

Page 313

1. rat 5. bat
2. that 6. flat
3. cat 7. sat
4. mat 8. hat

Page 314

Ann, Billy, Dan, Fran, Hank, Jill, Kate, Lola, Matt, Olivia, Pablo, Will

Page 315

1. 2, 1, 3 6. 1, 2, 3
2. 2, 1, 3 7. 3, 2, 1
3. 3, 2, 1 8. 2, 3, 1
4. 3, 1, 2 9. 2, 1, 3
5. 3, 2, 1

Page 316

1. bird, cat, dog, lizard
2. elephant, giraffe, lion, tiger
3. cow, horse, pig, sheep
4. crab, fish, octopus, shark

Page 317

The following words should be circled:

1. gave 5. hat 9. tap
2. cat 6. net 10. lap
3. wag 7. sat 11. zag
4. big 8. peg 12. fin

Page 318

1. baby 7. ice
2. bath 8. igloo
3. dash 9. mirror
4. dress 10. monkey
5. foot 11. wombat
6. football 12. wooly

Page 319

1. bring 7. leopard
2. brought 8. pickle
3. camp 9. play
4. coyote 10. playground
5. lamp 11. wombat
6. lazy 12. wooly

Page 320

1. dog 3. mop 5. tub
2. bat 4. log 6. web

Page 321

1. pig 4. bell
2. cat 5. sock
3. star 6. ring

Page 322

1. thirty 7. knife
2. wheat 8. cherry
3. knee 9. whip
4. chips 10. knock
5. sheep 11. church
6. think 12. throne

Page 323

1. swing 5. bring
2. twig 6. spot
3. clock 7. brain
4. slip

Page 324

7. May 10. April
8. June 11. March
9. October 12. July

The rule is that all words are the names of months.

Page 325

7. orange 10. yellow
8. brown 11. green
9. purple 12. red

The rule is that all words are the names of colors.

Page 326

Roses are red.

Page 327

Violets are blue.

Page 328

Stop needling each other!

Page 329

The missing word is "from."

Page 330

1. late 4. skate
2. gate 5. hate
3. plate 6. date

Page 331

Across: 2. June, 4. January, 5. April

Down: 1. February, 3. July

Page 332

from top to bottom: d, l, r, n, s, k

Page 333

1. bake 4. rake
2. cake 5. quake
3. lake 6. fake

Page 334

He was a snow-it-all!

Page 335

They've forgotten the words.

Page 336

hot croako

Page 337

1. blue 7. white
2. red 8. silver
3. purple 9. orange
4. green 10. pink
5. black 11. gold
6. yellow 12. brown

Page 338

1. l 5. p, w 9. o
2. p 6. t 10. r, w
3. n 7. t 11. t
4. o 8. k 12. y

Answer Key *(cont.)*

Page 339

1. p, t
2. k
3. f, m, s
4. l, r
5. c
6. l
7. h, k, l, w
8. h
9. o, u
10. a, n, u
11. b
12. d, g

Page 340

1. Little
2. Three
3. Baby
4. Old

Page 341

1. Pigs
2. Bears
3. Billy
4. Snow, Seven
5. Little
6. Beast
7. Lamp
8. Jack
9. Goose, Egg,
10. Sleeping

Page 342

1. bed
2. dog
3. hut
4. fin
5. pen
6. rug
7. web

Page 343

Answers will vary.

Page 344

1. monkey
2. lion
3. tiger
4. hippo
5. giraffe
6. gorilla

Page 345

1. ate
2. pear
3. son
4. right
5. sale
6. not
7. flour
8. aunt
9. tale

Page 346

1. cold
2. light
3. on
4. under
5. low
6. out
7. down
8. full
9. sad
10. dry
11. short
12. dirty

Page 347

1. awake, asleep
2. close, open
3. hot, cold
4. big, small
5. up, down

Page 348

Across: 1. come, 4. adult, 6. boy, 8. black
Down: 2. young, 3. deep, 5. heavy, 7. kind

Page 349

The following sentences should be underlined:

1. We're eating candy.
2. The bunny hopped away.
3. The clothes are drying.
4. We're making popcorn.
5. He's riding a horse.

Page 350

Susie is 8, Katie is 7, Jimmy is 6.

Page 351

Tran likes baseball, Henry likes basketball, and Maya likes soccer.

Page 352

1. bed
2. lamp
3. oven
4. TV
5. table
6. sink
7. glass
8. chair
9. towel
10. plate

Page 353

Answers will vary.

Page 354

1. doghouse
2. seashell
3. teapot
4. rainbow
5. football

Page 355

Answers will vary.

Page 356

Answers will vary. Possible answers include car, cap, can, carpet, crate, parent, pear, rat, rate, enter, ear, ten, tar, trap, tear, tree, near, net, ant, art, and rent.

Page 357

Answers will vary. Possible answers include ear, tear, hear, heart, art, wear, more, store, shore, home, seat, sweat, stare, share, rose, and hose.

Page 358

1. snack
2. sneeze
3. snail
4. snow
5. snore

Page 359

1. what
2. wheel
3. whistle
4. whisper
5. when
6. where

Page 360

hay, barn, tractor, chicken, fence, horse, farmer, cow, pigs, milk

Page 361

Beginning: duck, fall, milk, nut, play, sack
Middle: ladder, gift, camel, ring, apple, vest
Final: lid, leaf, gum, rain, cup, bus

Page 362

1. four legs
2. True
3. red, white, and blue
4. in the shape of a rectangle
5. green
6. down
7. usually brown
8. 26 letters

Page 363

1. tennis
2. dance
3. baseball
4. hockey
5. basketball
6. soccer

Page 364

1. sunny
2. door
3. mailman
4. cars
5. gas station
6. grocery store
7. school

Practice and Learn
WORKBOOK
You Did It!

Practice and Learn

WORKBOOK

This Award Is Presented To

____

for

- Doing Your Best
- Trying Hard
- Not Giving Up
- Making a Great Effort